KU-075-411

Contents

Figures

Introduction

The Problematic Relationships Between Science, Technology, and Business

To most people in the industrialized world of today, science and technology are so closely intertwined that any attempt to separate them analytically would seem both strange and strained. Scientists and engineers have a similar educational background and share several tasks. The difference between universities and technological institutes are often minute, and both science and technology are intimately tied to economic endeavors. The borders between science, technology, and business began to blur significantly about a century ago, not least with the construction of large technical systems. Referring to Thomas A. Edison's notebooks, the editors of the anthology *The Social Construction of Technological Systems* write that he "so thoroughly mixed matters commonly labeled economic, technical, and scientific that his thoughts composed a seamless web" (Bijker *et al.* 1987, p. 9; cf. Hughes 1983, p. 29). The present study will contribute to the discussion of this allegedly seamless web of science, technology, and business.

In the same volume Trevor J. Pinch and Wiebe E. Bijker (1987, pp. 19 ff.) advocate a social constructivist approach to the study of technology and rightly claim that many scholarly treatments of the science-technology relationship are dissatisfactory. Philosophers often suggest by introducing *a priori* some cognitive dichotomy, that science aims at explanation and technology at production (Küppers 1978). It is also common to argue that the goal of science is to discover truth and that of technology is to be useful and functional (Nordin 1988; Zweckbronner 1986). Pinch and Bijker criticize those historians and sociologists who make use of such axiomatic notions in their research; they suggest instead that "science" and "technology" are always contextually defined concepts. The present study follows their suggestion that "the social construction of the science-technology relationship is clearly a matter deserving further empirical investigation" (Pinch and Bijker 1987, p. 21), by examining the creation in the nineteenth century of "science," "technology," business," and their relations.

The science-technology relationship is also problematic in modern research policy, where the idea that technology is identical to applied science still persists (Rosenberg 1990). This idea is part of what Georg Wise (1985) has tellingly called the "assembly line" view, according to which scientific and technological change follows the path basic research - applied research - technological development - application - diffusion (Laudan 1982; Staudenmaier 1985; Ströker 1983). Wise's analysis of the academic debate on this topic shows how the most influential historians abandoned the assembly line model in the decade around 1975 (Constant 1980; Kranzberg 1967, 1968; Layton 1971, 1974; Price 1965, 1982; Vincenti 1979, 1982, 1984). They opposed the notion of technology as applied science, and began to regard "science and technology as separate spheres of knowledge" (Wise 1985, p. 244), each with a distinct character of its own, but also able to affect the other. Since, according to Wise, this position has not yet fully matured, the present study will hopefully contribute to that maturation process.

The growing influence of science on technological and economic matters in the second half of the nineteenth century lies at the core of the study. Particular attention is given to the impact of thermodynamics on refrigeration technology and of chemistry on beer brewing in the German-speaking world. These *scientification* processes were propelled by certain educators, industrialists, and politicians. Cognitively, they included the incorporation of some of the concepts, methods, results, and ontological positions of science into the sphere of technology; socially, scientifically educated people became increasingly involved in technical and economic matters. The proponents of scientification opposed those who held that science was an unnecessary luxury and claimed instead that science was the key to a perfect technology and a more profitable economy. It would be easier to control the production process with science, thus making the former more predictable. This study borrows Hugh Aitken's (1976, p. 300) idea of science, technology, and economics as three "spheres of human action" between which information, material, and people may flow and focuses on the activity of certain "translators" (p. 331) who made science bear on the other two spheres.

Unlike Edison, most people who appear in this story did in fact distinguish between "science," "technology," and "business." In contrast to electricity in the United States, several seams still remained within machine design and beer brewing in Germany, even though they slowly became more permeable. The difference between Edison and the participants in this story may be partly due to tradition, partly to national style: electrical engineering has always been more closely connected to science, whereas mechanical engineering has a long tradition of practicality; American engineers might have been more pragmatically oriented than their German counterparts and therefore did not find any principal reason to distinguish between science and technology (Ferguson 1979; Schryock 1962). Without attempting to make national comparisons, the present study will indicate how the three key concepts, *Wissenschaft*, *Technik*, and *Wirtschaft*, were conceptually and organizationally conceived in the German setting.

Historical discussions of technology and science in Europe and North America consider the period when Edison was active to be particular significant. Historians of technology and science have not been the only scholars to describe how engineers and scientists in various areas began to approach each other during this so-called Second Industrial Revolution (Cardwell and Hills 1976; Layton 1979; Mauel 1969). Economic historians like David Landes (1969) and Nathan Rosenberg also mark these years as the beginning of a new epoch. Rosenberg (1982a, p. 231) claims that the revolution was extremely important, calls for more research on this period, and asks "... what role did science play in those technological innovations that created modern industrial societies?" The present study is one of many attempts to answer this and similar questions—attempts which cover a wide range of subjects, from the foundation of research laboratories in the chemical industry (Beer 1981) to the struggle of engineering educators to bring institutes of technology on a par with the universities (Manegold 1970, 1970a).

The importance of science for the development of technology is not only of interest to historians. It is also a central concern for scholars in the interdisciplinary field of technology-and-society studies. After having paid much attention to the social consequences of new technology, these scholars have in recent years become increasingly interested in the determinants of technical change (Dierkes and Hoffmann 1992). This shift of focus can be seen, for instance, in the move away from technology assessment and *Technikfolgenabschätzung* toward constructive technology assessment and *Technikgenese* (Dierkes and Marz 1991; Rip and Belt 1988). This book deals with the ways in which science affects the generation and development of technology and should be seen as a contribution to this emergent discourse within technology-and-society studies. Like most works in this field, the present study focuses on the social and cultural aspects of this influence. Unlike most works in the field, however, it presents a Weberian analysis of the social and cultural roots of technological change.[1]

Science, Technology, and Capitalism in Max Weber's Developmental History

Max Weber's impact on the sociology and history of technology has not been of great significance. Apart from attempts by Randall Collins (1986) to create Weberian macro theory of technological development and by Gert Schmidt (1981) to introduce Weber into industrial sociology, Weber's direct influence has been slight. Indirectly, however, his analysis of capitalism has been of considerable importance, particularly as mediated by Georg Lukács (1968) and members of the so-called Frankfurt School (Horkheimer 1941, 1985; Horkheimer and Adorno 1969; Marcuse 1964, 1968). A large portion of Weber's writings is socio-historical and aims at understanding the unfolding of Western civilization—including its economic system and the role of science and technology therein. Weber's comprehensive and challenging perspective suggests that it might be worthwhile to explore the possibilities of introducing Weber into the history and sociology of science and technology. The present study therefore suggests

---

1 Archival research for this study was made while the author was associated with the Department of History of Science and Ideas at Gothenburg University. The manuscript was completed during a research stay at the Technical University of Berlin and at the Unit of Organization and Technology at *Wissenschaftszentrum Berlin für Sozialforschung* (WZB), where the author took part in a research project, "Technological Development in an Organizational Context," financed by the German Ministry for Research and Technology (BMFT).

a Weberian interpretation of the phenomena of the scientification of technology and business.

Weber discussed the importance of science for the development of the West in both theoretical and practical terms. Most well-known is the analysis of "the disenchantment of the world" which Weber (1958d, p. 155) made in his speech "Science as a Vocation" of 1918.[22] By "disenchantment"—a term borrowed from Friedrich Schiller—Weber meant that modern people do not have to invoke spirits or gods in order to understand or control their surroundings. Everything in our world is accessible to reason. Weber did not say that we know everything, but he did emphasize that we believe that we could, in principle, learn anything without referring to mystic forces. The great symbol for this ability in our society is science, with its abstract concepts and rational experiments. The scientist has replaced the magician. Accordingly, the present study suggests that the scientification of technology can be interpreted as one aspect of the more general Occidental disenchantment process, which Weber so eloquently described and analyzed.

Weber (p. 138) claimed that "[s]cientific progress is a fraction, the most important fraction, of the process of intellectualization ...," and that "... this intellectualist rationalization [is manifest] in science and scientifically oriented technology ..." Science indeed played a central role in Weber's investigations into the peculiar developments of the West, but it did not do so only on an intellectual and theoretical level. Science had also become in practice what Karl Marx would have called a "productive force," in particular after the mid-nineteenth century. Weber (1981, p. 306) writes in his *General Economic History*:

> The connection of industry with modern science, especially the systematic work of the laboratories, beginning with Justus von Liebig, enabled industry to become what it is today and so brought capitalism to its full development.

The present study suggests that the scientification of technology and industry can be regarded as an example of "intellectualist rationalization" on the one hand and of the unfolding of capitalism on the other.

Even if the above quotations clearly indicate that Weber found science to be of fundamental importance to modern society, they are not enough to

2 The original can be found in Weber (1922, pp. 524-555). References are generally made to English translations of Weber's writings wherever such are available—otherwise to German originals.

warrant the reconstruction of a Weberian approach to scientification. Weber's brief discussions about the historical impact of science need to be put into a larger framework. This will be done by treating the scientification process as a special case of the overall rationalization process of the Occident.

Guenther Roth (1987) and many other Weber scholars argue that Weber's concept of *rationalization* is the key concept in his "developmental history" of the modern Western world (Sprondel and Seyfarth 1981); it enabled Weber to go beyond mere economic history and find parallel rationalization processes in other realms of society, such as law, administration, religion, music, politics, personal conduct, science, and technology. Weber (1930, pp. 13-31) summarizes these developments in the introduction to his sociology of religion, reprinted in his most famous work, *The Protestant Ethic and the Spirit of Capitalism*. In the legal community, rationalization means the coming of positive law governed by abstract and uniform principles (Bertilsson 1985); in the administrative sphere it indicates an increasing bureaucratization and a strict regulation of tasks (Mitzman 1971); in religion it stands for universally valid ethics and implies an effort to control the world intellectually (Schluchter 1980); in the world of music it comes with harmonic chords and a formalized notation system; in politics it represents the replacement of charismatic leaders with predictably acting parties (Beetham 1985; Lindskoug 1979; Mommsen 1974); within the personal sphere it means an orderly and calculable behavior based on the notion of duty; and in the sphere of knowledge it stands for intellectualization and systematic experimentation. Jürgen Habermas (1981, Vol. 1, p. 226) is no doubt right in suggesting that this lumping together of such disparate processes is, at least at first sight, "confusing."

The confusion might diminish, however, if we sift some key elements from the list, and if we bring economics more into focus. Randall Collins (1986, p. 11) suggests that the formulation of a Weberian "theory of the social conditions for technology" requires us to consider texts other than *The Protestant Ethic*.

The present study consequently seeks inspiration in some of Weber's monumental works, like *General Economic History* and *Economy and Society*, in addition to some of his works on the methodology of the social sciences and some of his less well-known works on the sociology of religion.[3] Inspiration has been found for the title of this book in Weber's (1958, p. 320) political writings, where he discusses both dead and living machines—mechanical devices and bureaucratic institutions, that is—in terms of "frozen spirit" (*geronnener Geist*).

Whereas in *The Protestant Ethic* Weber traces the emergence of capitalism's economic structures back to some Protestant ideas about providence and predestination, his concern in *General Economic History* is how to account for the emergence and unfolding of modern capitalism on a much broader scale. Weber (1981, pp. 276 ff., 286) goes beyond mere ideological elements in the latter work and presents the following factors as crucial to Western capitalism: all means of production rest in the hands of an entrepreneur or a firm; a free trade market and a market with formally free labor; a speculative mentality which operates on a financial market and a stock market; and, last but not least, legal, administrative, and technical systems which are calculable and predictable. Weber takes these factors to be prerequisites for the effective application of rational capital accounting. Such accounting, which began in fifteenth-century Italy and is carried out in monetary terms, is treated by Weber as the epitome of modern capitalism.

Several common denominators can be found by comparing these aspects of Western capitalism with the previous list of factors which characterize the Occidental rationalization process. This is hardly surprising: Weber regarded the coming of capitalism as a central element of the rationalization of the West (Lindskoug 1979; Marcuse 1968). Both processes involve elements of abstraction and intellectualization (Giddens 1972), quantification and calculation (Abramowski 1966), systematization and formalization (Schluchter 1980), control and regulation (Dieckmann 1961), as well as prediction (Collins 1986). These elements can be derived neatly from Weber's (1958e, p. 293) own definitions: rationalism is "an increasing

---

3 *The Protestant Ethic* is Weber (1930) and the German original is Weber (1920, Vol. I, pp. 1-206). *General Economic History* is Weber (1981), the German original being Weber (1923). The first part of *Economy and Society* has been published in English as *The Theory of Social and Economic Organization* (1964), and other sections can be found in Weber (1958a, 1958b); the original is Weber (1922a). Some parts of his methodological writings have been translated as Weber (1949) and others in Runciman (1978); originals can be found in Weber (1922). His main work on religion is Weber (1920); in English we have Weber (1958c, 1958e, 1965).

theoretical mastery of reality by means of increasingly precise, abstract concepts," and it appears in "the methodological attainment of a definitely given practical end through an increasingly precise calculation of adequate means." These definitions correspond to what Stephen Kalberg (1980) has called *theoretical* and *practical* rationality, respectively.

In short, *the main thesis of the present study is that the growing use of science in technology and industry and of machinery in industry can be regarded as a special case of Western rationalization in Max Weber's sense.* A scientific approach to technological problems in our society usually implies that intellectual abstractions are made from reality, that various relationships are expressed in formalized terms, and that calculations about means and ends are made (Bogner 1989; Frängsmyr *et al.* 1990). Furthermore, science is applied to regulate and control the production process in order to predict its behavior and thereby commonly plays an instrumentalist role in industry (Beniger 1986; Schluchter 1979). Compare Weber's (1930, p. 24) statement that the rationality of "the peculiar modern Western form of capitalism ... is to-day essentially dependent on the calculability of the most important technical factors."

Science in Refrigeration and Brewing

The present case study in the history and sociology of technology is not a theoretical contribution to Weberian exegesis. Rather, a case is made for a Weberian interpretation of the application of thermodynamics to mechanical refrigeration and of the use of science and technology in the brewing industry in the second half of the nineteenth century. The account will move between the levels of sociology, economics, history, science, and technology.

When the first cold-producing machines appeared on the market in the middle of the century, a limited demand came from firms belonging to the food industry (Anderson 1953; Goosman 1924-26). Refrigeration machinery was produced on a small scale in countries like Australia, France, Germany, Great Britain, and the United States. There were three different kinds of machines, representing three *classificatory ideal types* of refrigeration technology (Burger 1976; Weber 1949a). Even though the pioneering innovators did know some heat theory, their scientific knowledge was fragmentary and usually outdated. It was expressed in very general terms and was never systematically applied to their technical work.

Carl Linde, a professor of theoretical mechanical engineering at the Polytechnic in Munich, was the first to analyze mechanical refrigeration systematically from the point of view of thermodynamics. Linde adopted the ontology of and some concepts from thermodynamics in the early 1870s and argued that the most efficient refrigeration machine would be that which comes closest to the reversed Carnot cycle. He analyzed existing machines, compared them with the Carnot ideal, and determined that they were thermodynamically hopeless. The Carnot cycle served as a *Leitbild* for Linde and other thermodynamically trained engineers—Linde's famous student Rudolf Diesel among them (Dierkes *et al.* 1992; Marz and Dierkes 1992).

The secondary literature on the history of refrigeration technology mentions this origin of the scientification process only in passing. Roger Thévenot (1978, p. 22) writes without further analysis in the most comprehensive survey of the subject:

> There was a transition from ingenious versatility to rational studies during this extraordinary fertile quarter [1850-74] of the century, studies which began to be founded on thermodynamics, notably through the work of Linde, from 1870 onward.

The scientific, technical, and commercial activities of Linde and his colleagues are at the core of the present study. Central questions are: Why did Linde choose a scientific approach to the problems of mechanical refrigeration, an area which had a very different technical *tradition* (Berner 1990; Constant 1980; Dierkes and Knie 1989; also Knie 1989)? How was his approach, characterized by W. R. Woolrich (1967, p. 50) as "a thorough thermodynamic analysis," a scientific one? What was the nature of refrigeration technology before 1870, and how did scientification affect it?

The largest demand for refrigeration equipment in the German market came from the brewing industry. What technical, organizational, economic, and geographical factors made certain breweries prone to invest in mechanical refrigeration systems? Is Hans Friedrich Tillmann (1972) right in claiming that small breweries developed into large ones as a result of their installing mechanical refrigeration? When representatives of the largest breweries on the European Continent learned about Linde's ideas, they incited him to go from theoretical deliberations to practical innovation. At the beginning, they even defrayed the expenses for Linde's experimental work. Why did these breweries become strong *supporters* of Linde's endeavor (Berthoin Antal 1992), and what role did his allegedly "scientific" approach play in enticing their interest? To what extent will an analysis on the levels of *ideology* (Liedman 1984) and *organizational culture* (Dierkes 1988, 1989; Kenngott 1990) help us understand their behavior?

Linde and his collaborators managed to get his first refrigeration machines onto the market in the mid-1870s. They criticized the contemporary standard of mechanical refrigeration and created a new research and development program. This program can be seen as one aspect of "technical thermodynamics"—a technological school founded by the mechanical engineering educator Gustav Zeuner (1866) in the late 1850s and early 60s and emphasizing scientific methods. Success was instant, and the Linde corporation became market leaders within a few years. Why did Linde's design become so influential in mechanical refrigeration that it served as a pattern among refrigeration engineers during several decades? Is there anything to the often repeated statement that Linde's machines produced twice as much ice per energy unit as those of his predecessors (Krug 1981, p. 91; Lohmann 1972, p. 13)?

The Weberian Perspective

The Weberian analysis of these events will rest on three of four "cornerstones for the analysis of rationalization processes in history" which Kalberg (1980, p. 1145) has distilled from Weber's writings—primarily from his essay "The Social Psychology of the World Religions" of 1913 (Weber 1958e).[4] They are *theoretical*, *formal*, and *practical rationality*. The fourth cornerstone discussed by Kalberg is value-oriented *substantive* rationality, a phenomenon whose impact is reduced by the Western rationalization process and which will therefore be of limited importance to the present analysis.

---

4 Weber (1958e) is a translation of the introduction to the essay "Die Wirtschaftsethik der Weltreligionen," the original is Weber (1920, vol. I, pp. 237-275).

The unfolding of theoretical rationality is obvious in the work of Linde and his fellows. Their work included what Kalberg (p. 1152) calls

> a cognitive confrontation with one's experience ..., thought processes as logical deduction and induction, the attribution of causality, and the formation of symbolic "meanings" ...

This study treats Linde's approach to problems within mechanical refrigeration as an example of "intellectual rationalization." Linde's, Zeuner's, and Diesel's application of abstract, thermodynamic concepts and a mechanical ontology was an attempt to "disenchant" the world.

However, the Zeunerian school of technical thermodynamics was not just a theoretical attitude. As educator, Zeuner took great pains to construct auxiliary formulae which could be directly applied by engineering students; Linde emphasized the importance of systematic experimentation. The formulation, in quantitative terms, of universally valid laws was paramount in their engineering science. Such formulae literally helped to formalize engineering practice. While the formalization of organizations means that tasks are strictly regulated and that a system of rules are created, the formalization of scientific and technological activities appears as "strict empirical observation, quantification, and systematic measurement" (Kalberg 1980, p. 1159). Methodical investigations had replaced haphazard tinkering. In Kalberg's (*ibid.*) words:

> As opposed to the formulation of hypotheses, which belongs to the domain of theoretical rationality, experimental scientific procedures are ... judged, by Weber, to be fully formally rational.

Teaching was not an end in itself. The ultimate aim of Zeuner and Linde was to facilitate the design and construction of better machinery, "better" typically meaning more fuel-efficient and more economical. The maximization of profits is an important goal in capitalist establishments, and technical devices often serve as tools for reaching this goal. In this view, technology becomes a means for reaching a given end, and it thus illustrates what Weber (1964, p. 115) called means-end, or purposive, rationality. "The practical rational way of life," Kalberg (1980, p. 1152) writes, "accepts given realities and calculates the most expedient means of dealing with the difficulties they present."

In this study we will encounter practical rationality not only among engineering educators, but also in the brewing industry. Brewers adopted sophisticated instruments and chemical and biochemical analyses as a means of making the quality of the final product more predictable. Temperatures were continuously measured, sugar content was determined, and the viability of yeast cultures was analyzed in order to make the production process more reliable. The immediate goal was to avoid unpleasant surprises—in other words to control production.

Control is a key term not only in the exercising of practical rationality. Kalberg (1980, p. 1159) writes that "... mental processes that consciously strive to master reality are common to all types of rationality." The adoption of a scientific view of the world, the systematization of experimental work, and the breaking-down of the production process in quantifiable entities can all be subsumed under headings like control and mastery. The adoption of mechanical refrigeration by the large brewing companies fits nicely into this picture. Ice-producing machines allowed these firms to create uniform conditions year-round and become independent of an unreliable supply of natural ice. Even though they could not master the weather, they were able to control the temperature.

I. Refrigeration Technology Before 1870

The first part of this study consists of four chapters that serve as a historical and conceptual background to the following two parts, but should also be seen as a contribution in its own right to the history and historiography of technology.

Chapter 1 sets the stage by sketching the general economic, technological, and scientific background, and the other chapters discuss the main developments of refrigeration technology in the nineteenth century. Because only two books on the history of refrigeration technology have been published since the Second World War (Anderson 1953; Thévenot 1978), and because both concentrate on the period after 1890, these chapters fill a gap in the existing literature. Rather than describing each and every ice-machine, Chapters 2 and 3 present a systematic treatment of various technologies of cold production before 1870, classifying them according to different characteristics and historical significance. Only the most influential features of these machines will be described at length. Terms that might contribute to general discussions in the philosophy and history of technology will be presented, since terms like "classificatory ideal type" and "archetype" can help scholars to organize and present their sources. The final chapter will consider first of all why some individuals and firms developed successful refrigeration technology while others did not, and will subsequently analyze what kind of technological knowledge was available to these agents.

The Weberian heritage will be expressed in the historical background, the application of the ideal type concept, and the emphasis on certain social groups as historical agents.

1. The Economic, Technological, and Scientific Background

Industry and Capitalism in Europe and the United States

Max Weber detested mono-causal and uni-directional accounts (Abramowski 1966; Roth and Schluchter 1979); he did not believe that historical explanations could always be found in one and the same area of human life. Despite Weber's (1930, p. 90) [in]famous proposal that *The Protestant Ethic* was to be read as "a contribution to the understanding of the manner in which ideas become effective forces in history," all his later works are remarkably pluralistic and many-sided. History does not follow one path in a teleological manner. In spite of his well-known analysis of Occidental rationalization, Weber never regarded this process as irrevocable or pre-determined.

Weber's approach comes out particularly well in his *General Economic History* (1981), a monumental text where the roots and character of Western capitalism is analyzed at depth. The book might not contribute much to present-day economic history on the level of single observations, but its comprehensive scope makes it unusually rich and challenging—also seventy years after its first publication. Randall Collins (1986, Ch. 2) has shown that Weber's book describes how modern capitalism was fostered by a dynamic interplay between a large number of institutional factors—religious, legal, monetary, administrative, political, and technological. In other words, the emergence of modern industry cannot be explained by reference *only* to Protestantism, the inflow of precious metals from South America, or the invention of the steam engine. It is this Weberian emphasis on anti-reductionism and anti-determinism that has also inspired the present study. Or, in Ira J. Cohen's (1981, p. L) words:

> Weber ... maintained an exquisite sensitivity to the complexity and ironic consequences contained in the weave of various social, economic, technological, political, and cultural forces as they are involved in the production of a given set of circumstances.

The seams remain in Weber's weave of history, and the historian's task is to analyze the relationships between the various threads.

Several of the factors that Weber places at the core of modern capitalist developments were mentioned in the Introduction: free markets for goods, labor, money, and stock. Organizations like banks, factories, joint-stock companies, a bureaucratically organized state, and predictably acting courts had to be founded for these markets to function in a rational manner.

The first country where these lines of development converged was Britain (Deane 1965; Hobsbawm 1968; Landes 1969). Partly as a result of its global trade, Britain had become one of the wealthiest countries in Europe by the seventeenth century. Credit institutes like the Bank of England channeled parts of this capital into mines, iron works, and factories. Like most observers, Weber (1981, p. 303) points to the importance of the textile industry in the history of technology: "The decisive factor ... in the triumph of the mechanization and rationalization of work was the fate of cotton manufacture." Serving a large market and experiencing intense competition, this industry became an important engine for technical change.

Britain became known as the workshop of the world; both domestic and foreign demand grew (Dillard 1986; Kenwood and Lougheed 1983). Other countries desired to catch up with Britain and tried to persuade British artisans to go abroad. Their attempts were often successful, despite British restrictions on the exports of both skilled labor and advanced machinery. At a time when technical textbooks and manuals were scarce, engineering knowledge was very closely tied to a few individuals. Technological espionage was another way to get hold of essential knowledge, and in Part III one such example will be described.

An eighteenth century observer might well have expected France to be the first country to follow in the wake of Britain (Price 1981). However, despite a good start the economy developed sluggishly in the first half of the nineteenth century. On the other hand, French technical and scientific ability was very advanced, and French products were known for their high quality. We will later encounter a French refrigeration machine system that for a long time was regarded as the best of its kind.

In the United States the food industry became the largest buyer of refrigeration systems. This industry had mechanized early and was organized on a large scale (Yeager 1981). The coming of the railroad, which Weber (1981, p. 297) called "the most revolutionary instrumentality known to history," made Chicago a center of the food industry.

It is common in the historiography of nineteenth century technology to distinguish between the American industry on the one hand and the French and British on the other (Ferguson 1979; Habakkuk 1967). American mechanics and industrialists are often said to have been geared toward the manufacturing and application of novel, labor-saving machinery, whereas their French and British counterparts are supposed to have been more conservative, or at least to have encountered stronger labor opposition. A host of inventions was made in the two European countries, but in a number of instances their full technological and economic potential was realized first in the United States (Rosenberg 1976, Ch. 10). It was not uncommon for American engineers to "borrow" design solutions from Europe and to develop them substantially (Cochran 1981), and in this study we will encounter such examples from the area of refrigeration technology.

It is also common to distinguish between the United States and Europe—in particular France and Germany—when it comes to the attitude toward science (Birr 1966; Cochran 1981; Schryock 1962). Whereas science was a highly regarded activity in the German and French speaking parts of Europe, the Americans are usually said to have been more hesitant, at least until the last third of the nineteenth century. Practicality and usefulness were more highly valued than excessive theorizing in the Anglo-Saxon world (Buchanan 1983; Roderick and Stephens 1973). The historian Michael Calvert (1967, p. 53) writes that

> Thermodynamics, or the science of heat and energy, was first explored by French and German engineers and scientists ... American engineers recognized this debt to Europe for basic principles in their science. *Engineer* in 1860 complained that the United States had no first-class theorist in the field of mechanical engineering.

This state of affairs slowly began to change a decade later, with the foundation of colleges like the Stevens Institute of Technology at Hoboken, New Jersey (Rogers 1979). Mechanical engineering students were here given a firm footing in basic mathematics, chemistry, and physics.

Weber also discussed the importance of science in modern industry. Even though he somewhat prematurely suggests that Edmund Cartwright, the man behind the power loom, was "one of the first inventors who combined technology with science," it is clear that Weber (1981, p. 304) regarded the coming of science in the productive sphere primarily as a phenomenon of the nineteenth century: "... most of the inventions of the 18th century were not made in a scientific manner" (p. 306).

German industry began to catch up in the middle of the nineteenth century (Henderson 1975; Hoffmann 1965; Kellenbenz 1981; Kuczynski 1947; Milward and Saul 1977; Sartorius 1920). At the beginning of the century Germany had been a conglomerate of minor states; the economy had been largely rural. In the 1830s the foundation of the German customs union, the *Zollverein*, and the opening up of the first railroad lines started the process of political and economic unification. Simultaneously, old bonds hampering rational economic activity and labor mobility were removed. Weber (1981, p. 99) describes this development:

> ... the peasants received freedom of movement and finally, favorable property rights. This happened in almost all of south and west Germany in the course of the [18]20's and 30's; only in Bavaria the substance of it was not achieved until 1848.

The economy now became more dynamic. The production of coal, iron, machinery, and foodstuffs increased substantially in the period 1851-1857.

Some legal institutions remained unaltered in spite of these changes. For example, the guild system did not disappear until the late 1860s, and a general standard for money, weights, and other measurements had to wait until the foundation of the German *Reich* in 1871. This event was followed by two years of intensive economic activity—a period known as the *Gründerjahre*, the founding years. New joint-stock companies were started by the hundreds, but the bubble suddenly burst in 1873. The crisis began in Vienna in May, and it soon spread to most of Europe and North America. Scholars debate about the length and severity of the following depression, but by 1880 most German economic figures, including real income, started to climb again (Desai 1968).

The economies of Bavaria and Austria-Hungary remained small-scale, rural, and agricultural much longer than the northwestern parts of Germany (Good 1984; Gross 1973; Kaizl 1879; Michelson 1907; Zorn 1962, 1975). True, a polytechnic had been founded in Vienna already in 1815, but the historian N.T. Gross (1973, p. 252) nevertheless calls the industrialization of the Habsburg monarchy in the former half of the nineteenth century a "patchwork" process. The government of the Bavarian kingdom directly counteracted the industrialization of certain branches of business. Brewing did not belong to these branches however, and we will later encounter large brewing companies in both Bavaria and Austria. These firms were situated far away from coal resources and the economic centers of the continent and could grow only as the railroad expanded; Munich was connected to Augsburg in 1840, to Berlin in 1851, and to Vienna in 1860 (Jacobs and Richter 1935).

In contrast to Austria-Hungary and Bavaria, most of the Swiss cantons had already gone through bourgeois and industrial revolutions early in the nineteenth century (Biucchi 1973; Hauser 1961). Thanks to its large, mechanized textile mills, Switzerland had become second only to Britain in cotton manufacturing. In textile centers like Zurich and Winterthur a machine industry slowly began to grow with the help of an industrialization policy (Hofmann 1962). As we will see in Part II, one result of this policy was the foundation of a very advanced engineering school by mid-century.

The Central Position of the Machine Industry

Of course, the machine industry was by no means limited to Switzerland.[1] If textiles and mining had been at the center of early industrialization, the machine industry became the very hub of the nineteenth century economy. Rosenberg (1976, p. 18) claims in a discussion of the period 1840-1910 that

> ... the machine [tool] industry may be regarded as a center for the acquisition and diffusion of new skills and techniques in a machinofacture type of economy.

This industry worked the increasing amounts of iron which were being produced, and it supplied itself and other branches of the economy with everything from simple screws to complex machines. Bessemer and other new processes supplied it with more and more steel, enabling an improvement in quality (Becker 1962). The technology of the machine industry was versatile, but at its base were drilling, milling, and grinding (Hallendorff 1967; Rolt 1986). This flexible ability—both concerning production, processes, and products—is part of a phenomenon which Rosenberg (1976, pp. 15-28) calls *technological convergence*. The phenomenon will be illustrated in the following story, as we encounter several cases where machine firms were able to adjust to the production of mechanical refrigeration systems because of technological knowledge acquired in manufacturing other items.

---

1 A firm in the *machine tool industry* uses machine tools in its production process. It does not necessarily make machine tools, even if some companies in this branch do. Certain firms use machine tools in order to manufacture machines, and thus they belong to the *machinery producing industry*. To make things more complicated, machine tools can also be used in carpentry, of course. However, the term is normally restricted to metal working establishments. The broadest term, also covering pure assembly plants, is the *machine industry*—or machine shop if we deal with smaller firms. The technology of mechanical engineering is primarily tied to this industry.

The flexibility and importance of the machine industry as a whole are also stressed by Walter Becker (1962) and Ernst Barth (1973) in their accounts of the German developments in this field between the years 1850 and 1914. However, they also make it clear that at least two trends during this period counteracted versatility on the level of individual companies. There was a differentiation between firms as each became more specialized. For instance, in 1871 85% of all locomotive producers made nothing but locomotives (Becker 1962, p. 212). There was also a move away from made-to-order production toward a standardized production-for-stock. Under the latter system, which Weber (1981, p. 118) calls "price work," the customer had to choose between a limited number of models in stock, each of a certain size and performance.[2] We will see below how refrigeration systems were indeed standardized in this manner—in opposition to Barth's (1973, pp. 14 ff.) claim that refrigeration technology was not standardized in the nineteenth century.

There were other interconnected trends in the German machine industry (Barth 1973). The number of workers increased constantly, and the energy demand and the accumulation of capital increased even faster (Hoffmann 1965, pp. 69, 196). The overall trend was that the small machine shop, with a craftsman or mechanic at its head, yielded to the large joint-stock firm, where well-educated engineers played significant roles as owners or employees. However, this does not mean that the small firms disappeared altogether. Just like today, small machine shops serving a local market could co-exist with large, export-oriented companies.

The Foundation of the Mechanical Theory of Heat

The main purpose of the present study is to analyze the influence of science on technology, in particular of the science of heat on refrigeration technology in the period 1870-1890. Such an analysis obviously presupposes that a science of heat existed by the late 1860s. At the time this

---

2 Please note that (1) the standardization of machine models does not necessarily require that (2) the parts of the machines are standardized (i.e., made interchangeable in accordance with the "American system"). In Germany (1) generally predated (2) (Barth 1973, p. 67).

science was commonly called the mechanical theory of heat, even if its modern name, thermodynamics, was also used.

Fire was one of the Aristotelian elements; it inhered in most substances, but was not a substance itself (*DHS* 1981). This classical scheme was challenged in the seventeenth century, when Pierre Gassendi suggested that there are certain fire particles and Robert Boyle claimed that heat is nothing but an effect of matter in motion. Gassendi represented the substantialist and Boyle the kinetic theory of heat. During the next century most natural philosophers, Isaac Newton included, adhered to the kinetic theory, even though misgivings concerning this idea increased. Chemists, from Hermann Boerhaave to Antoine-Laurent Lavoisier, regarded the total quantity of heat in chemical reactions as constant, and argued that this conservation principle appeared most conducive to the substantialist theory. The substance of heat was named caloric. The caloric theory became highly developed and influential in the first decades of the 1800s, even though a kinetic approach was vigorously defended by some natural philosophers (Brush 1976; Fox 1971; Mendoza 1961; Rosenfeld 1941; Truesdell 1980). Despite this struggle, both camps could share several notions of a more phenomenological kind, such as latent and specific heats. Important experimental results could be communicated even between people with different ontological points-of-view.[3]

Thermometers had been considerably improved in the eighteenth century, and standard temperature scales had been adopted (Meyer 1913) Ole Roemer's thermometer, employing mercury instead of alcohol, and Daniel Fahrenheit's graduation, based on two fixed points, became a very popular combination. Thermometers of an accuracy down to one twentieth of a degree Celsius (1/10°F) were available already at the end of the century, and after 1800 the liquid thermometer was replaced by the gas version in measuring extreme temperatures. In particular, the gas thermometer became a useful tool for scientists and engineers interested in very high or very low temperatures. The science of heat owed much to the technology of thermometer making—just as biology became dependent on the micro-

---

3 One reason why C. Truesdell (1980) called his book on the early history of thermodynamics a tragicomedy is that fruitful misunderstandings abounded. Cf. Thomas S. Kuhn's (1970, pp. 129 f., 184) paradigm theory, admitting that scientists are able to share concepts and instruments, even if they do not have the same "metaphysical paradigm."

scope. Without good instruments the natural philosophers would not have been able to reach much beyond pure speculation.

The importance of technology for the development of science—that is, the reversal of scientification—has recently caught the attention of several historians and social scientists (Collins 1990; Hård 1993a; Lindqvist 1988; Price 1986). It is clear that not only thermometry, but also steam engine technology, was crucial for the birth of thermodynamics. Donald S. Cardwell writes that (1971, p. xii):

> [Thermodynamics] originated substantially (but not of course wholly) in the power technologies of the eighteenth and early nineteenth centuries.

The steam engine, the great symbol of the Industrial Revolution, transformed heat into work as nothing before had, and aroused interest among scientists and engineers in energy conversions. The most important early contributor was the scientifically trained French engineer, Sadi Carnot, who in 1824 published a book called *Reflexions on the Motive Power of Fire* (1978). Like many before him, Carnot here aims specifically at the improvement of the steam engine, but he also wants to furnish a general theory of heat.

Denouncing the possibility of perpetual motion, Carnot (1978, p. 74) claims that "*wherever a temperature difference exists, motive power can be produced*" (Carnot's emph.). The larger the temperature gap is between the furnace and the cooling water, the more work a steam engine can produce. Since at this time Carnot still supported the caloric theory of heat, it was natural for him to draw a parallel between a waterfall and a decrease of temperature—in other words the fall (not the destruction) of caloric. Carnot thus demonstrates that the temperature gap sets a limit of the available "motive force" and goes on to ask what engine process comes closest to this limit. The starting-point is the repeating cyclic process of a steam engine; compare Figure 1.1:[4]

1. Heat (Q_1) is added to water in a boiler, turning the water into expanding steam;
2. The steam continues to expand in a cylinder, doing work;

---

4 Even though Carnot did not draw diagrams such as that in Figure 1.1, it has been included here to lay a foundation for Part II. However, Carnot *did* talk about a "circle of operation" (Truesdell 1980, p. 86).

3. The steam is condensed to water again, as heat (Q_2) is removed (work may here be performed by the atmosphere);
4. The water is pumped back to the boiler, and the cycle starts over again.

Carnot's great discovery was how these four steps should be arranged for maximum efficiency:

1. Heat should be added at constant temperature;
2. Expansion should continue without heat being lost to the surroundings, the temperature of the steam continuously sinking;
3. Heat should be removed from the steam at constant temperature;
4. The steam should be compressed without heat being lost to the surroundings.

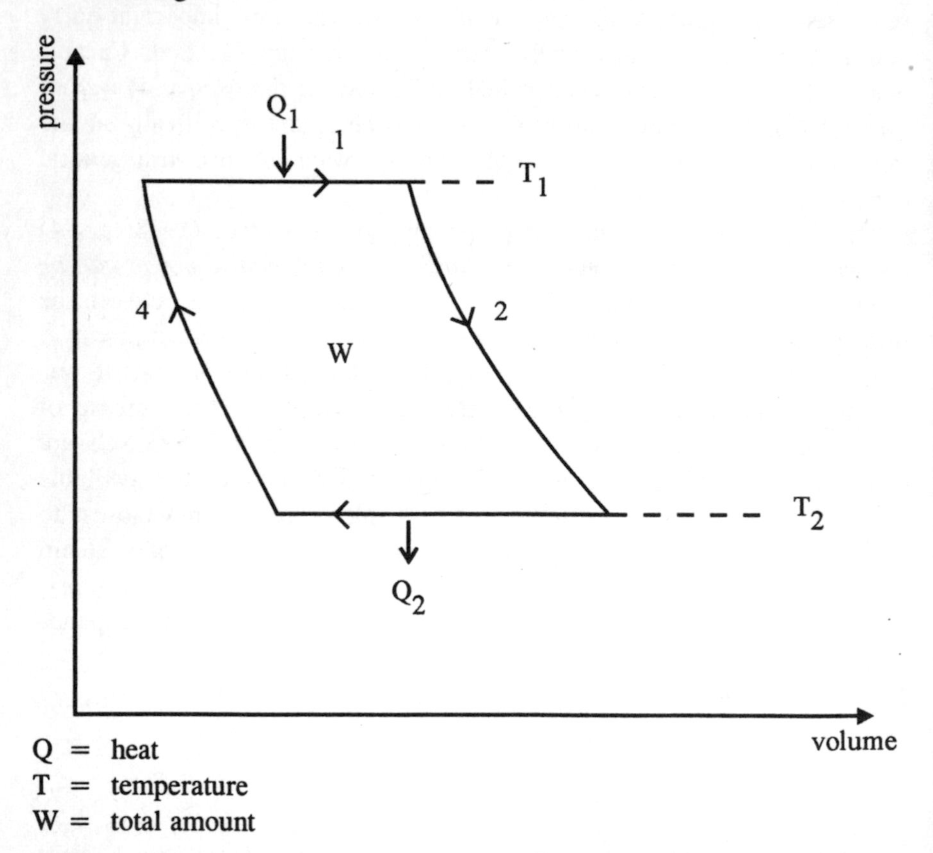

Q = heat
T = temperature
W = total amount

Figure 1.1. Schematic representation of a steam engine cycle

A heat engine fulfilling this ideal would be a theoretically perfect machine. This ideal can never be reached in practice, but the goal of achieving this "Carnot cycle" came to be of immense importance as a *Leitbild* for generations of later engineers (Dierkes *et al.* 1992): Rudolf Diesel tried to reach this ideal in the 1890s when designing his internal combustion engine (Knie 1991). In Part II we will see how the Carnot cycle also influenced one of Diesel's teachers, Carl Linde, in his work on mechanical refrigeration.

Carnot's work remained obscure for a decade, and after yet another decade the synthetic science of "thermodynamics," or the mechanical theory of heat, was born (Liedman 1983). Fundamental to the foundation of thermodynamics was the appearance of its so-called first law—independently formulated in the 1840s by several people, including Rudolf Clausius, Hermann von Helmholtz, James Prescott Joule, Rober Mayer, and William Thomson (Lord Kelvin) (Hiebert 1962; Kuhn 1959; Mach 1883). This law is the principle of the conservation of energy, or of "the preservation of force," as it was usually called. A similar law for the conservation of vis viva (mass times velocity squared) had been suggested by Gottfried Wilhelm Leibniz as early as 1700, but the new law made it possible to find connections between a much wider range of phenomena: mechanical work, electric power, heat, and chemical affinity, for instance. Energy cannot be created, it can only be transformed into other forms. Clausius was probably the most important person apart from Thomson in developing a strict, mathematical foundation for thermodynamics. They presented the second law of this science in the 1850s, saying that heat cannot pass from a cold to a warm body without the exertion of work. In 1865 Clausius (1867, p. 44) phrased the first two laws of thermodynamics in this manner:

1. The energy of the world is constant;
2. The entropy of the world strives for a maximum.[5]

By 1870 thermodynamics had thus developed into a distinct field of science studying heat and energy conversions, along with the behavior of matter at various temperatures and phases. It had its own ontology, laws, concepts, and research program. Technology had affected its development, and in Part II we will see how it, in turn, came to affect the technology of mechanical refrigeration.

---

5 "Entropy" is a notoriously difficult concept; the most accessible definition is probably one later suggested by the science of statistical mechanics: "degree of disorder."

2. The Classificatory Ideal Types of Natural and Mechanical Refrigeration

Max Weber's Concept of Classificatory Ideal Type

People have observed since time immemorial that cold may have a refreshing and preserving power, but this chapter focuses on the nineteenth century. A systematic treatment of various methods of natural and artificial sources of refrigeration in the 1800s is presented, thereby laying a foundation for the following story.

It is important in most scholarly activity to divide and discuss the objects of study in a systematic manner (McKinney 1970). It is common in the history and sociology of technology literature to distinguish, for instance, between different theoretical and practical traditions (Constant 1980), relevant social groups (Pinch and Bijker 1987), or technological systems (Mayntz and Hughes 1988)—depending on the desired perspective. Since large parts of the present study treat changes in apparatus and machinery, a terminology distinguishing between such devices will be proposed. Instead of terms already being used in the secondary literature, a Weberian concept is chosen.

Authors of engineering textbooks normally describe machines and processes in general terms for reasons of clarity. For instance, it is common to give a schematic account in writing and drawing of the four-stroke Otto engine in chapters on internal combustion. Idealizations are preferred to a description of a modern, existing, actual piston and cylinder from a car engine. Historians of technology usually divide their subject-matter along the same lines, and the invention and development of the Otto and the Diesel engines are often central topics in histories of internal combustion (Knie 1991). Both the engineering and the historical accounts presuppose that all so-called Otto engines share some characteristics. I suggest that Weber's concept of *ideal type* can be applied to any schema depicting the common trait of a class of technical objects. A technological ideal type may formally be defined as a visual, literal, or oral representation of the basic features inherent in an area of technics. An ideal type is an image which might be used for scientific and pedagogical ends; it is constructed by a method which could be called empirically based inductivism, but it is not a mere reflection of real items. If an ideal type exists in reality, it does so only on paper or as a demonstrative model. Unlike an invention or innovation, an ideal type is not patentable.

Weber himself never did apply the ideal type concept to material objects, so the extension here proposed may, of course, be questioned. For Weber (1922, p. 190) ideal types like "capitalism", "Catholic," and "craftwork" were mental constructs used by historians and social scientists in a "pragmatic" and "heuristic" manner to orient themselves in the chaotic world of social agents and events. Without such concepts, scholars in the human sciences would literally be unable to see the forest for the trees. The science of economics had in Weber's age successfully used a similar method when discussing and analyzing the behavior of rational individuals and organizations in a perfect market. Even if nobody in the real world acts absolutely rationally, it has nevertheless proven quite useful to suppose that the market is inhabited by "economic men." We will see in Part III below how Weber applied terms like "workshop" and "factory" in an ideal-typical way.

According to Weber, ideal types belong "neither to historical reality nor to 'actual' reality" (p. 194). They belong to the world of ideas, but they are not the result of free speculation or deductions from an isolated mind (Küttler and Lozek 1986, p. 174). Weber instead "views types as inductively abstracted from reality" (Burger 1976, p. 124). An ideal type includes those characteristics which are considered representative of a certain group of phenomena; everything that is "occasional," contextual, or accidental is excluded (Weber 1922, p. 201).

Even if Weber only used the ideal type concept for highly complex social phenomena, I would like to try to apply it to technological matters. After all, Weber's concern was to further research in the human sciences, not the natural ones (Hekman 1983, pp. 35 f.), and technological artifacts are certainly human products. Take the automobile as an example. As an ideal type the automobile may be defined as an engine-driven vehicle covered by a metal body with four wheels and a chassis, or it may be depicted by a simple drawing. Both descriptions are mental constructs and have been abstracted from reality; neither of them *is* a car; both of them are stripped of everything that is not characteristic of all cars. And, last but not least, an ideal type of this kind is a great auxiliary tool for anyone discussing or analyzing the history of modern transportation.

One possible objection is that here the automobile is actually being used as what Weber (1922, p. 202) calls a "simple class concept" (*einfacher Gattungsbegriff*)—that is, one which includes "a complex of traits which are common to several phenomena." While an ideal type contains everything that the scholar considers significant, a simple class concept includes everything that, from an empirical point of view, appears common to a group of objects (Psychopedis 1984, p. 258). If *automobile* were considered as a simple class concept, a vehicle with six wheels or a plastic body would be something else. Such a definition would obviously cause trouble for anyone discussing or analyzing, for instance, traffic policy. But if *automobile* were regarded as a "classificatory" ideal type (*gattungsmäßig*; *ibid.*), this strange vehicle could easily be treated as an automobile. Judith Janoska-Bendl (1965, p. 26) has pointed out that this may indeed sound paradoxical: "The ideal type is a class concept which does not encompass all individual cases belonging to the class."

Thus, the main proposition in this chapter is that classificatory ideal types could be useful tools in the history of technology; they help the scholar to organize and present his or her material in an orderly manner. Since these types are supra-historical, they facilitate temporal and geographical comparisons without implying historical links between various machines and apparatuses. The concept itself carries no evolutionary or diffusionist bias.

Equivalents to ideal type in the literature on the typology of artifacts are not easy to find. A century ago, Camillo Sitte, a well-known architect and town planner, introduced the term "original form" (*Urform*) in an article on the classification and history of furniture design. Sitte (1888) distinguishes between two original forms, the principles of which are inherent in all furniture: the box and the shelf. For instance, the modern cupboard and closet illustrate the box form. However, the big difference between Sitte's concept and that of ideal type is that original form is an historical and genealogical term, not a supra-historical one. Sitte claims that all furniture has historically developed from early boxes and shelves.

Much closer, both literally and figuratively, to ideal type is Karl Heimpel's "basic type" (*Grundtyp*). Heimpel (1894) used it at the end of the nineteenth century in a technical account of mechanical refrigeration, dividing this subject into three basic types. In fact, they correspond exactly to the last three ideal types in the account below. However, Heimpel only introduces his term in passing (p. 6), giving no theoretical motivation for it. The primary reason for preferring the ideal type is that this concept directly reveals its imaginary, non-genealogical character. Basic type is more ambiguous in this regard.

The same criticism can also be directed at the term "basic model," launched by the historian of technology Alfred Wislicki (1985). He finds in the history of pumping technology that there are only three basic models at the root of all pumps. Like an ideal type, a basic model has to reflect historical or contemporary reality. However, unlike an ideal type, a basic model has actually existed. Wislicki mentions as an example Ktesibios' double piston pump—not the double-acting pump in general. If we combine the two terms, we could say that the basic model is the first recorded example of a product or process being classified as an ideal type.

Refrigeration Without Machines

Let us make the discussion less abstract and see how the ideal type concept may help us organize the refrigeration technology of the nineteenth century. The reader interested in refrigeration before the year 1800 may consult the fragmentary accounts found in Roger Thévenot's (1978, pp. 22-25) survey and the journal *Ice and Refrigeration* (1901, Vol. 21, pp. 3-6).

The first ideal type is as old as it is simple: the widespread method of storing perishables in *cool cellars or caves*. It is unique because it can be adopted by virtually all social agents. In the nineteenth century, cellar or cave refrigeration could be found in the family household, as well as in the small grocery and in the large, industrial brewery. Some breweries had multi-stored cellars reaching more than sixty meters (two hundred feet) under ground, its galleries sometimes totaling one and a half kilometers (one mile) (Arnold and Penman 1933, p. 55; Baron 1962, pp. 230 f.). Of course, the construction of such establishments required special knowledge and skill, the greatest problems being connected to ventilation. Moist and mold might ruin the stored products without a continuous exchange of air.

The second ideal type is *natural ice*, that is, all ice not man-made. It had been a custom for centuries in rural areas to harvest ice from ponds, lakes, and rivers, and to store it in food cellars in order to ensure that their temperature remained low throughout the hot summer. This method entails considerable problems of humidity and exact temperature control. The air becomes damp, and water has to be drawn off. An ice-house could become "a veritable sweatbox" in the summertime, as a nineteenth-century observer noted (*Ice and Refrigeration* 1897, Vol. 12, pp. 442 f.). Furthermore, the ice might be unwholesome, contaminating the stored product. This danger became a matter of public concern after the mid-nineteenth century, when a scientifically inspired "controversy" (Engelhardt and Caplan 1987) developed in the wake of bacteriology. Ice dealers vigorously fought what they distastefully labeled "germ theories" with varying success. Ice harvesting was forced to take place farther and farther away from towns and industries (Goosman 1924, Vol. 67, pp. 110 ff.; *Ice and Refrigeration* 1893, Vol. 5, p. 103, 1898, Vol. 14, pp. 99 ff.).

However, despite these problems—in addition to the simple fact that the supply of natural ice is dependent on long, cold winters and therefore always insecure—the use of natural ice spread to a number of trades during the century, vividly demonstrating the large market for cold production (Anderson 1953; Cummings 1949; Goosman 1924, Vol. 67; Hall 1888; *Ice and Refrigeration* 1901, Vol. 21, pp. 6-16; Thévenot 1978, pp. 66-73). Ice-house construction was improved, and the technology of ice harvesting grew in scale and complexity. Figure 2.1 illustrates how horses were used for cutting the ice into conveniently sized blocks, and steam engines for hoisting them into storage buildings. The processing of natural ice became an industry in the hands of large and powerful companies. At least initially, this business depended heavily on the market-oriented foodstuffs industry. In 1870 natural ice was the most important refrigeration technology in Europe and North America.

The processing of natural ice had become a special business by the early 1800s, when Frederic Tudor of Boston began shipping ice to the West Indies. The first ice-houses were erected in the American South where New England ice was stored and subsequently sold to local restaurants and similar establishments. This business grew during the following decades, even though supply was always insecure and prices sometimes one hundred times higher in New Orleans than in Chicago. A growing number of Southern firms, among them breweries, became increasingly dependent on ice. Their position became especially precarious during the Civil War, when supply was frequently cut off. By this time, a steady demand for ice had developed. It is not surprising to find several people experimenting with mechanical refrigeration during the war. The need for natural ice had paved the way for artificial refrigeration.

Figure 2.1. Harvesting and storing of natural ice at the Knickerbocker Ice Co., Philadelphia, PA; from Fasbender (1881, Vol. 1, p. 28); courtesy *Deutsches Museum*, Munich

In the northern United States natural ice became particularly important in the meat packing trade (Clemen 1923; McCarty 1902; *Report* ... 1905; Unfer 1951; Yeager 1981). The expansion of the canal and railway networks had made it possible to raise animals farther away from the densely populated eastern areas of the country. Initially live cattle and hogs were transported eastward to local butchers. These long trips were problematic, however, since the animals lost weight and some did not even survive. Some firms began at mid-century to slaughter the livestock in the Midwest and to transport dressed beef and pork to the Northeast to get around this problem, a solution which meant that no inedible parts of the animals had to be transported. The rapidly growing city of Chicago soon became the center for these meat packers (Pierce 1937-1957). "Disassembly lines" were designed to speed up butchering. At first the whole sequence from slaughtering to shipping had to be carried out in the wintertime, but once the first ice-house for dressed beef was erected in 1858, dressing began to take place in the summer as well (Unfer 1951, pp. 10 f.). Slowly but gradually, the packers grew independent of the season.

The next step was to introduce (natural) ice-cooled railroad cars. The first American refrigerator car patent was issued in 1867, but ice had already been used a couple of years earlier to cool food in normal railroad cars (Leech and Carroll 1938, pp. 125 f.). The new cars were soon adopted by several meat packers, most notably by Gustavus F. Swift, "the Yankee of the Yards," who even supported technical experimentation in this area (Unfer 1951; Pierce 1937-1957, Vol. 3, pp. 113-119). Some historians stress the "technology push" activity of inventors supplying the initially passive market with refrigerator cars (MacManus 1925; Yeager 1981, p. 241), whereas others emphasize the "market pulling" force exercised by the packers demanding innovations (Chandler 1977, pp. 299 f.). Either way, the technology of natural ice refrigeration clearly was very important to the growth of this industry.

The "*ice-boxes on wheels*," as Rudolf A. Clemen (1946, p. 13, his emph.) has called the refrigerator cars, gave the packers a better chance of handling and controlling their products throughout the year—granted a large enough natural ice harvest. However, this does not mean that there were no problems connected with the ice-cooled car. Like in the ice-house, the air inside the car often became damp because of insufficient ventilation, or the temperature rose too high as a result of a short ice-supply. If the refrigerator car solved some of the meat-packers' problems (cattle dying during transportation), it created new ones (unfresh meat reaching its destination).

It also failed to solve many problems for other concerned parties. Local butchers, who wanted to remain in control of slaughter and dressing, battled the ice-cooled car, for instance through its newly founded National Butchers' Protective Association. The railroad companies did not want to invest in expensive, new cars and charged the same price for transporting dressed meat as life cattle—until Congress acted against them in 1887. Customers, who found the quality of the meat deteriorating, disliked chilled meat (Yeager 1981). Only as a result of the packers' political power and economic strength did the ice-cooled railroad car eventually take over in the 1890s.[1]

The European natural ice trade found its large sources of ice in Norway and the Alps, but some ice was in fact imported all the way from the United States. Norwegian ice exports to Britain had already started in the 1820s, and they grew constantly during the rest of the nineteenth century (*Ice and Refrigeration* 1901, Vol. 21, p. 12; Smith 1942-1943, p. 100; Thévenot 1978, pp. 69 f.). More than one hundred vessels were involved in this trade by the turn of the twentieth century. Some of the ice went all the way to Bavaria, a long and expensive rail or boat journey. In contrast to the United States, in Europe the ice was not primarily used for cooling meat (Perren 1978). The fish trade was its largest consumer in Britain, and in Germany most of the ice went to the brewing industry.

Like the two previous classificatory ideal types of refrigeration, examples for the third type can be found in ancient times. Here, *porous pots and pans*, made of unglazed clay, are filled with water and stored in the open air over night. If the weather is clear and the wind is brisk, the vaporization of the water might be so rapid that the water in fact turns into ice. Vaporization always requires considerable amounts of energy, and in the case of clay pots and pans, the energy is taken as heat from the water itself, whereby the temperature of the water decreases. (Physically, this is the same principle that causes someone to shiver after having taken a swim during a cold day.) Even though the method is too cumbersome to ever have become of any large economic significance, it was still the only way for many cultures to obtain ice.

A fourth ideal type is the lowering of temperature by *mixing water with salts* like ammonium nitrate or saltpeter. Heat is absorbed as the salt turns from solid to liquid, the temperature of the mixture hence decreasing. The

1 Arguing in favor of a social constructivist approach to technology studies, Trevor J. Pinch and Wiebe E. Bijker (1987) claim technology is shaped by various "relevant social groups" and that the technology in question has a specific "meaning" to each group. The authors apply their approach to the early history of the bicycle, showing how various user groups—that is, not only engineers—influenced its design. However, they seem to have forgotten the power dimension in their endeavor to give all relevant groups a chance to influence technological development. The ice-cooled car is a nice example of how power relations decide what technologies are introduced; it was an outcome of conflicting interests rather than consensus (Hård 1993; Russell 1986).

method has been known for centuries and in the 1800s was found in confectioneries and fancy restaurants.

Mechanical Refrigeration

Mixing obviously requires mechanical work, but only the following three classificatory ideal types are usually placed under the heading of mechanical refrigeration: air expansion, vapor compression, and absorption. A controversy developed in mechanical engineering over the pros and cons of these three systems in the decades around 1870. Rapidly expanding firms experienced difficulties in finding large and cool enough cellars or caves, and many industrialists felt that non-mechanical solutions would not be able to meet the increasing demand for a constant supply of cold. The use of natural ice continued to increase, but its bulkiness, occasional unwholesomeness, irregular supply, and fluctuating prices caused severe problems. If a reliable, continuously working, and not too expensive method could have been found, many business directors—brewers among them—would have welcomed it. After mid-century it looked as if this dream might come true. The general upsurge of the industrial economies, better raw materials (especially steel), and the growing skill of the machine industry were factors that made mechanical refrigeration seem more likely and promising. I shall review in abstract fashion the three classificatory ideal types of mechanical refrigeration before examining these developments (Kalide 1976; Van Wylen and Sonntag 1985).

Let us begin with the *air expansion* (or *cold air*) type. It is based on the physical principle that the temperature of a gas (air in this case) sinks if the gas is allowed to expand while doing external work. Since some of the energy of the gas is used to perform mechanical work, its temperature is lowered. The complete cycle of this ideal type is depicted in Figure 2.2. Since the goal is to produce cold by allowing air to expand, it is first necessary to acquire air at high pressure. This is done in cylinder a, as atmospheric air is compressed—a process requiring work (W_a). Anyone who has used a bicycle pump knows that compression increases the temperature of the air. The hot and compressed air is subsequently cooled by means of well or stream water drawing off heat (Q_1), its temperature sinking from T_1 to T_2. Now that we have cool and compressed air, we sub

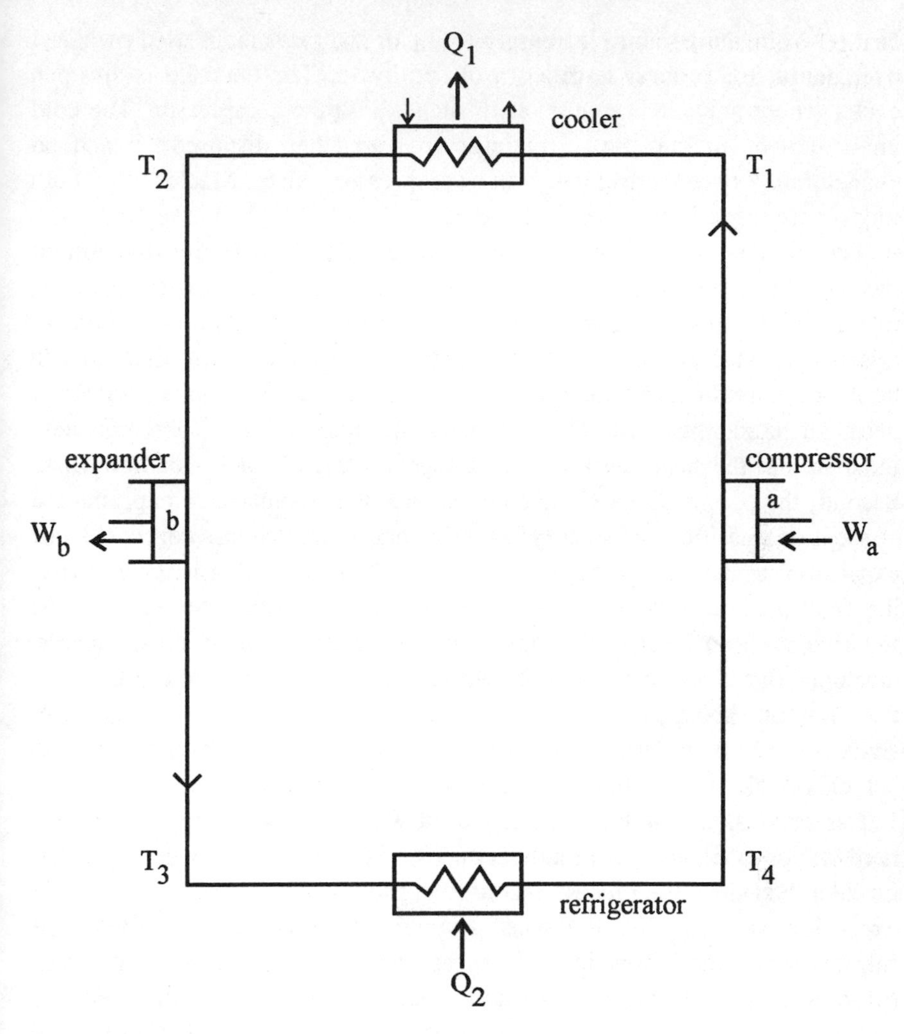

Q = heat
T = temperature
W = total amount

Figure 2.2. The classificatory ideal type of air expansion (cold air)

sequently allow it to expand in cylinder (or turbine) b, while performing work (W_b). Its temperature falls from T_2 to T_3 during this process, and with this cold air we can cool a refrigerator area, where the air absorbs heat (Q_2), its temperature increasing to T_4. If the same air is used over and over again, the process is called a closed cycle. The opposite is an open cycle, where new air is continuously sucked into the compressor. The cold air is blown out into the refrigerator area and then disposed of, and no connection between refrigerator and compressor exists. Machines of both kinds were made in the nineteenth century.

Two methodological points can be made here. First, the division of mechanical refrigeration into three different kinds existed already in the middle of the nineteenth century and is no modern invention. Of course, this fact is no drawback for the historian of technology who discusses in terms of classificatory ideal types. However, the historian's categories need not be identical with those made at the time of study. The important thing is that the historian finds the categories useful for his or her work. Second, the open cold air cycle demonstrates the advantage of applying the concept of classificatory ideal type rather than a simple class concept. If air expansion, as depicted in Figure 2.2, had been a class—that is, encompassing the common denominators of all air expansion machines—a machine working with an open cycle could not have been called an air expansion machine. But if we focus on what we find to be the significant rather than the common aspects, the inclusion of the open machine poses no problem. Even if it has no connection between refrigerator and compressor, we can still classify it as belonging to the air expansion ideal type.

Gas expansion is today primarily used when very low temperatures are needed, for example in the manufacturing of liquid helium, whereas in the nineteenth century the process was used at more ordinary temperatures. Air expansion was often hailed for being simple and safe. Since no poisonous substances except lubrication oil are applied, these machines were often regarded as suitable for hospitals and groceries. An obvious drawback was that air is a bad heat conductor, and that it takes a considerable amount of time for it to cool down liquids or solids. In practice, this meant that the air entering the refrigerator had to be much colder than the items to be cooled. If the air had not been properly dried its humidity could also cause ice to clog the pipes or valves.

Figure 2.3 illustrates that the next ideal type, *vapor compression* (or *cold vapor*), is rather similar to air expansion. The main difference is that cold is produced in a vapor compression machine as the circulating substance turns from liquid to vapor in an evaporator, not as air rapidly

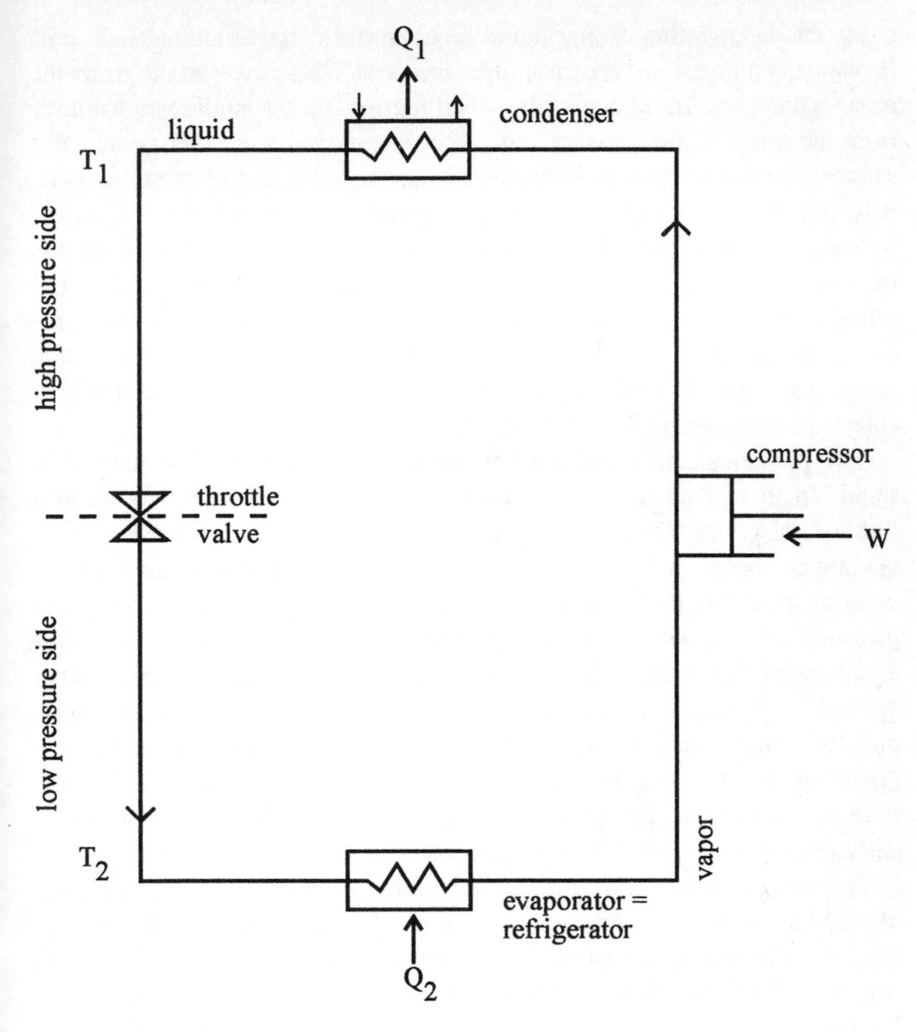

Q = heat
T = temperature
W = total amount

Figure 2.3. The classificatory ideal type of vapor compression (cold vapor)

expands. The substance is called refrigerant or working fluid. For practical reasons the expansion cylinder is usually replaced by a throttle valve. As we learned in the cases of porous pots and pans and of shivering swimmers, the vaporization of any liquid requires considerable amounts of heat. In vapor compression type machines this heat (Q_2) is absorbed from the refrigerator area. In other words, when the refrigerant is allowed to move from the liquid to the gaseous state, heat is removed from that area. After evaporation the refrigerant is returned to the liquid state in two steps: first, it is compressed in a cylinder, whereby mechanical work (W) is applied; second, the compressed, hot vapor is cooled and condensed as heat (Q_1) is removed from the refrigerant, usually by means of cooling water. The refrigerant is now once more liquid and can be evaporated again, thus producing more cold. The liquid is led to the evaporator through the throttle valve, and the cycle restarts. The vapor is usually dry and superheated as it enters the compressor. If not, the cycle is called "wet."

The problems and benefits of vapor compression will be discussed at some length in Part II, since this ideal type was preferred by the central figure Carl Linde. Only a few general aspects will be explicated here. It has always been understood that the choice of refrigerant is crucial; the working fluid has to be highly volatile at pertinent temperatures (T_2) and pressures; it may not freeze at any point of the cycle; it has to be compatible with the metals, oils, and packings of the machine. Diethyl ether and sulfur dioxide were most commonly used in the 1860s, but ammonia, dimethyl ether, and carbon dioxide were also applied. Although Thévenot (1978, p. 43) has claimed that ammonia was not used until 1872, the Frenchman Charles Tellier (1910) experimented with this compound as early as in the late 1850s, receiving a patent in 1860.

A serious problem with vapor compression is leakage, which is especially dangerous when poisonous substances like sulfur dioxide and ammonia, an inflammable compound like diethyl ether, or, as in the twentieth century, CFCs that destroy the ozone layer are used. The comparative harmlessness of carbon dioxide clearly contributed to the popularity of that substance in the second half of the previous century—its main disadvantage being its requirement of fairly high pressures (*Scientific American* 1876, Vol. 34, pp. 228 f.). By and large not many vapor compression machines were sold before the mid-1870s. Their technical and economic drawbacks were prohibitive. Prospective customers also felt that this system was a disaster waiting to happen.

Finally, we have come to the last ideal type: *absorption*. In 1870 it was commonly regarded as the most promising mechanical refrigeration method, and machines of this type could be found in a number of countries (Thévenot 1978, pp. 46 f.). The following chapter will describe how the most popular absorption system spread from France to other countries. Only the general features of the absorption ideal type will be sketched here.

Figure 2.4 demonstrates that the condensation and evaporation steps of absorption are identical to those in vapor compression. Cold is produced as a refrigerant is vaporized, drawing off heat from a refrigerator area. However, how the vapor is moved from the evaporator and how it is made to return to the condenser are different. With absorption, the compressor is replaced by a system consisting of a generator and an absorber. A mixture of refrigerant and liquid circulates through this system. The refrigerant has to be both volatile and soluble in this liquid. After evaporation the refrigerant is absorbed by and dissolved in the liquid—hence the name of this ideal type. The liquid is consequently called the absorbent. Water was usually used as absorbent and ammonia as refrigerant in the period 1860-1890, while today other substances are applied. For reasons of clarity only water and ammonia will be discussed in the following.

When the ammonia vapor coming from the refrigerator is absorbed by the water, heat is released. This heat (Q_4) has to be drawn off—usually by cooling water surrounding the absorber. The mixture, rich with ammonia, is led to the generator by means of a mechanical pump or gravity. If no pump is used, this ideal type has the big advantage in that no mechanical work is required. A famous system of this kind was developed by the Swedes Baltzar von Platen and Carl Munters in the 1920s (Johansson 1983; Rydberg 1983; Strandh 1979, pp. 227 ff.; Thévenot 1978, p. 177), but throughout our period all important machines included a pump.

The mixture is in the generator set to simmer at temperature T_3, heat (Q_3) being added. Most of the ammonia vapor is driven out of the water and piped to the condenser in this process, while the water vapor, now containing only small amounts of ammonia, is led back to the absorber. This ideal type thus includes two cyclic processes.

Absorption has two big drawbacks. First, the heat (Q_3) just mentioned is quite substantial, since a large amount of water has to be evaporated over and over again in the generator. Second, since it is rather complex, involving two cyclic processes and two substances, absorption is difficult to analyze in mathematical, physical, and chemical detail. This disadvantage hardly played any role before 1870, but it became a serious problem with the scientification of refrigeration technology.

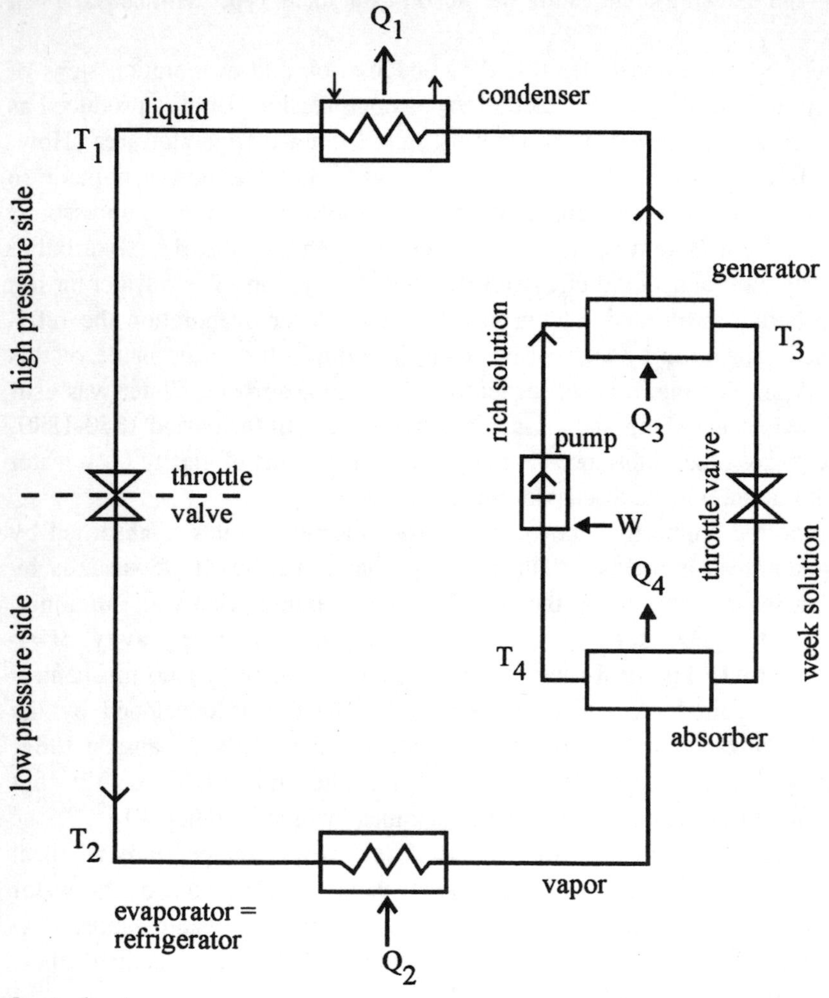

Q = heat
T = temperature
W = total amount

Figure 2.4. The classificatory ideal type of absorption

We will see in Chapters 5 and 7 how thermodynamic tools could be applied to the analysis of air expansion and vapor compression early on, whereas a comprehensive theory of absorption was not put forth until the very end of the nineteenth century.[2]

2 This was done by Lorenz (1899) in a paper that appears to be unknown to Thévenot (1978, p. 47) who claims that the first theory of absorption was not introduced until 1913.

3. Archetypes and Types in Mechanical Refrigeration

The Concept of Archetype

The central concept in the previous chapter was classificatory ideal type. Even though ideal types have a supra-historical character, they have to be grounded in historical or contemporary reality.

It is important that we do not lose sight of which refrigeration systems were actually designed and most widely used in our period. Since a controversy over the advantages and disadvantages of various mechanical refrigeration systems erupted around 1870, in this chapter I will examine more closely the most influential air expansion, vapor compression, and absorption machines of that time.

All historians have to face the complexity and manifoldness of historical data and decide what is significant and what is "only" interesting. One way of doing this in the history of technology is to isolate and describe the most influential products and processes and explain why they became so important. I propose the term *archetype* as a tool for achieving this end, here defined as a product or process which has served as a pattern for later developments in an area of technology. The German term *Vorbild*, literally meaning "pre-picture," brings out the model character of an archetype very well.[1] While ideal types and the psychoanalyst Carl Gustav Jung's term "archetype" are imaginary phenomena, a technological archetype designates a real object, and it is usually patentable. An archetype has actually existed (or still exists), and it has exerted substantial influence on the course of history. Like in Darwinian biology, it is a historical concept, not a supra-historical one.[2]

---

1 In their discussion of how the Underwood typewriter served as a pattern for later developments in this field of technology, Lutz Marz and Meinolf Dierkes (1992, p. 18) call the Underwood a *Leitbild*. It seems to me, however, that the term *Vorbild* is more suitable for an analysis of the model character of artifacts.

2 Archetype was earlier used as an abstract, classificatory tool in nonevolutionary theories, but Darwin gave it a true historical meaning (*DHS* 1981, p. 23). By archetype, Jung meant an image (of the good mother, for example) which is found among all human beings, regardless of cultural background (*DHI* 1968-1974, Vol. 3, p. 597; *FDMT* 1977, p. 34).

N.A. Otto's and Eugen Langen's 1876 engine illustrates the archetype concept. Their machine created an important precedent in four-stroke engine technology that lasted several decades (Bryant 1966). Their so-called "silent Otto" eventually influenced the design of other engines to a considerable degree. It became an archetype in the area of internal combustion and served as a model for later *types*—a type being defined as a modification of an existing product or process. Like archetype, a type is a real object, but it has not had any decisive impact on later developments. A classificatory ideal type may well encompass more than one archetype, and an archetype might develop into several directions at the same time. This gradual evolution of types is a branching process, whereby some characteristics change and others do not. Several archetypes, as well as types, may exist simultaneously and compete with each other.

These concepts will be related in the following to four areas of debate in technology studies: technological conservatism, closure and stabilization processes, the continuous or discontinuous character of technical change, and the distinction between invention and innovation. This discussion will remain on a fairly impersonal level, and it should always be borne in mind that behind the creation of archetypes and the design of types stand various social agents; we will return to them more explicitly in Chapter 4.

The archetype concept might well lend itself to an analysis of technological inertia and stability, addressing the question why certain technologies linger on and continue to set the agenda for further developments, whereas others fade away. Such problems can often be explained in economic terms by reference to substantial investments; if existing artifacts are not used, capital is destroyed. However, technological conservatism may also be seen as an outcome of the complex character of machines and technical systems. Andreas Knie (1992a) has discussed the inability of the automobile industry to undertake anything but minor modifications in engine design, and has shown how designers resist external demands for radical change. Renate Mayntz and Thomas P. Hughes (1989) have analyzed on a more aggregate level how the interrelatedness of artifacts makes it difficult to change one part of a technological system without considerable harm being done to the functionality of the system as a whole.

However, inertia may also be explained by referring to social and intellectual rather than economic and technical aspects. The historian John M. Staudenmaier (1985, pp. 155 f.) writes that:

> Dominant technical concepts tend to perpetuate themselves ... because of the influence they exert on the imaginations and intellectual expectations of mainstream practitioners.

Technologists become acquainted with certain artifacts and methods through education and professional experience, and considerable efforts are needed to move into completely new directions; a *professional culture* resistant to change often develops (Helmers 1991). Paraphrasing Thomas S. Kuhn (1970), Giovanni Dosi (1982) has chosen the term "technological paradigm" in order to cover the epistemological frameworks and problem-solving procedures of a group of engineers. Such paradigms are a kind of "inertial frame" and create "corridors" inside which most engineers are active (Knie 1989). Wiebe E. Bijker (1987) has gone even farther and also includes the goals and practices of nonengineers under the concept of "technological frame." Consumers, business administrators, technicians, and other groups have different technological frames; they emphasize different aspects of the technology in question and give it different meanings. Thus, Bijker's model is a dynamic one, but he does in fact discuss examples where only one frame remains. The technological artifact has stabilized in these cases, and a Kuhnian "exemplar" has been created.

Discussions of stabilization processes, whereby one among several solutions becomes dominant, have become quite common in technology studies (Bijker *et al.* 1987; Bijker and Law 1992). Technology-and-society scholars follow a line of investigation that began in the social studies of science (Engelhardt and Caplan 1987), and analyze how certain artifacts and procedures become accepted as what Knie (1991) has called "ruling standards." Controversies and conflicts that take place during the most creative and formative periods are highlighted and the factors contributing to closure and "black-boxing" are investigated (Latour 1987; Hård 1992).

Although these studies usually end when closure has been reached, the present study goes somewhat further. The definition of the term "archetype" facilitates an analysis not only of the establishment, but also of the maintenance of a stable artifact. The interesting question is not only why certain artifacts become paradigmatic exemplars, but also why they remain influential over the years. "Archetype" has its roots in the Greek word for ancient and implies something old and conservative. Of course, "exemplar" carries a meaning close to *Vorbild*, and it has been used in a similar fashion not only by Bijker, but also by Donald MacKenzie and Judy Wajcman (1985a, p. 11). But I hope to avoid philosophical discussions about incommensurability and *Gestalt* switches by keeping away from Kuhnian terms. For the same reason, the concepts of technological school (social aspects) and research and development program (theoretical and practical aspects) will be used instead of technological paradigm.

Two extremes may be found in discussions about the qualitative and quantitative aspects of technical change (Rosenberg, 1982, Ch. 1). Some scholars emphasize the revolutionary role played by a small number of epoch-making novelties. The economist Joseph A. Schumpeter was a well-known proponent of this point of view. For instance, he calls "the history of the productive apparatus of the iron and steel industry" a "history of revolutions" (Schumpeter 1978, p. 23). He stressed the discontinuous character of socio-technical change and claimed that technical and organizational innovations occur by leaps, not gradually. Schumpeter (1935, p. 4) writes in his neo-classical vocabulary: "... innovations are changes in the production function which cannot be decomposed into infinitesimal steps."

The opposite view quite naturally focuses on piecemeal, continuous changes in technical developments. This evolutionary position can also be found among economists—Paul David (1975) and Nathan Rosenberg (1982, Ch. 3), for example. Even though there are other so-called evolutionary theories that make explicit parallels between technical change and natural selection (Elster 1983, Ch. 6), the word "evolution" here does not suggest any biological parallels. Instead, it only alludes to a process of gradual change, as Rosenberg (1976, p. 192) explains:

> ... inventive activity is, itself, best described as a gradual process of accretion, a cumulation of events where, in general, continuities are much more important than discontinuities.

David does not deny that radical innovations take place, but he claims that their overall significance is minor compared to the cumulative effect of the many small changes which are made continuously. It seems to me that the relative significance of continuity and discontinuity has to be decided in each special case; revolution and evolution are mutually dependent processes. Rosenberg (1982, p. 68) also makes the point that a discontinuous revolution is a prerequisite for later evolution.

In the terminology of the present study ideal types are always distinctly different. A shift from one ideal type to another is certainly a revolution, whereas types evolve in a comparatively continuous process. A change from archetype to type, or from one type to another, is defined as a modification—a slight shift. However, things are not so clear when it comes to archetypes. At first glance, all archetypes may seem to represent something radically new. However, the only criterion for an archetype is that it has been influential for subsequent developments. Of course, it might have become influential because it has broken with historical tradition, but public relations and superficial design aspects are often more important for the setting of new trends. I want the term archetype, representing a central historical object, to determine the influential products or processes, not necessarily the revolutionary ones.

Another common distinction is between invention and innovation. These words are not always separated in everyday language, but in technology studies an important distinction is usually made (Edquist 1977, pp. 43 f.; Lindner 1982). An invention is the first description of a novelty. It is usually presented on paper or as a *prototype* for later production—prototype being defined in its ordinary sense, a device that is made as a test before real manufacturing can commence. An innovation, however, is the economic implementation of something new, the introduction of a novelty in the market. Whereas inventing is here primarily an engineering process, innovation includes a great amount of business-oriented activity as well. If an invention is the result of a technical feat, then the successful move to innovation requires entrepreneurial, managerial, and capital-raising skill (Glete 1987; Kocka 1975, pp. 13 ff.). An innovation always supersedes one or several inventions, but it goes without saying that most inventions are never turned into innovations. There is also a third concept which is often connected to the previous two: diffusion, defined as the geographical dissemination of the means for reproducing the innovation, not as the spread of the results itself.

Thirty years ago, the German philosopher of technology Friedrich Dessauer (1958, p. 168) used the concepts pioneering and development inventions (*Pionier-* and *Entwicklungs-Erfindungen*), which seem to come close to archetype and type (Tuchel 1964, p. 51). However, a pioneering invention is much more general than an archetype. Dessauer mentions the first steam engine and telephone as examples. Since a pioneering invention designates a real, historical object, it is not identical with ideal type; since the word pioneering implies discontinuity, whereas persistence and historical durability are inherent in the word archetype, Dessauer's term is not particularly similar to archetype.

Gerhard Mensch's (1979) terms, basic invention, basic innovation, improvement innovation, and pseudo-innovation (*Basiserfindung*, *Basisinnovation*, *Verbesserungsinnovation*, and *Pseudo-lnnovation*), are closer to my terms. Basic invention and basic innovation both designate revolutionary novelties, albeit at various levels of the creative process. Mensch (1979, p. 144) defines a basic invention as "a formula for a new type of product or process." His central problem was how such basic inventions can be turned into economically epoch-making basic innovations that bring something distinctly new onto the marketplace. Mensch came out of the Schumpeterian tradition and claimed that the economic crisis of the mid-1970s was due to a lack of basic innovations. Whereas a basic innovation represents discontinuity, an improvement innovation is just a minor change along "lines of development that have already been established" (p. 48). Finally, a pseudo-innovation also represents a small change, but cannot be considered an improvement compared with the existing technology. This last distinction seems meaningless; in practice, virtually every change can be considered an improvement by somebody, and hardly ever can a change be regarded as an improvement by everybody.

Archetypes are no doubt similar to basic inventions and basic innovations, and types are not far from the other two concepts. However, an archetype does not necessarily have to be revolutionary. We could say that some archetypes are basic inventions or basic innovations, and that some basic inventions and innovations become archetypes for a period of time. The archetype concept subsumes both inventions and innovations. Mensch himself shows that there is often a long time span between invention and innovation. It is not uncommon during that lag time for an invention (a patent description or a prototype, for example) to become an archetype. For instance, Beau de Rochas' four-stroke engine patent was an invention serving as an archetype up till 1876, when the "silent Otto" appeared.

The economist Simon Kuznets (1978) has put forth a vocabulary similar to Mensch's. Kuznets discusses "major inventions," which after some time may turn into economically useful "major innovations." A major innovation is both "a marked advance and a substantial economic contribution" (Kuznets 1978, p. 336).

I will examine the most influential refrigeration machine systems in the decades around 1860 below. Both qualitative and quantitative factors are taken into consideration when deciding what machinery ought to be labeled archetypes. The few general surveys of the history of refrigeration technology have been very helpful in evaluating the importance of and examining the ties between various machine systems (Anderson 1953; Goosman 1924-1926; Schwarz 1888; Thévenot 1978). Their accounts have been compared fruitfully with a comprehensive list of articles and books on mechanical refrigeration published before 1873, compiled by John Bourne (1873-1874) for the *Minutes of Proceedings of the Institution of Civil Engineers*. Engineering journals no doubt played an important role for the establishments of archetypes, not least through their increasingly detailed drawings (Belofsky 1991; Björck 1987).

Gorrie's Air Expansion Apparatus

When transoceanic trade in chilled meat began in the 1870s, natural ice was the safest cooling method. Several experimental journeys with refrigeration machinery were also made, but this technology was not firmly established until the following decade. Since shippers disliked having poisonous and inflammable substances on board, air expansion systems were usually favored. If leakage occurred, air was of course very preferable to ammonia or diethyl ether.

A Scottish machine was by far the most commonly used device of all cold air machines for meat transport in the 1880s (Thévenot 1978, p. 62). It had been developed by the Bell-Coleman Mechanical Refrigeration Company of Glasgow in the late 70s, a company illustrating a combination of user interest and technical skill which was common among ice-machine firms. We have already encountered such an example in the case of the ice-cooled car, where meat packers and technicians collaborated. We will study examples of cooperation between brewers and engineers in the next part. Henry and James Bell owned a meat packing business in Glasgow and needed low temperatures in their plants; James Coleman was a chemical engineer at a near-by oil refinery, Young, Meldrum & Co., where he had gained first-hand experience from an air expansion machine. This device had been designed and installed in the early 1860s by Alexander C. Kirk, an engineer at the refinery, for the cooling of paraffin.[3] Kirk had in turn been influenced by the work of John Gorrie, an American physician (Anderson 1953, pp. 67 f.; Kirk 1873-1874, p. 246).

Gorrie's machine acted as an important archetype within the air expansion ideal type throughout the period 1850-1880. There is a clear line of continuity from Gorrie over Kirk to Coleman, whose system replaced Gorrie's as an archetype around 1880. Bourne's (1873-1874) list of published technical articles showed that before 1870 Kirk's and Gorrie's machines received more attention than any other cold air system; Bourne lists nine papers on Kirk and seven on Gorrie. J.C. Goosman (1924, Vol. 67, p. 428) could write as late as 1924 that Gorrie's machine "included practically every important element of the present day dense air refrigerating apparatus." Even if that may be a slight exaggeration, some features of the Gorrie machine were definitely found among cold air machinery of the 1860s and 1870s, even if no direct links can be proven. For instance, Gorrie's machine shares several features with Franz Windhausen's system which was used widely in Germany during the seventies (Knight 1876, p. 1168).

What did the Gorrie archetype look like, and why had it been invented? Since Gorrie lived under the merciless sun of Florida and was concerned with the well-being of his patients, he had designed a simple air-cooling device applying natural ice already before he got into mechanical refrigeration (Becker 1972). As we have seen, natural ice prices were extremely high in the South. When Gorrie learned in 1842 about the chilling effect of expanding air, his mind was set in motion. Two years later he discussed in a local paper the features of an air expansion machine employed for what we today would call air conditioning:

> It is proposed to compress the external atmosphere by means of a force pump, and transfer it into a reservoir, and thence transmit it to a similar pump, there to exert its expanding mechanical force, and, finally, be discharged into the room of a house ...[4]

This is indeed a nice description of the cold air ideal type working on an open cycle.

---

3 Short descriptions of his and other early British patents in refrigeration technology can be found in *Abridgements* ... (1877).

4 Quoted in Becker (1972, p. 109); originally in the *Apalachicola Commercial Advertiser* of 1844.

It is not known exactly when Gorrie actually designed his first prototype, but by 1848 a Cincinnati firm had manufactured a couple of ice-producing machines following his specifications. One of them was apparently sent to Washington, D.C. along with a patent application, and another was transported to New Orleans for further experimentation. A third Gorrie machine was built in Britain by the firm "James Watt & Co." (MPICE 1882, Vol. 68, p. 177). Despite technical problems, it elicited the interest of others, who propagated information about Gorrie's ice-machine through articles in British engineering journals, including *Mechanic's Magazine* (1851, Vol. 54) and *Journal of the Society of Arts* (1854, Vol. 2). In fact, Gorrie was granted a patent in the United Kingdom in 1850 (MPICE 1882, Vol. 68, p. 153), one year before he received one in the United States, even though he never worked his patents commercially in either country. According to his own account, there were three reasons for this failure: no market existed for very large quantities of ice or cold; potential machine buyers were hesitant because they did not understand how the machine worked; opponents claimed that ice-making was both unnatural and ungodly.

The first explanation does not seem warranted, considering the steady growth of the natural ice trade, whereas the other two might have something to them (Becker 1972, p. 160). More important, however, was probably the sudden death of his most interested financier (Whiteside 1897, p. 160). A schematic picture of Gorrie's machine system can be found in Figure 3.1.

Each cycle began with atmospheric air entering the compressor at the right; compare the classificatory ideal type of Figure 2.2 (*Ice and Refrigeration* 1901, Vol. 21, pp. 47 f.; Woolrich 1947, pp. 197 ff.). A jet of cooling water was pumped into the cylinder after compression, lowering the temperature of the compressed air. In order not to clog any pipes with ice, the air then had to be dried before it was led to the expander at the left. The air was allowed to expand in this cylinder, whereby work was performed and the temperature of the air sank. The expander, serving as a refrigerator as well, was "surrounded by a cistern of an unfreezable liquid," as Gorrie wrote in his patent application (Woolrich 1947, p. 198). In other words, when the air expanded, it drew off heat from a brine which continuously passed over the cylinder walls. Simultaneously, part of the mechanical work done during expansion was used to drive the compressor.

The air was subsequently expelled into the atmosphere, and the cold brine was piped to a large ice-generator.

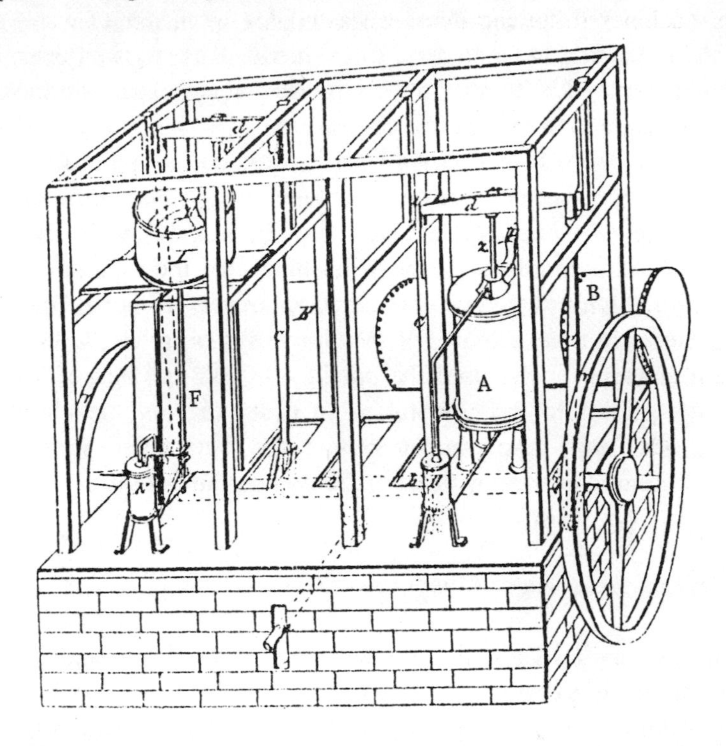

A = compressor
B = ice generator
F = expander surrounded by a brine jacket

Figure 3.1. The main characteristics of Gorrie's air expansion apparatus of the mid-19th century; from Woolrich (1947, p. 197)

Although it is difficult to tell from the picture, Gorrie's system was quite intricate, with a complex network of pipes and a sophisticated driving mechanism. When this archetype is compared with Kirk's later type, we find both similarities and differences. Kirk's machine consisted of three cylinders rather than two (Kirk 1873-1874; *Practical Mechanic's Journal* 1863, Vol. 8, pp. 113 f.). Instead of one expander, Kirk used two identical ones; instead of a vertical compressor, Kirk's was placed horizontally.

This machine worked on a closed cycle, the same air being pumped back and forth between the expanders, through the compressor. When the compressed air entered the expanders it was cooled by means of water passing along the bottom of the cylinders. Like Gorrie, Kirk allowed brine to pass by the expander—albeit only on the top side, where expansion took place. The cold brine was then used for ice-making.

It could be claimed that Kirk's machine was not a type modeled on the Gorrie archetype, because the two machines were rather different. However, they are alike in principle, and, more importantly, we know that Kirk was directly influenced by Gorrie's machine—the most decisive criterion when deciding what should be considered an archetype. Furthermore, if we move forward in time, features of the Gorrie system return in the Bell and Coleman apparatus, who used the open cycle and the idea of injecting a stream of water into the compressor in order to cool the air (Schwarz 1888, pp. 190-196). Like a true archetype, the characteristics of the Gorrie machine appeared at various times in the decades after 1850.

The Harrison-Siebe Vapor Compression Machine

The world of artificial refrigeration was small in the 1850s and 1860s, and a move from air expansion to vapor compression brings us back to the Young-Meldrum oil refinery. A vapor compression system had been at work there for a couple of years before Kirk began his experiments. That system, employing diethyl ether as refrigerant, had been made by the Siebe Bros. of London, one of the comparatively few manufacturers of vapor compression machines in this period. Why did the management of Young, Meldrum & Co. want Kirk to develop a new ice-machine, when the firm already owned one? The main reason was simple: leaking ether had caused a fire in the refinery; the dangers of vapor compression were real (Kirk 1873-1874, p. 246; Oldham 1946-1947).

However, one or two fires did not ruin the reputation of the Siebe company. It launched a modified machine in 1862 which received considerable attention. The Siebe machine was boosted by its success at the London industrial exhibition in that same year and soon gained wide publicity in engineering journals like *Practical Mechanic's Journal* (1863-1864, pp. 6 f.), *Dingler's Polytechnisches Journal* (1863, pp. 434 ff.), and *Engi-*

neering (1868, Vol. 6, p. 483). More papers were published on this machine up until 1870 than on any other vapor compression system; Bourne (1873-1874) lists sixteen articles about Siebe and twelve for Charles Tellier. As we will see in Part II, when Carl Linde initiated the scientification of refrigeration technology in 1870 by making a thorough analysis of various machines, he chose the Siebe design as *the* representative vapor compression system. When Linde later went ahead and constructed his own machine, he also borrowed several ideas from Siebe. Linde's second compressor model from 1875 is particularly close to Siebe's. The Siebe model of 1862 served as an archetype within vapor compression in general up until the late seventies, when Linde's third compressor model made its breakthrough.

The pre-history of the Siebe system brings us all the way to Australia, where in 1855 a Scottish emigrant had received a patent for a vapor compression machine using diethyl ether (*Ice and Refrigeration* 1901, Vol. 21, pp. 48 f.; Smith 1942-1943, p. 102; Thévenot 1978, pp. 38-41). His name was James Harrison, a man with a varied background and apparently without formal education. Among other things, he was the editor of a local paper and a member of the legislative council for Victoria. Not quite satisfied with his invention, Harrison traveled back to Great Britain and began to collaborate with a London machine firm: the Siebe Bros. Their cooperation was successful, and in 1856-1857 they received two British patents and could continue onto the level of innovation. The machine which had been installed at Young, Meldrum & Co. dates from this period. Harrison's ideas simultaneously returned to Australia, where P.N. Russell & Son began manufacturing the Harrison-Siebe machine. In London the Siebe Bros. went through a number of reorganizations, first becoming Siebe, West & Co., and then splitting into Siebe, Gorman & Co. and West & du Vallon, later H.J. West & Co. The basic features of the original design remained despite these changes. H.J. West's son Ernest West could write that "the design of the ether machine was not radically altered until 1888" (Oldham 1946-1947, p. 8). Like all archetypes, the core of the Harrison-Siebe design survived in more than one disguise.

The main features of the Siebe Bros.' 1862 machine can be seen in Figure 3.2, and it may also be compared to Figure 2.3. The single compressor in the middle is a vertical, double-acting pump, meaning that compression takes place below and above the piston, alternately. When compression occurred at the bottom, vapor was drawn into the space above the piston, and the compressed ether vapor was subsequently led to the condenser—a wooden tank with a copper coil submerged in cooling water, where the ether became liquid. Evaporation took place within a network of horizontal copper tubes in the refrigerator. The tubes were surrounded by brine which slowly flowed down the ice-generator and was subsequently pumped back to the refrigerator. The ice-generator was loaded from the lower end with metal troughs filled with water, and ready-made blocks of ice could then be removed at the top of the generator.

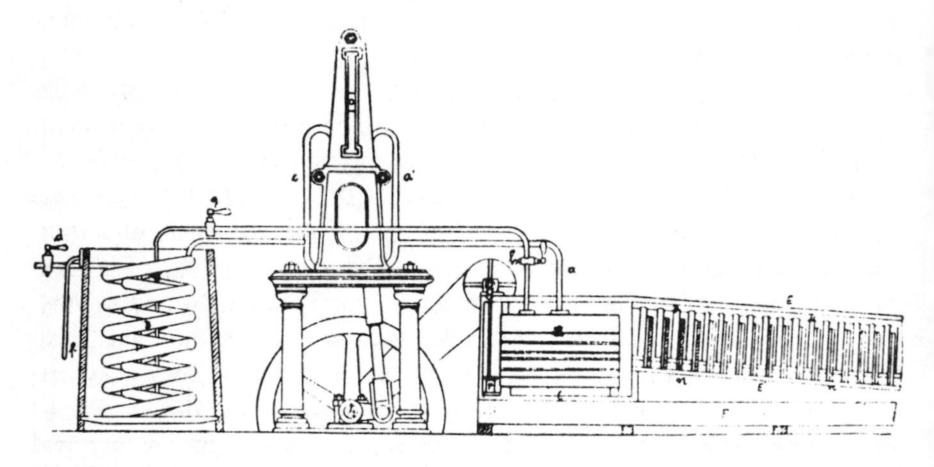

From left to right: condenser — compressor — evaporator — ice generator

Figure 3.2. The Harrison-Siebe vapor compression machine of 1862, applying diethyl ether; from Schwarz (1888, p. 306)

Machines built around 1860 were often enormous. At the Truman-Hanbury brewery, a Siebe machine with a one-odd meter (40") high cylinder was installed. Despite its size, the refrigeration compressor ran at a speed of forty double strokes per minute. It must have been an impressive and frightening machine. It was driven by a steam engine of fifteen horsepowers, a prime mover also made by the Siebe company. The technologies of steam engine design and of vapor compression refrigeration are not very different, and it was quite common for firms to combine the two. The temperature of the brine could reach -12°C (+10°F), and roughly three tons of ice could be produced in twenty-four hours. A peculiar feature of the Siebe design was the very low pressures applied in order to minimize ether leakage; the pressure in the condenser was only about 20% above that of the atmosphere. Leakage was a serious problem that plagued vapor compression machines in particular. As is illustrated by Figure 3.3, various more or less complicated techniques were developed to take care of it. If we apply the terminology of Thomas P. Hughes (1983, 1987), we could say that leakage was a "reverse salient" that hampered the expansion of mechanical refrigeration as a "technological system" (or "machine system," if you like). The cleaning-up outfit was a "conservative invention" in the sense that it helped the system overcome such problems without requiring it to change trajectories.

Figure 3.3. The dangers involved with the leakage of ammonia and other poisonous refrigerants led to the development of various respiration apparatuses, such as this one from the König Co. of Altona; from Behrend (1900, p. 297)

Mechanical refrigeration technology was still in flux around 1870. Machines representing the three classificatory ideal types and applying various working fluids tried to find their share of the market during this unstable phase.[5] Air expansion machines were often preferred in hospitals, and carbon dioxide was commonly chosen on board ships. We could paraphrase Knie (1991) and say that there were a number of technical "options" available and that no system had become the "ruling standard" (*herrschender Stand*) for all refrigerating machines.

However, if any system was close to becoming *the* standard one in the 1860s, then it was ammonia absorption. *Scientific American* (1870, Vol. 22, p. 40), by that time a leading engineering journal, was not alone when it stated that absorption was "the most philosophical of any method thus far proposed." The good reputation of absorption was partly due to the performance of a French machine designed around 1860 by Ferdinand Carré. This machine aroused more interest than any other refrigeration system in the 1860s; three times as many articles were published on the Carré system than on the Harrison-Siebe design (Bourne 1873-1874). Even though ammonia absorption never managed to become the ruling standard of mechanical refrigeration, the Carré machine acted as an influential archetype at this time.

Carré had been experimenting since the mid-fifties, but it was not until 1859 that his work began to show promise. After he had tried diethyl ether, calcium chloride, and sulfuric acid, Carré discovered that ammonia was a suitable working fluid for absorption machines (Loverdo 1903, pp. 9 f.). It is extremely soluble in water, it is highly volatile, and it was fairly cheap and easily accessible at the time.

The structure of Carré's continuously working machine is depicted in Figure 3.4 (Knight 1876, pp. 1165 f.; Loverdo 1903, pp. 8-13; Schwarz 1888, pp. 220-26; Swoboda 1868, pp. 18-24). A mixture of ammonia and water was heated in the generator to about 130°C (265°F) at a pressure of eight atmospheres. Ammonia gas was then piped to the condenser, where it became liquid while passing through a network of pipes immersed in cooling water. Liquid ammonia then evaporated at a pressure of slightly more

5 For a discussion about unstable technologies in flux, cf. Hård (1992).

than one atmosphere in the refrigerator coils surrounded by brine. Heat was thus transferred from the brine to the ammonia. A large number of vessels containing the water to be turned into ice were placed within the brine and between the coils. In 1867, for example, the largest Carré machine could produce as much as 200 kg (440 lbs) per hour and the smallest one 25 kg (55 lbs).

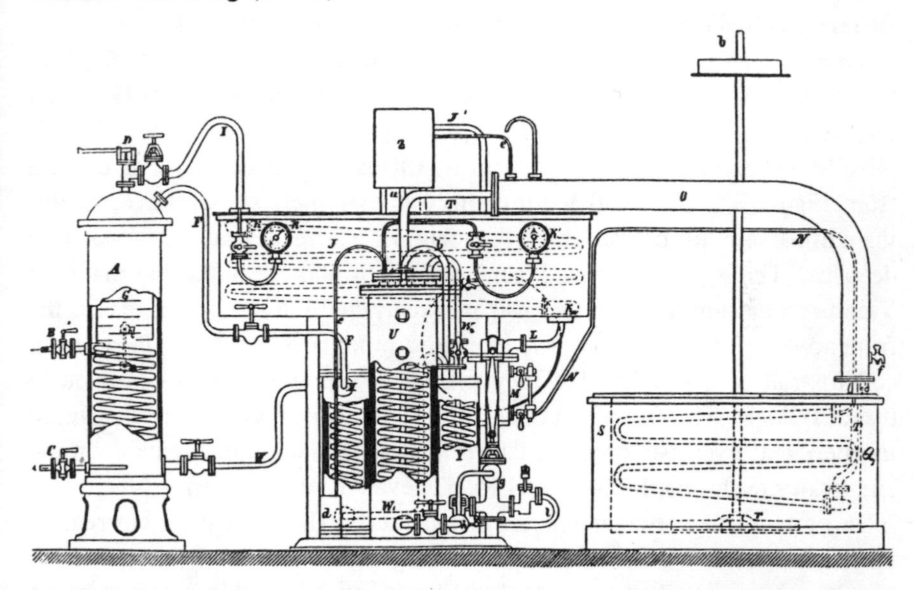

Figure 3.4. The Ferdinand Carré continuously working ammonia absorption machine, which became an influential archetype for later absorption designs from the early 1860s and throughout the nineteenth century; from Schwarz (1888, p. 221)

After vaporization the ammonia was led into the absorber containing a weak solution of ammonia in water. This solution had come to the absorber by way of two heat exchangers, one where it had given off some of its heat to the strong ammonia/water solution, and one (a cooler) where its temperature had been further lowered by means of cooling water. The weak solution was enriched with ammonia in the absorber and pumped back to the top of the generator. There, the ammonia was separated from the water in a rectifier, consisting of several perforated trays. Finally, the whole process could start over again.

The Carré system was exhibited at the Crystal Palace fair of 1862—just like the previously mentioned Siebe compression machine (Oldham 1946-1947). Carré had by then associated himself with a reliable machine company, Mignon & Rouart of Paris, and won an unforgiving patent struggle with another French firm, Tellier, Budin, & Hausmann.[6] The phenomenon of technological convergence is neatly illustrated by the ability of Mignon-Rouart and Siebe to turn to a completely novel area of production.

Carré was now ready to conquer the world; license production began in Great Britain by Reece & Stanley and by Pontifex & Wood, in Germany by Vaaß & Littmann and by Oscar Kropff, and in Australia by Mort & Nicolle. In other words, the process of diffusion had begun. It is evident from Figure 3.5 that Vaaß & Littmann was extremely conservative, retaining almost all the essentials of the original Carré design for about two decades. The system depicted here had been shown at the international Vienna exhibition in 1873, and was still marketed ten years later. True, the firm could offer other features, like an ammonia generator with a steam coil instead of a furnace, but they primarily followed changes previously made in Paris. The British and Australian companies were somewhat more independent, even beginning to take out their own additional patents in the late sixties (Schwarz 1888, pp. 241 f.; Thévenot 1978, p. 46).

In none of the above-mentioned cases did the 1862 Carré system remain unaltered, and it was never radically changed. Its basic archetypical structure remained. The British and Australian changes, an additional pump and a new kind of rectifier among them, were peripheral. What Alois Schwarz (1888, p. 230) writes about German absorption in a 500-page technical survey could also be said about changes made in other countries:

> The principle of the *Kropff* ice-machine is absolutely identical with both the *Vaaß & Littmann* machine ... and the *Carré* machine. It only differs from these when it comes to details of design and the arrangement of various parts.

If Carré became influential in Europe and Australia, his conquest of the United States was still more effective (Oldham 1946-1947). Absorption remained the most widely used mechanical refrigeration ideal type for quite a long time in this country. The 1862 Carré machine acted as an archetype

---

6 Accounts of this fight can be found in *Practical Mechanic's Journal* (1863-1864, pp. 8 f.) and Tellier (1910, pp. 12 ff.). Despite the loss, Charles Tellier later returned to mechanical refrigeration, making some spectacular trips with chilled meat from South America to Europe.

almost to the end of the century, or, in W.C. Woolrich's (1967, p. 24) words: "[It] became the pattern for many American absorption plants."

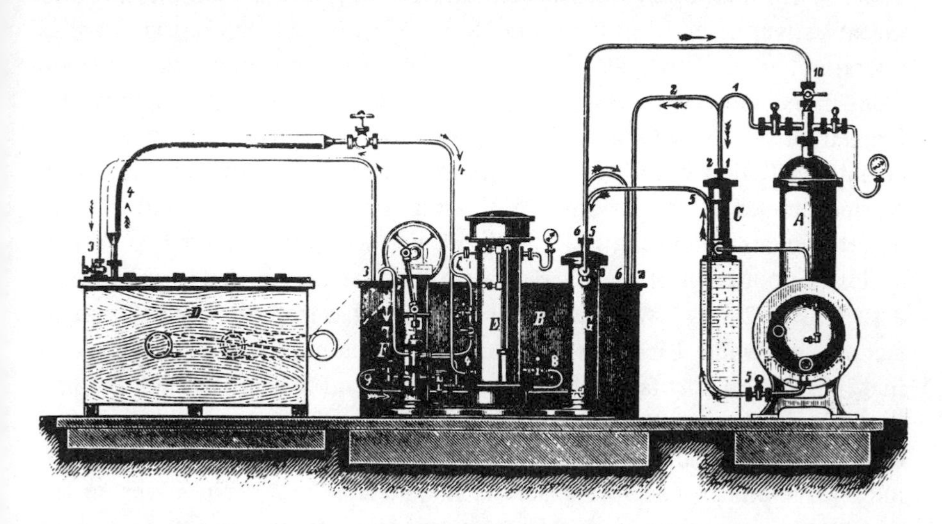

Figure 3.5. The ammonia absorption machine manufactured by Vaaß & Littmann, Halle, its design being very similar to that of Carré; from Schwarz (1888, p. 227)

Carré had taken out his initial American patent at an early stage, but he soon sold the patent rights to a local firm, Bujac & Girarde of New Orleans. As the historian of technology Hans-Joachim Braun (1983, p. 239) has observed, at this time it appears to have been more common for European (at least for German) machine firms to prefer this strategy to founding subsidiaries in the United States. Bujac & Girarde had imported the first Carré systems at the time of the Civil War, when the supply of natural ice was particularly haphazard. However, these machines never worked satisfactorily. According to Daniel Holden, an engineer who participated in installing several Carré machines, the failure resulted from technical inability on the part of the American firm (*Ice and Refrigeration* 1901, Vol. 21, p. 50). Only when it began to cooperate with other companies did the worst technical problems seem to have been overcome. Word about the Carré system spread rapidly in the latter half of the 1860s when several firms became involved in installing, manufacturing, and even developing it. The Southern firm, Mepes, Holden, Montgomery & Co., replaced the furnace in the ammonia generator with a steam coil as early as 1865. The Louisiana Ice Manufacturing Co., where six large Carré machines were erected in the years 1868-1870, was extremely important as a kind of "educational site" for interested technicians. Drawings had come from Paris, but construction took place at the machine firm of Sylvester Bennett outside New Orleans (p. 51). Among the engineers involved in the actual installation were Thomas Rankine and Harrison Stratton, who went on independently to design their own absorption systems and receive several patents (Goosman 1925, Vol. 69, p. 100; Woolrich 1967, p. 27).

The introduction of the Carré system into the United States was clearly a successful case of what is called technology transfer. The historian of technology Svante Lindqvist (1984, Ch. 15) has made an important point in his book on the failed introduction of steam power technology into Sweden: the fate of technology transfer does not depend only on technical factors. He lists four other areas which affect the process: cultural, economic, geographical, and social factors. If we adept these perspectives on our case, then we could say that Carré's choice of French descendants in a Franco-American city as collaborators was culturally advantageous and understandable, since it made it easier for him to communicate across the Atlantic; the economical incentives to try artificial ice were especially strong in the South—largely due to the geographical disadvantages of producing such things as beer; the Civil War created severe social problems for the natural ice trade; we know that Bujac & Girarde had technical difficulties at first, but also that the level of American engineering turned out to be high enough both to adopt and to adapt the foreign technology.

Monsieur Carré has brought us around the world. In fact, he could have taken us to even more machine shops where his tradition was carried on. These stories would have even more substantiated the claim that the Carré-Mignon-Rouart system of 1862 remained an absorption archetype for about three decades. The designs made by other engineers and machine firms had their roots in the French machine. They differed from it in various degrees, but all of them can be considered as types in relation to the 1862 original.

4. The Social Carriers and Concerned Parties of Refrigeration Technology

The Agency Perspective

Max Weber's theories for the emergence of Western capitalism and the unfolding of rationality are macro theories that describe historical development on an aggregate level (Collins 1981). Even if Weber is best known for such grand perspectives at least among historians, it must not be forgotten that he always saw individual action as the basic unit in all social processes (Parkin 1982, Ch. 1) and that he believed that all macro events were connected to micro events in a causal way (Rossi 1986). In short, Weber was a methodological individualist who opposed all kinds of teleology (Cohen 1981, p. XX).

Weber's most comprehensive discussion of the nature of social action is found in the famous first chapter of *Economy and Society*. Weber (1964, p. 88) gets to the heart of the matter at the very beginning:

> Sociology ... is a science which attempts the interpretive understanding of social action in order thereby to arrive at a causal explanation of its course and effects. In 'action' is included all human behaviour when and in so far as the acting individual attaches a subjective meaning to it.

The goal of his sociology, like his history and his economic history, is to understand (*verstehen*) why individuals act in certain ways; to reach such understanding the social and human scientist has to suppose that these individuals believe that their actions have some meaning (*Sinn*). Physiological processes and simple, reflexive behavior do not belong to the fields of sociology and history. If we furthermore want to explain (*erklären*) certain actions, we have to investigate the individual's motives (*Motive*) (p. 95).

Weber (p. 101) is of course aware that such an extreme micro approach is untenable for much sociological research:

> ... it may ... be convenient or even indispensable to treat social collectivities, such as states, associations, business corporations, foundations, as if they were individual persons. [...] But for the subjective interpretation of action in sociological work these collectivities must be treated as *solely* the resultants and modes of organization of the particular acts of individual persons ...

In other words, a Weberian approach does not preclude an agency perspective on social events. If we wish to follow Weber, then we do not need to stay on the level of historical macro processes.

Individual and collective agents have been well-studied in the history and sociology of technology; heroic inventors, innovative entrepreneurs, and system-building organizations abound (Beckman 1990). Even though structuralist and functionalist accounts were quite influential in the 1950s and 1960s (Dennis *et al.* 1969; Ellul 1964; Marcuse 1964), the purposive agent made a strong return in the 1970s and 1980s—often in Schumpeterian or Machiavellian disguise (Dosi *et al.* 1988; Knie 1992).

Agency-oriented approaches can also be found among social constructivists and actor network theorists, who have moved far beyond the level of the heroic inventor by taking several groups and individuals into account when discussing the course of technological change (Bijker *et al.* 1987; Bijker and Law 1992). While constructivists like Pinch and Bijker (1987) have introduced the term "relevant social groups" to designate all agents for whom a certain artifact has a particular meaning, scholars like Michel Callon (1987) and John Law (1987) stress the need for actors to build complex networks, consisting of both humans and artifacts, when trying to make technologies work. Both approaches are important in that they insist that not only engineers and businessmen, but also users, social movements, and even natural phenomena may influence the ways in which technology is shaped. However, this insistence seems to have taken them somewhat too far. Pinch, Bijker, and Callon lack a discussion of the relative power between various agents and thereby create an impression that disadvantageous groups like today's environmental activists and nineteenth-century women have, or have had, the same chance of affecting technical change as do technicians and industrialists (Hård 1993; Russell 1986).

This study has been greatly inspired by the constructivist and actor network perspectives, but does not directly apply any of them. Since power and persistence are essential factors in the promotion of technical change (Knie 1991), this study focuses primarily on those agents who have exercised a decisive influence on the development of refrigeration technology; these agents will henceforth be called its *social carriers*. Since the historical source material only seldom allows a thorough analysis of what meanings various relevant social groups attributed to refrigerating devices, the acting units are concrete institutions and individuals rather than groups of more or less anonymous people; these units will be called *concerned parties*.

The concept of "social carrier of technique" was introduced some years ago by Charles Edquist and Olle Edqvist (1978, 1979) in their analysis of the introduction of technology into the developing countries. They define it as "a social entity which chooses and implements a certain technique" and take as examples agricultural cooperatives or multi-national companies investing in agricultural tools or machinery (Edquist and Edqvist 1979, p. 31). A social carrier may be an individual or any societal body acting in a unified manner. Edquist and Edqvist (p. 9) limit their discussion to the carriage of "tools, equipment, instruments, and machines," or what they call techniques. Since this hardware aspect of technology is so intimately connected with softer parts like knowledge and organization, I will talk about social carriers of technology instead of techniques.

When Edquist and Edqvist study the transfer of technology from industrial countries to the Third World, they assume that the technology in question already exists in the industrial world, and that it is not altered by the transfer process. Both presuppositions appear unnecessary. Concerned parties in the developing countries frequently need tools that no one is able to supply. Technology is often modified when transformed into a new setting —a point which has been made by Nathan Rosenberg (1982, p. 272): "The successful transplantation of a technology involves the domestic capacity to alter, modify, and adapt in a thousand different ways." Edquist's and Edqvist's social carrier concept will be modified below to cover each level of technological development. Although they do not discuss this idea at any length, Edquist and Edqvist (1979, p. 34) admit that it would be possible to expand their concept to cases involving invention and innovation, in addition to diffusion and transfer. They use the development of new grain hybrids as an example, where research institutes, large corporation, and powerful farmers acted as what they call *linked* social carriers.

In order to make their carrier concept useful for a social analysis of technology, Edquist and Edqvist (pp. 31 f.) list six conditions, all of which have to be fulfilled, if a technique should be introduced. For an actor (Edquist and Edqvist explicitly avoid the term "agent" because they find it too voluntaristic) to become a social carrier of technique, he, she, or it has to (i) be interested in introducing the technique; (ii) be organized properly; (iii) be socially, economically, and politically powerful; (iv) be informed about the existence of the technique; (v) have access to it; (vi) know how to handle it. If an actor is not able to meet all six requirements on its own, then it can cooperate with others, thus forming a *combined* social carrier. This means that the actors fulfill the conditions collectively. These six requirements can be easily modified in the manner described below in order to facilitate a theory of social carriage of technology that also covers the phenomenon of technological change.

This expanded version of the social carrier concept is intended for the analysis of how existing technologies are introduced into new settings, or how novel technologies are developed. We have to regard such acts as meaningful in Weber's sense in order to be able to analyze and understand them. This implies that we have to investigate the agents' motives rather than their interests. Weber (1964, p. 115) has also suggested that all social acts can be treated as rational, traditional, or affective. Thus, the first issue on the checklist is that each social carrier of technology has to be rationally, traditionally, or affectively (1) *motivated*.

Like neo-institutional economists, Edquist and Edqvist are right to stress the central role organizations play in technological change. Agents have to be properly (2) *organized* in order to become social carriers of technology. This can be done either by creating new institutions or entering into existing ones. The inventor who is the only user of his own work represents an uninteresting exception.

Histories of failed innovations and the advent of so-called alternative technologies illustrate that agents who lack power often remain what Edquist and Edqvist call a *potential* social carrier (Braun 1992; Dickson 1974; Schumacher 1973). The agent has to be able to influence the course of events and other agents in order to become an *actual* social carrier.[1] We can follow Weber (1964, Part III) and set as a prerequisite that the agent acquire traditional, legal, or charismatic authority; if this has been done it may be (3) *powerful* enough.

The importance of information flows for technological change in general and for the diffusion of technological knowledge in particular is obvious. During the discussion in the Introduction of the flow not only of information, but also of agents and artifacts, reference was made to H.G.J. Aitken's (1976, 1978) model of three spheres of human action. I would like to

1 A similar discussion is to be found in Berthoin Antal (1992), where it is suggested that the successful introduction of organizational and technical novelties requires the existence not only of a purposeful *champion*, but also of a powerful *supporter*.

combine Aitken with Edquist and Edqvist and argue that an agent has to be (4) *informed* keenly and selectively about the pertinent technological and economic spheres if it is to become a social carrier of technology. If needed, the agent might also have to take the scientific sphere into account.

So far, the conditions applied to a social carrier are not too different from those of Edquist and Edqvist. The major divergence from their scheme concerns what they call "access to the technique," a point which will here be replaced by (5) *resources* needed by a social carrier in order to be able to complete certain tasks. Some distinctions have to be made depending on the case under consideration. When an already existing technology is carried into a new geographical or economic area, then not the same resources are needed as when a new technology is carried from idea to product. In the first case, resources for adaptation, diffusion, marketing, and purchasing may be required. The functions may be carried out by a single actor or by several. A large government-owned railway firm which builds its own cars is an example of a single social carrier. In the case where the technology does not yet exist, then research, development, design, and manufacturing might be needed. These four functions may be fulfilled by one agent or a combination of agents.

The process of technology carriage does not end when, for example, a machine is installed. Someone has to run it, and someone has to maintain and repair it. All these tasks require particular (6) *skills*, or practical know-how (Bergström 1985).

Success and Failure in Social Carriage of Refrigeration

I will now test the social carrier concept by applying it to the previous study of archetypes and types in the history of refrigeration technology. What agent was the initial driving force in the various cases? Which of the six requirements of social carriage did it fulfill, and which conditions were left for other agents to meet? Why did some agents succeed and others fail to become social carriers of refrigeration technology? It has to be borne in mind in this connection that the social carrier concept is an analytical, not an explanatory concept, which might give us a better grasp on processes of technological development and diffusion. It can be used as a first step toward a more profound understanding of these processes, but it does not help us explain them in a causal way.

Let us begin with the introduction of the American railway car cooled with natural ice. At the outset large meat packing firms like Swift and Hammond were most motivated to introduce such a technology. They also had a nation-wide organization and substantial economic power; they were well informed about the economic situation. However, they lacked the resources to develop and manufacture ice-cooled cars, they were not particularly well informed about technical details, and they were not able to operate such cars alone. Thus they needed to cooperate with other agents who could meet these conditions and form a combined social carrier. First of all, the meat packers had to find a technician or a firm that could acquire the pertinent technological information and had the resources for research, development, design, and manufacturing. Gustavus F. Swift cooperated with an inventor, Andrew J. Chase, whose ideas were transformed into a product by the Michigan Car Co. of Detroit (Unfer 1951, pp. 33 ff.). The railroad companies were not happy about the new car, because less cars were needed to transport dressed meat than livestock, but after having been put under pressure, the Grand Trunk Co. finally agreed to run Swift's cars. Thus the Swift company, a powerful and motivated organization, became a combined social carrier of ice-cooled railway transportation technology together with Chase, Michigan Car, Grand Trunk, and a number of ice-harvesting firms situated along the railroad lines. Butchers and consumers in the Eastern cities were affected by the cooled transportation of dressed meat, but since they simultaneously battled its introduction, these groups were not among the social carriers of this technology. Since it is not clear what meanings they attributed to ice-cooled railway cars, they cannot be treated as a "relevant social group" in Pinch and Bijker's sense, but they were certainly *concerned parties* in this struggle.

When we move on to mechanical refrigeration, we find more agents forming combined social carriers. Independent agents also formed new bodies in some cases, thereby creating a new social carrier—usually a firm. For instance, the meat packers Henry and James Bell were motivated to acquire an ice-machine, they were well informed about the economic sphere, and they had some economic power, but they still lacked several components. James Coleman (1882, p. 154) himself recalls that they asked the well-known physicist William Thomson (Lord Kelvin) for advice:

> attention ... was directed to the subject by Sir W. Thomson, who had been consulted by Messrs. Henry and James Bell, of Glasgow, as to the possibility of constructing machinery to supersede the use of ice in the preservation of fresh meat during its passage across the Atlantic.

Thomson directed them on to Coleman, who was well informed about the technological aspects of mechanical refrigeration and had acquired operative skills at Young, Meldrum & Co. As it turned out, Coleman was also able to do some research and to design a new cold air machine. The final step was taken when the Bell-Coleman Mechanical Refrigeration Co. was founded. It became possible for the Bells and Coleman through that body to reach a larger group with their machine. They now had an organization that could slowly conquer a growing market. They obtained more economic and social power as an incorporated machine firm, and were able to start manufacturing machines to order and help maintain and repair machines they had sold.

Other agents were not as successful as Bell-Coleman; John Gorrie was one of them. Let us see if the social carrier concept might help us explain why he never was able to get beyond the building of a few prototypes. Gorrie was certainly a motivated actor. He wanted air-cooling partly on affective grounds to alleviate the discomfort of hospital patients—indirectly a concerned party, in other words. Gorrie seems to have been well informed about the technological, and even partly about the scientific aspects; he had the resources for research and design; and he presumably was able to run and repair his own machines. A machine firm in Cincinnati took care of the manufacturing. However, a number of factors was missing, not least a proper organization. Despite Gorrie's own efforts to find collaborators, his project remained pretty much a one-man show, at least in the United States. Gorrie lost with the death of his financier not only the economic power to begin large-scale production and marketing, but also an important channel through which information about the economic sphere could pass. Furthermore, he did not have enough charismatic power and influence to persuade potential customers of the excellence of his ice-machine. This point is proven by Gorrie's own description of the hesitancy observers felt regarding the operation of the machine and the opposition to artificially produced ice. But why did Gorrie fail in Britain as well, despite the help of an established machine firm? The available sources are thin, but the main problem seems to have been that no suitable organization developed that could coordinate the various agents. Some skills and resources were on one side of the Atlantic, and some on the other.

The case of James Harrison and the Siebe Bros. is quite straightforward. Harrison was a lonely inventor in Australia and lacked an organization, economic power, and the resources to begin manufacturing. All this, and probably a little more, was supplied by the Siebe firm. Hence, Harrison and Siebe became a combined social carrier of vapor compression refrigeration.

The introduction of the Carré system into the United States is theoretically close to what Edquist and Edqvist originally wanted to describe. Whereas the analyses above have dealt with the development of new technologies, this case has to do with the introduction of an existing technology into a new geographical area. Carré's own research and design will not concern us here, but because he took out United States patents at an early stage, he became an important agent in the transfer process. He was apparently motivated to begin exploiting the American market. He and Mignon-Rouart sent ready-made ice-machines, along with technological information, to the United States importers, Bujac & Girarde, whereas only drawings were mailed to Sylvester Bennett. Bujac & Girarde initially bought the machines from France and succeeded in marketing a couple of them. They obviously had power enough to persuade some firms of the blessings of mechanical refrigeration, and they understood that this technology could play an important economic role in the South. However, they severely underestimated the difficulties of technology transfer; none of their imported machines operated satisfactorily. Bujac & Girarde simply forgot that a proper organization, including sufficient technical skill, is necessary to make a technology work. The act of social carriage was completed only after firms like Mepes, Holden, Montgomery & Co. brought with them manufacturing resources and operative skills.

The first, general conclusion to be drawn from the above cases is that the social carriers of novel mechanical refrigeration technology in the mid-1800s encompassed a wide group of technicians, machine firms, and users. The technicians ranged from self-taught, individual amateurs to formally educated, employed engineers. The machine firms were sometimes established companies already producing various items and sometimes new firms founded with the immediate aim of making ice-machines. Meat packers and chemical firms were among the active users. A railroad firm and ice-harvesting firms were also involved in the case of the ice-cooled car. When it finally came to the transfer of existing technology, a trading firm became involved. The introduction of refrigeration technology required a large number of agents.

Another conclusion can be drawn if we look closer at those agents who instituted the introduction process; only in the case of technology transfer was a machine firm among the initiators. In all other cases the process of social carriage was begun by a technician or a user, that is, a firm in need of ice or some other means of cold. Harrison and Gorrie were amateur technicians who began by making their own inventions before approaching a machine firm which could produce them commercially. The Swift and the Bell meat packing firms asked some technicians to design a workable refrigeration system. According to his own description, Kirk (1874, p. 246) "was requested by Messrs. Young and Meldrum to investigate the subject thoroughly" and to come up with a machine better than Harrison's. Thus the existing machine firms appear to have been very passive, at least at the outset. The capital and experience of these companies were often crucial for the successful completion of a project, but the firms played a surprisingly marginal role in the initial phase. Established machine firms were often able to begin manufacturing ice-machines or ice-cooled cars rather quickly as a result of technological convergence, but they seldom took this step on their own initiative.

The apparent passivity of the machine industry must remain a mere suggestion, since the sources do not allow a stronger conclusion. Moreover, this conclusion only covers the childhood of mechanical and railroad refrigeration—roughly 1840-1880. When these technologies came of age around 1880, the machine industry became a driving force in their development. This is also implied by Oscar Anderson (1953, p. 94):

> About 1880 leadership passed from individual mechanics to companies which could command greater financial and technical resources.

In other words, we can say that Anderson, stressing the role of technicians and machine firms supplying the market with novelties, emphasizes the push aspects of technological change. In contrast to Anderson's suggestion, the present account has shown that pull aspects were also important; users often demanded technologies that were not extant. The pushing side prevailed in the case of Harrison-Siebe, whereas the Swift case shows how pulling forces predominated. The role of large and powerful users could be just as important as that of technicians and machine firms. In fact, even concerned parties among the public were of some importance through their criticism of the use of infectious natural ice; artificial ice made from distilled water was much preferred.

Technological Knowledge Before Scientification

Technology is not only machinery; it is also knowledge (Layton 1974). In Part II we will see how scientific knowledge began to influence the technology of mechanical refrigeration in the 1870s, whereas previously science had played a rather minor role. Those individuals who published in this field concentrated on the engineering side of the coin, discussing such things as materials, performance, and design specifications. If heat theories did appear, then they did so briefly and in quite a superficial manner.

Since most social carriers and other concerned parties had only a limited education, it is not surprising that the emphasis was on the practical hardware side. Harrison had received no formal engineering education, and his technical accounts were devoid of scientific analysis (*Polytechnisches Centralblatt* 1857, pp. 1031, 1506, 1863, p. 902; *Scientific American* 1861, Vol. 5, p. 72). Carré's work came somewhat closer to a scientific approach. Carré (1860) uses the term "latent caloric" in an early paper for the amount of heat that has to be added in order to vaporize a certain amount of liquid, and he refers to H.V. Regnault's famous experimental tables of the properties of various substances. However, science does not pervade his paper; it only appears in his defense of ammonia as a working fluid, where he claims that this substance has the largest latent caloric.

A similar discussion can be found in a pamphlet written by an American refrigeration engineer, Alexander C. Twining (1857, p. 3), suggesting that diethyl ether is the most "highly evaporable freezing liquid" which could be applied in ice-machines. We have not met Twining before, but his 18-page pamphlet is worth mentioning, since it is one of the more ambitious discussions of refrigeration theory and practice published before 1870. Nevertheless, the scientific level is still not beyond Carré's. In the booklet Twining has included a couple of letters from famous American professors having evaluated his ideas. The geologist J.D. Dana agrees with Twining in that, at least in principle, it ought to be possible to produce cold by means of a vapor compression cycle. Like the chemist and natural historian, Benjamin Silliman, Senior, Dana does not venture beyond general qualitative statements. Writes Silliman, for example:

> The production of cold by evaporation, is, of course, a familiar fact. Every Professor of chemistry and physic [*sic*] has frozen water in [the] presence of his audience, by the evaporation of ether.[2]

Gorrie had quite a good understanding of natural processes as a physician, and his texts include references to well-known natural philosophers—William Herschel, John Dalton, and J.L. Gay-Lussac, among others. However, Gorrie's knowledge of the science of heat seems to have been restricted to the insight that the total amount of caloric is always preserved and never destroyed in a process, a substantialist version of the energy principle (Becker 1972, pp. 79 f., 109). The many quotations in Raymond Becker's (1972) biography of Gorrie suggest that Gorrie's own writings on refrigeration were primarily technical and that the theoretical parts were of a qualitative nature. Even if Gorrie was inspired by scientific works, it would be an exaggeration to say that his engineering was in any way scientific (*DPJ* 1850, Vol. 115, p. 159; *Journal of the Society of Arts* 1854, Vol. 2, p. 250). Like Carré and Twining, Gorrie had a fragmentary and non-mathematical knowledge of heat theories, implying that it was possible to produce cold by the evaporation of a liquid, but not really affecting the engineering as such.

Because Gorrie's British machine worked inefficiently, the owners asked the engineer William Siemens to examine both it and the underlying theory. Siemens' report from 1857 is rather detailed, including diagrams of the working of the compressor and expander, as well as a theoretical section (*MPICE* 1882, Vol. 68, pp. 179-186). However, theoretical is not identical with scientific. Rather, the scientific content of the section is limited to a couple of references to "the dynamical theory of heat," primarily to what we today call its first law. In qualitative terms only, Siemens states that heat may be converted into mechanical work and *vice versa*, but he appears to have been unaware of Clausius's and Thomson's discussions about the losses that often occur in such processes. Ignorant of the limits imposed by the Carnot cycle, Siemens claims that in an "ideal machine ... the production of ice does not necessarily involve an expenditure of power"

---

2 In Twining (1857, p. 14); quoted from a letter by Silliman of August 19, 1857.

(p. 183). Of course, it could still be claimed that Siemens' report was a case of scientification, even if his science was not up to the standards of his day. However, the important point is that there is no connection between Siemens' scientific account and his engineering theory. After he describes the scientific basics, Siemens goes directly on to discuss what technical reasons there might be behind the inefficiency of Gorrie's machine, and how these could be adjusted. In short, Siemens believed that the science of thermodynamics was important for the technology of mechanical refrigeration, but he was neither able to nor interested in making the former act on the latter. The process of scientification had to wait.

It was Siemens's report that inspired Kirk in turn to commence working with cold air machines. Kirk was a mechanical engineer by profession, and his successor at Young-Meldrum, Coleman, was a chemical engineer. This shift of generations also illustrates a change in the character of technological knowledge. While Kirk's (1873-1874) own published account of his machine is a practical description of its features, including figures of performance, Coleman's (1882) writings contain simple scientific formulae and technically important deductions taken from them. For instance, Coleman includes both the general equation of state for an ideal gas (pV/T = constant) and a formula for the efficiency of a refrigeration machine. We have seen that his collaborators, the Bell brothers, had asked if William Thomson could help them design an ice-machine. The Bells presumably had approached Thomson because he was an outstanding physicist and had written a paper on air engines in 1852.[3] Both Coleman and the Bells must have been optimistic about the ability of science to solve technical problems. However, these concerned parties have brought us well into the 1870s and 1880s, and by then the process of the scientification of refrigeration technology had already begun to take shape.

---

3 Thomson (1852) is in part a comment on a paper by J. P. Joule. Both deal with the hot air engine, i.e., a prime mover, the reversal of a cold air machine.

II. The Scientification of Refrigeration Technology, 1870-1893

When we leave the early history of refrigeration technology, we approach a watershed. In Part I we saw that only a few, awkward attempts were made before 1870 to solve problems in this area by scientific means; the spheres of mechanical refrigeration and the mechanical theory of heat were separated, both intellectually and socially. In Part II I will investigate how this situation began to change in the 1870s, when the concepts, methods, results, and ontologies of thermodynamics were slowly incorporated into refrigeration technology, and as the barriers between technical and scientific institutions and circles were lowered. The person who initiated the process of scientification had received a scientifically-inspired engineering education and was well suited to act as a *translator* between science and technology (Aitken 1978). Please note that refrigeration technology did not thereby become an applied science. Since it already existed as a distinct technical area and retained several of its traditions and aims after scientification, the designation applied science does not seem suitable.

The scientification process arguably began in 1870-1871 with the publication of two papers. After their content has been discussed below, they will be placed in the contemporary institutional, intellectual, and economic context. There are two main questions to be addressed: why did the scientification of mechanical refrigeration begin in the German-speaking world at this time? What were its immediate consequences? The following chapters focus on the experience and contributions of Carl Linde (1842-1934), but it does not have a strictly biographical character. Its goal is instead to treat Linde as a representative of certain general movements and as a mirror of his time.

This part illustrates in Weberian terms the process of intellectual rationalization which became increasingly important during the nineteenth century. The scientifically-trained engineer formalized technological problems by means of abstract concepts and quantifiable methods and hoped thereby to solve problems in a more reliable manner; he applied scientific concepts and ontologies in order to "disenchant the world." Science promised not only greater accuracy and more efficient machinery, but also a means to master reality and to control the market place.

5. The Beginning: Carl Linde's Early Papers

The Thermodynamic Approach

Two unusual articles appeared at the beginning of the 1870s in the "Bavarian Journal of Industry and Trade," a technical and economic journal published by the Bavarian Polytechnic Society.[1] They furnished a sophisticated thermodynamic account of the central problems of artificial cooling and thereby approached refrigeration technology from an angle very different from the one described in the previous part. Their author was Carl Linde, a young assistant professor at the Munich Polytechnic School and a co-editor of the journal. Linde (1870, 1871) introduced a novel element into refrigeration technology by using the tools provided by the burgeoning science of thermodynamics. We have seen that limited attempts in this direction had been made earlier, but Linde's effort was clearly pioneering. It was comprehensive, well informed, and would later become critical in the development of a highly successful refrigeration system that remained archetypical for several decades. Linde did not explicitly intend to move from paper to practice when writing the articles, and he could not have foreseen that they would lead to the foundation of a successful industrial enterprise.

Linde's interest in mechanical refrigeration had been aroused by a contest sponsored by the Mineral Oil Society of Halle (Linde 1870, p. 206). Such prize contests, which assign very concrete problems, have a long tradition in both science and technology (Hård 1979). At this time paraffin was one of the economically most interesting products being refined from coal tar (Buchner 1864) and the prescribed task was to invent a method by which it would be possible to keep twenty-five tons of paraffin at a temperature of -5°C (23°F) year-round by artificial means (*ZVDI* 1870, Vol. 14, p. 394). The solution had to include a description of such an apparatus, along with a cost analysis. Linde sought to organize the problem more formally and first asked what the most efficient refrigeration process ought

1 Its German name was *Bayerisches Industrie- und Gewerbe-Blatt*. The name of the journal had been changed in 1868-1869 from "Journal of Arts and Trade" (*Kunst- und Gewerbe-Blatt*), reflecting the general transformation of German economic life at the time.

to look like; he then went on to compare a number of existing machines with this ideal and finally was able to present a design of what he claimed was the most fuel-efficient ice-machine. His conclusions were based on theoretical as well as practical considerations.

Linde begins his first paper with a short discussion of basic thermodynamic concepts, the immediate roots of which will be discussed in Chapter 7. After this introduction he determines that external work (W) is needed in order to keep a body continuously cold at temperature T_2. A certain amount of heat (Q_2) is thereby removed from the body. Figure 5.1 demonstrates how the circulating refrigerant gives off its excess heat (Q_1) at temperature T_1.[2] If path 1-2-3-4 of this figure is compared with Figure 1.1, it can be seen that in principle the refrigeration cycle is a reversed steam engine cycle. For an ice-machine to be most efficient—other things being equal—the quotient Q_2/W should be as large as possible; in other words, for a certain amount of work one wants as much ice as possible. This quotient is called the coefficient of performance (for cooling) in modern terminology.

Linde thus rephrased the original problem in a formally rational way; instead of discussing paraffin cooling, he asked what refrigeration cycle will maximize Q_2/W. Since ice-machines remove heat Q_2 at a constant temperature—0°C (32°F), Linde (1870, pp. 208, 321 f.) determines in an axiomatic manner that the optimal process ought to be the reversal of the perfectly efficient power engine cycle. We learned in Chapter 1 that the latter cycle is today commonly called the Carnot cycle, but Linde did not use this name (Beckman 1976; Kalide 1976; Van Wylen & Sonntag 1985). For him, like many other post-Carnot engineers, this perfectly efficient power engine cycle served as an important, collectively held *Leitbild*. The Carnot cycle told these engineers what was desirable (*wünschbar*) and in what direction to aim, and thus gave them a common goal that *guided* their work; this is its *Leit* function.[3] Since it was furthermore possible to compare the performance of existing machines with the Carnot cycle by means

2 Linde (1870, pp. 207 f.); the notation has been modified to correspond to that used in the previous chapters.

3 This interpretation follows Dierkes *et al.* (1992, pp. 42, 52, 82, 100), who have made the point that the Carnot cycle served as a *Leitbild* for Rudolf Diesel's work in interal combustion engineering. Since Diesel was Linde's student and had been his employee for some time, the similarities between the two men are not surprising.

of the indicator diagram, this ideal also had an important visual component. It was a picture (*Bild*) with great attractive power (*Anziehungskraft*).

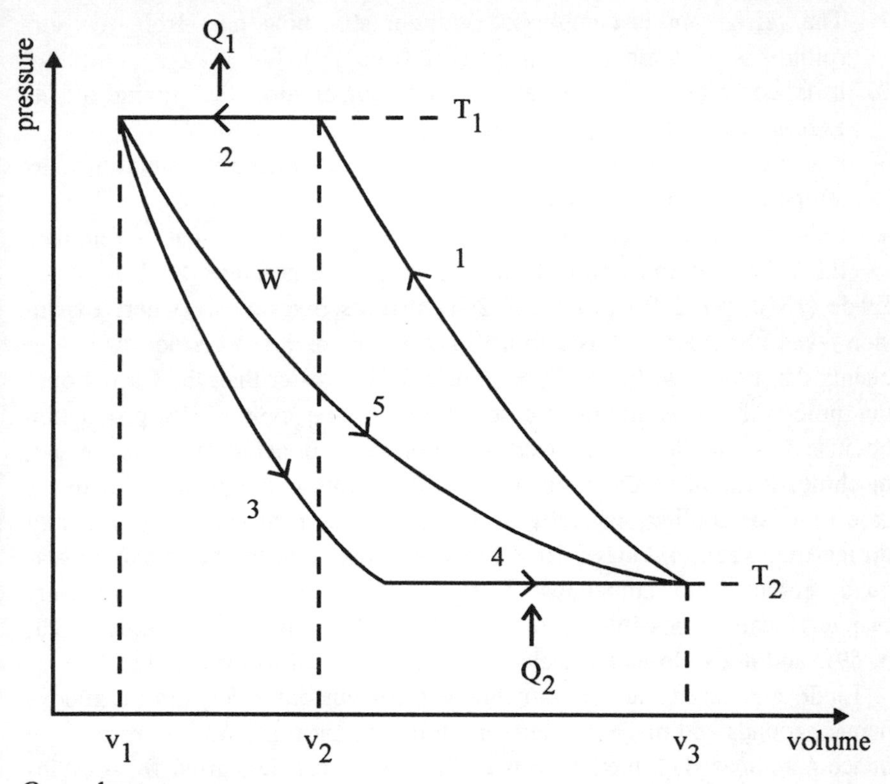

Q = heat
T = temperature
W = total amount

Figure 5.1. A schematic representation of an ice-machine cycle (1-2-3-4), being the reversal of the steam engine cycle; from Linde (1870, p. 321)

While a power engine turns heat at T_1 into mechanical work and runs clockwise with a thermal efficiency of $(T_1-T_2)/T_1$, a refrigeration cycle has to run counterclockwise and absorb heat at T_2. Linde concludes quite straightforwardly that the maximum coefficient of performance is $Q_2/W = A[T_2/(T_1-T_2)]$, A being a constant. Linde tells us with this expression how a theoretically "perfect" (*vollkommen*) ice-machine should work; it ought to produce ice at as high and use cooling water at as low a temperature as possible (Linde 1870, p. 209). According to Figure 5.1 it ought to run as follows:

1. The refrigerant is compressed without absorbing heat from the surroundings, its temperature increasing from T_2 to T_1;
2. it is compressed further at constant temperature T_1, giving off its excess heat to the cooling water;
3. it is expanded without heat being transferred to the surroundings, its temperature returning to T_2;
4. it is expanded at constant temperature T_2, whereby heat is removed from the body to be cooled; that is, water is turned into ice.

Linde (1870, pp. 209 f., 1871, p. 264) also discusses a case where expansion takes place continuously in addition to this reversed Carnot cycle. He claims that this cycle (path 1-2-5, Figure 5.1) is better than the Carnot one, but notes that it is impossible to follow in the case of ice-production because heat has to be removed at a constant temperature T_2 in an ice-machine. It might be theoretically possible to follow the cycle 1-2-5 in the case of brine-cooling, whereby heat is removed from the brine gradually during the expansion phase. Here Linde supposes that the brine can be gradually cooled from temperature T_1 to T_2. It has to be observed, however, that it is hardly possible to follow this cycle in practice (Kalide 1976, p. 59), and it also loses its relevance for Linde's following account.

Linde arrived at the above-mentioned conclusions solely on thermodynamic grounds and made no mention of any extant refrigeration technology or ice-machines. His method was deductive in that he started from established thermodynamic definitions and laws and came to his conclusions using thermodynamic lines of reasoning, and it was visionary in that it introduced the reversed Carnot cycle as a *Leitbild* for refrigeration engineering. Up to this point, Linde's approach to his technological problem was highly abstract. Concrete, practical aspects return to Linde's account when he applies his rules to a technological problem. He concludes that if one has access to cooling water at 15°C (59°F) it would be theoretically possible to produce 98.5 kg of ice at -3°C (27°F) per horsepower and hour (hph).[4] This example is the last step on his deductive journey.

---

4 Linde (1870, p. 323, 1871, p. 272); the figures from 1870 have been modified in order to make comparisons easier.

Linde next turns his thermodynamic tools toward the world of real artifacts by means of a thorough analysis of three existing ice-machines. His purpose is to ascertain how close these machines come to the ideal cycle and to suggest pertinent improvements. He therefore picks a representative for each of the three classificatory ideal types of mechanical refrigeration: the Windhausen cold air machine, the Carré continuous absorption system, and the Siebe Bros. vapor compression apparatus. His discussion is based on information derived from several German and British technical journals.[5]

Figure 5.2 shows Linde's graphic image of the Windhausen cycle, which can be compared to the ideal type of Figure 2.2. Together with a novel formula of its coefficient of performance, this interpretation represents a new stage in mechanical refrigeration engineering. Linde immediately determines that only two of the steps (compression and expansion without heat transfer) correspond to the Carnot process, making the Windhausen machine of only limited interest. If we insert the figures from the example above into Linde's (1870, p. 323, 1871, p. 265) formula, we find that merely 50 kg of ice per hph could theoretically be produced by the Windhausen procedure. The gap between this cycle and the ideal one contracts, however, as the difference T_1-T_2 increases. This only means that a Windhausen machine comes closer to the perfect one when T_1-T_2 is large, not that its coefficient of performance is enhanced. The standard rules, to use cooling water as cold as possible and to produce ice at as high a temperature as possible, still hold for air expansion machines.

The 50 kg production mentioned above are never reached in practice, partly because of friction and leakages. Windhausen himself reported an ice production capacity of only 10-14 kg per hph, and Linde's (1870, pp. 265 f.) conclusion is that "[c]ertainly, an air expansion machine superior to the Windhausen design is not inconceivable ..." While he acknowledges that better technological solutions are possible, Linde (1870, p. 325) still relates this low figure primarily to some problems which are inherent to all air expansion machines.

5 *Dingler's Polytechnisches Journal* (1862, Vol. 164, p. 178, 1863, Vol. 167, pp. 171, 397, Vol. 168, pp. 434 f., 1870, Vol. 195, p. 115); *Mechanics' Magazine* (1869, p. 387), and *Practical Mechanic's Journal* (1863, Vol. 8, p. 321).

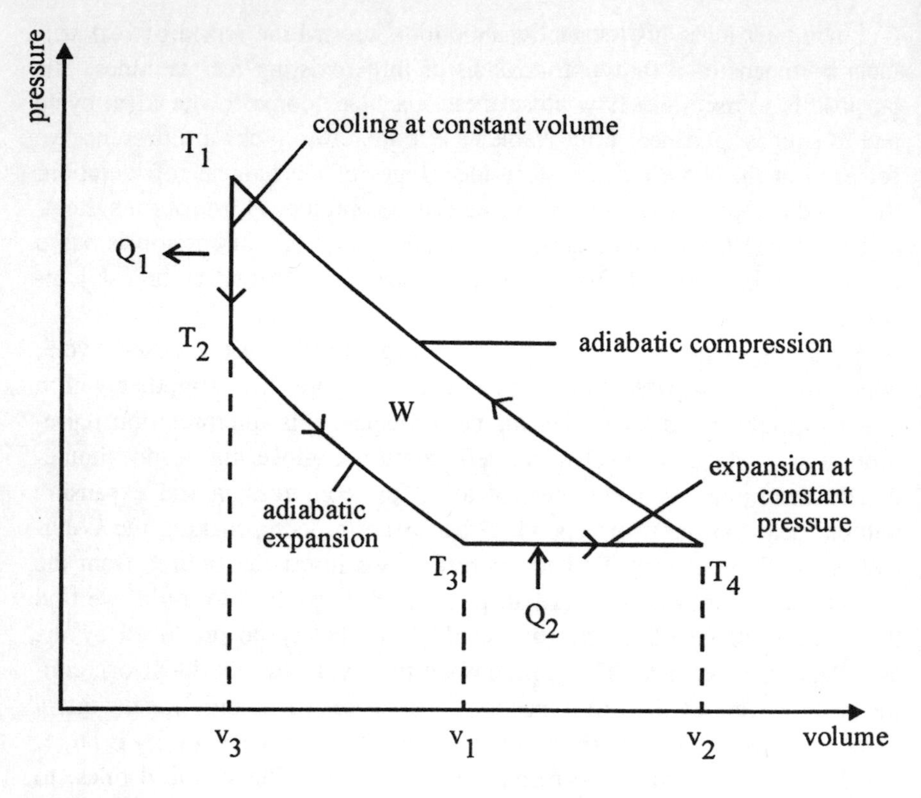

Q = heat
T = temperature
W = total amount
Adiabatic = process whereby no heat is communicated with the surroundings

Figure 5.2. The cyclic refrigeration process of Windhausen's air expansion machine; from Linde (1871, p. 265)

The low heat conductivity of air makes it necessary either to reduce its temperature considerably below the freezing point of water or to construct enormous contact areas between air and water. Nevertheless, Linde does not exclude the possibility that an air expansion system which works on an open cycle—where the cold air is released into the rooms to be cooled—

could be made fairly efficient. But he does not supply any figures for such a machine. He is also clearly aware of the benefits of air, its unlimited supply and harmlessness, even though his thermodynamically-centered method was not conducive to taking such factors into account.

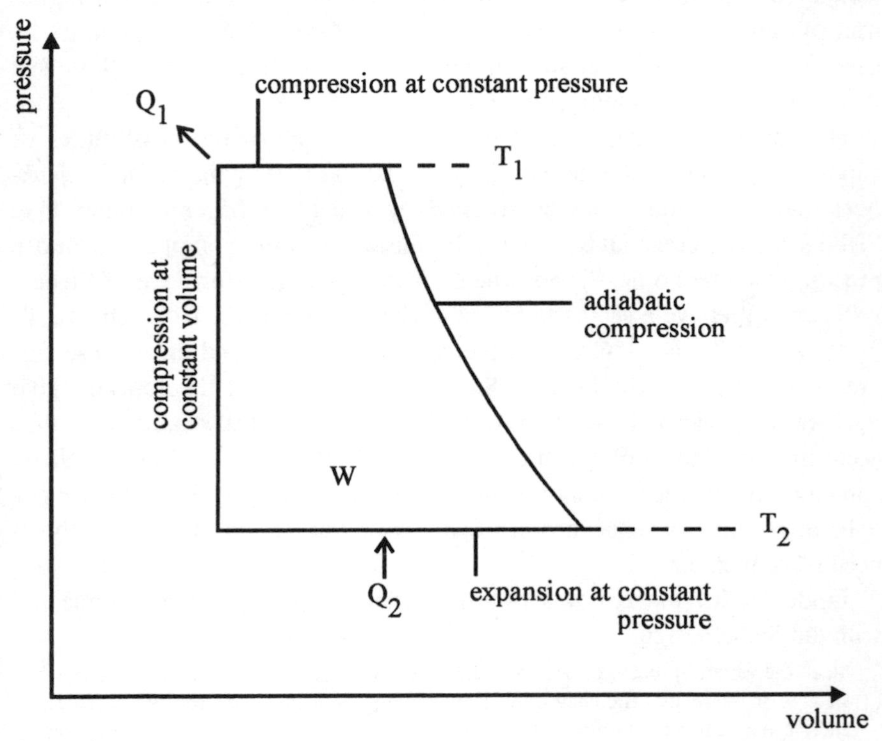

Q = heat
T = temperature
W = total amount
Adiabatic = process whereby no heat is communicated with the surroundings

Figure 5.3. The cyclic refrigeration process of the Siebe vapor compression machine; after Linde (1871, p. 266)

The Siebe vapor compression system, as depicted in Figure 5.3, deviates from the reversed Carnot cycle only in the compression at constant volume. Linde makes use of such thermodynamic concepts as heat of vaporization (r) and specific heat (c) in his analysis of this process. He uses a formula for the coefficient of performance to derive a rule which would guide a large part of his subsequent work on mechanical refrigeration: the larger its quotient r/c, the more efficient a refrigerant.[6] If two refrigerants are compared, then the better one, thermodynamically speaking, has a higher heat of vaporization (more heat is required to turn it from the liquid to the gaseous state) and a lower specific heat, or specific heat capacity (less heat is required to raise its temperature at constant volume).

His calculations make Linde quite optimistic about the possibilities of vapor compression, and he explicitly states that it is "conceivable" (*denkbar*) that perfection could be reached by using a refrigerant other than Siebe's diethyl ether and turning the constant volume compression into a process whereby no heat is absorbed. However, Linde's critique of Siebe's refrigerant and cycle seems to be somewhat off the mark. If we choose $T_1 = 15°C$ and $T_2 = -3°C$ like in the previous example and enter these figures into Linde's formula, then Siebe's machine would theoretically give 93.7 kg of ice per hph, which is only 5% below the ideal maximum. Since according to Linde's own sources (*DPJ* 1863, Vol. 168, p. 435) the Siebe apparatus in practice did not achieve more than roughly 9 kg of ice per hph, there must have been other features of the design more urgently in need of refinement.

Linde (1870, p. 326) was aware of the technical problems connected with the Siebe design:

> Since the general process of this machine is relatively satisfactory, it would be possible to increase its efficiency quite considerably by using large cooling surfaces and large amounts of cooling water. However, it is obvious that the behavior of the ether vapor in the expansion cylinder presents some problems and makes leakage losses inevitable.

The main problem Linde has in mind is the corrosive tendencies of some refrigerants, but he does not consider it—or the leakage losses—to be insuperable. Despite this positive assessment, Linde insisted on replacing the Siebe cycle with the reversed Carnot cycle and diethyl ether with another refrigerant. The reason for this critique of Siebe seems to be some severe miscalculations by Linde of the Siebe coefficient of performance.

---

6 Linde (1871, p. 266); the formula is $Q_2/W = A[r-c(T_1-T_2)]/[c(T_1-T_2)+r(T_1-T_2)/T_2-cT_1 \ln(T_1/T_2)]$.

Linde (1871, p. 266) wrongly states in a table that the theoretical maximum of the Siebe machine varies between 68 and 91% of the ideal maximum for the most common temperatures; the correct limits—using Linde's own formulae—should be 85 and 97%, respectively.

It is certainly acceptable to check the work of previous scientists and engineers, if this is done on their own terms, without being Whiggish and anachronistic. For example, when entering T = 280K and r/c = 200 into the formula for Siebe's machine, Linde arrives at 18.275 instead of the correct figure 26.3. The coefficient of performance of the reversed Carnot cycle under the same conditions is 27.0, showing how theoretically close to perfection the Siebe cycle actually was. Furthermore, if we choose a refrigerant whose quotient r/c is twice that of diethyl ether, the amount of ice produced by the Siebe cycle would increase by only 2.6%—from 93.7 to 96.2 kg per hph. In other words, simple errors of calculation led Linde to underestimate the degree of perfection of the Siebe process and thus to criticize the use of diethyl ether and constant volume compression more intensely than he otherwise might have done.

Although Linde's final judgment of vapor compression is quite positive, he does not predict a bright future for absorption. Linde (1871, p. 265) argues that it is not possible to exceed 30% of the ideal coefficient of performance with machines of this kind, mainly because such a large part of the energy input is required to heat the mixture of water and refrigerant in the generator. If we use the same notation as in Figure 2.4, we can say that Linde found Q_3 to be prohibitively large. The mixture in the Carré system is heated to 130°C (266°F), which means that 20 kg of water has to be heated in addition to every kilogram of ammonia. The losses entailed by repeatedly heating such large amounts of water makes it unlikely that an ice production capacity of more than 30 kg per hph can be reached—to be compared with the 98.5 kg per hph from the reversed Carnot cycle. Linde's (1870, p. 365) thermodynamic calculations also show another drawback of the Carré machine: its need for excessive amounts of cooling water; 24 kg of water at 15°C are required for each kilogram of ice produced. He arrives at this figure typically by using a deductive method instead of citing the experience gained from existing apparatuses. However, Linde refers to one essential advantage of the absorption ideal type: such machines have no moving parts, with the exception of a pump that requires comparatively small amounts of energy:

> The Carré apparatus occupies an exceptional position in that it exerts no "detrimental resistance," except in the case of the pump which returns the saturated [water/ammonia] solution to the [distillation] vessel. (Linde 1871, p. 267)

In Chapter 3 we saw that absorption had received the most acknowledgement and praise of the three ideal types of mechanical refrigeration, and that this reputation was largely due to the Carré archetype. Machines belonging to all ideal types could be found on the market, but absorption devices were given the most attention in engineering circles. Absorption was close to becoming the "ruling standard" of refrigeration. We have to judge Linde's work in this light. The strength of his deductive method was that it enabled him to break with historical experience and turn to the theoretically most powerful process. Absorption appeared to Linde as a "presumptive anomaly," a term that has been coined by Edward W. Constant II (1987, p. 225) to describe the following situation:

> The old system still works, indeed still may offer substantial development potential, but science suggests that the leading edge of future practice will have a radically different foundation.

The propeller plane represents the old system in Constant's work on the emergence of the turbojet airplane, and its shortcomings were foreseen by a group of engineers that came to airplane design from other areas of technology and science (cf. Constant 1980). In our case the old system is absorption. Linde's thermodynamic analyzes convinced him of the limits of absorption and the extraordinary possibilities of vapor compression, despite its bad track record.

Practical Conclusions and Recommendations

These deliberations bring us to another section of Linde's papers, where he formalizes some of the practical aspects of ice-machine performance (Linde 1871, pp. 267-270). While his thermodynamic calculations had initially sought to determine the theoretically maximum efficiency of the three ideal types, they now focus on problems of a more practical nature. Linde takes into account losses through friction, heat conduction, and leakage by introducing the term "degree of efficiency" (*Wirkungsgrad*). He defines caloric degree of efficiency as the ratio between the actual coefficient of performance of a machine and the Carnot ideal. The coefficient of performance of a perfect machine would thus be 100%. Linde (1871, p. 269) takes a number of technical and economic factors into consideration and is thereby able to present a table of figures which once again shows that vapor compression is superior to cold air, unless the temperature gap is extremely large. He arrives at 1.2% for the cold air system and 17% for the diethyl ether compression machine at ordinary temperatures. These low figures facilitate a better appreciation of the ice producing capacity of existing machines and an understanding of why it was hard to exceed 10-15 kg of ice per hph. The figures also make Linde more cautious about the possibilities of constructing an ideal system, even though he suspects that he might have overestimated the friction losses in his calculations.

Linde has turned from theoretical to practical problems by estimating degrees of efficiency, but he has not given up his deductive method. Empirical data do not enter into his derivations; they only appear for reasons of verification. Linde (1870, pp. 268, 270) now deductively concludes that vapor compression is also to be recommended for practical purposes. This classificatory ideal type ought to be up to fourteen times more efficient than the expansion type at ordinary temperatures. Furthermore, Linde brings in economic considerations and claims that the relatively enormous dimensions of cold air machinery and corresponding large material costs make this ideal type even more unattractive.

Unfortunately, Linde does not furnish any comparable figures for absorption, which he has already denounced as hopeless. His account would certainly have been more complete if he had not abandoned the Carré system after he found that it did not even theoretically achieve more than 30% of the Carnot cycle.

At the very end of his papers Linde (1871, p. 272) arrives at the optimistic conclusion that a vapor compression machine with an ice producing capacity of 30 kg per hph is, "without a doubt," possible. Since the best machines at the time produced less than 15 kg, this remark suggests that a doubling of the fuel efficiency was feasible.

This conclusion appears after Linde has reviewed his most important results and made some practical recommendations for the design of a superior ice-machine. Since he has already considered cold air and absorption and found both ideal types undesirable, he now focuses his efforts on improving the Siebe Bros. machine. He proposes dimethyl ether as a refrigerant instead of diethyl ether, since the former substance has a higher heat of vaporization and is non-corrosive.[7] Linde uses published tables to demonstrate that more heat is required to vaporize dimethyl ether and that more cold is thus produced. He also points out that the steam pressure of this substance is relatively low, which would diminish the risk of explosion —at the time a common problem. These factors taken together make it possible to run a dimethyl ether machine ten times slower than a Siebe device of similar power—thereby reducing energy losses due to friction (Linde 1871, p. 272).

Linde's (1971, p. 271, Plate XXII, Figs. 7 & 8) account has here reached its most practical point: he describes and depicts in some detail a possible design for a single-acting compressor pump. His immediate goal has obviously been to suggest what a refrigerating machine ought to look like, not to lay a foundation for a new branch of engineering. He hoped that drawings and descriptions were so convincing that he would win the Halle Mineral Oil Society prize contest. Linde's technical suggestions are in line with the focus of his previous analysis and limited to the compressor. The design of evaporators and condensers had already become fairly standardized in refrigerating engineering by this time, but compressor designs were still very different. Thus compressor design was most in need of a thorough treatment. Linde's proposed compressor uses mercury to prevent the refrigerant vapor from escaping into the atmosphere. Leakage was perhaps the most troublesome problem for engineers building vapor compression machines, and with this mercury sealing method Linde hoped to solve it.

Linde's initial contribution to refrigeration technology opened up a path to the conceptual framework and the analytic tools of thermodynamics, even though it did not make full use of them. Linde's comprehensive application of this science to refrigeration technology began the scientification of this field. I have chosen to discuss the scientification of refrigeration technology in the sense that the science of thermodynamics was imported into that already established technological domain. Refrigeration technology was neither turned into a science through this process nor did it become an applied science, since it had already existed as a branch of

7 Linde (1871, p. 270) uses the word ether for diethyl ether and methyl ether for what we today call dimethyl ether. Their respective formulae are $(CH_3CH_2)_2O$ and $(CH_3)_2O$. Linde instead writes C_2H_5O for what he calls "methyl ether."

mechanical engineering for quite some time. Like Carré and other earlier refrigeration technicians, Linde ultimately strived for the design of technically and economically sound ice-machines. The scientification process did not alter the ultimate goals of refrigeration technology, but it did affect the relative importance of various goals, as well as the means. Linde himself conceived of his papers as a contribution to technology and economics, not to science.

It is possible to distinguish a number of methods in Linde's papers. After he stated his problem verbally and rephrased it in mathematical language, Linde defined the concepts he intended to use, drawing on available thermodynamic knowledge—especially as it had been formulated by Rudolf Clausius and Gustav Zeuner; see Chapter 7. Linde proceeded in a perfectly deductive manner to find the theoretically optimal refrigeration process and the maximum coefficients of performance for various ideal types. He then analyzed how close these types came to the optimum and in what respects they might be improved. When he came to practical problems, Linde first deduced a number of degrees of efficiency which he later used in a second analysis of existing machine systems. He introduced technical and economic factors into his thermodynamic calculations and arrived at the conclusion that it ought to be possible to double the efficiency of available ice-machines. Linde finally synthesized his central results and used them in a prescriptive way to describe the design of such an improved machine. This description was totally technical and devoid of scientific content.

Linde had not yet actually built an ice-machine in 1871. Linde (1870, p. 270) was well aware that the steps from formulae and drawings to an economical and practical machine was large. At this time, he was not confident enough to take this step.

Linde's final synthesis represented the embryonic stage of the scientification of refrigeration technology. His prescriptions outlined a novel research and development program, several parts of which are still vital to refrigeration technology. A.R. Trott's (1981, p. 25) modern refrigeration textbook lists, among others, the following "requirements" for a useful refrigerant. It ought to have a "high latent heat of vaporization," be "noncorrosive," and show "compatibility with materials of construction"—all factors mentioned by Linde. Linde's synthesis and prescriptions formed a technological program based on scientific principles. Like some of his teachers and other contemporaries, Linde tried to bridge science and technology, thus acting as a *translator* between these two "systems of human action" (Aitken 1978, p. 102). Aitken introduced this term in a study of the early history of radio technology, a system in-between the science of electro-magnetism and economics. Oliver Lodge plays the role in Aitken's story which has here been attributed to Linde. Linde picked up pertinent information from science, applied it to technology, and thereby created new technological knowledge. He showed by this act of translation how old problems could be addressed in new ways.

Did Linde, like Edison, mix science, technology, and economics so closely that they constituted a seamless web? Linde's papers, like Edison's notebooks, do contain information from all these spheres of human activity, and Linde moved freely from one area to another. However, this does not mean that the seams had disappeared. In his second paper Linde (1871) typically introduces three different degrees of efficiency: one "caloric," describing the theoretically optimal efficiency of a certain ideal type; one "effective," taking into account technical factors like friction; one "economic," being applicable to real situations. The first degree was scientifically based and concerned with how close various principal solutions came to the Carnot *Leitbild*; the second degree was technological and intended for engineers to use in the design process; the third degree was economic and would enable business owners to calculate how much coal was needed to run an ice-machine under certain given conditions. Linde discussed all three aspects, but knew how to distinguish between them.

We will next see why it was possible for Linde to bridge the gap between thermodynamics and refrigeration technology. Subsequently we will see how he continued into the sphere of economic life.

6. The Institutional Background: School Culture Education

School Versus Shop Training

Linde's papers will be put into their historical context now that the content and character of his early attempt at scientification has been described and analyzed. His immediate motive for turning to refrigeration technology was to win a prize. We next need to investigate Linde's personal background and discuss what structural developments might have affected him in order to understand the way in which he addressed the prescribed problem. His theoretical heritage will be examined in detail in the following chapter, but the present chapter remains on a more general, institutional level. Technological discovery will not be explained with a phrase like "a flash of genius." Instead I will accept an old invitation from Abbot P. Usher who rejected in his *History of Mechanical Inventions* (1954, p. 78) all explanations which are based on subconscious phenomena:

> It is not necessary to explain the final act of insight; the task now consists in explaining how the stage is set to suggest the solution of the perceived problem.

What needs to be explained is why Linde chose to answer the prize question in the way he did, and to this end an analysis will be made on the level of *professional culture* (Helmers 1991). At this time mechanical the engineering profession consisted of two opposing cultures, each with its own presuppositions, values, and conduct (cf. Helmers 1990, Ch. 3).

The main thesis in this chapter is that Linde can be treated as an exponent of the *school culture* of the mechanical engineering profession. Monte A. Calvert launched this concept in his book *The Mechanical Engineer in America, 1830-1910* (1967) and put it in opposition to *shop culture*. These labels designate two separate traditions in mechanical engineering and revolve around questions of training, social relations, institutions, and professional status.

The hub of shop culture was the machine shop with its machine tools for turning, milling, and grinding. Here knowledge was transmitted verbally and through practical experience, while theoretical education was often looked down upon. The young mechanic started out as an apprentice on the shop floor and worked his way up the hierarchical ladder by learning various skills on the job. However, shop culture was not especially egalitarian; Calvert (1967, pp. 12 f.) calls it elitist and maintains that it was a predominantly upper-class and upper middle-class culture (cf. Layton 1971, Ch. 3). Calvert also emphasizes that the roots of this tradition can be traced to Britain. The American shop culture apparently shared several ideals with that of the British "gentlemen engineers" (Buchanan 1983).

Calvert does not place shops within the guild system, even though some features and ideals, like the hierarchical order and the emphasis on practical experience, have obviously been carried over from this system into shop culture. Weber (1981, Ch. XII) also separated the shop (*Werkstatt*) from the guilds; whereas the former employ various mechanical devices, the latter manages with very little fixed capital. Even though Weber did not discuss mechanical engineers as such, he would probably have regarded this profession—unlike that of the master artisan—as a fairly recent phenomenon:

> ... a specific workshop technique ... first arose gradually in the 16th and 17th centuries and first definitely with the mechanization of the production process (p. 177).

Weber (pp. 165 ff.) mentions flour mills, iron foundries, and breweries (to which we will return in Part III) among the first large workshops, all of which required other skills and knowledge than did handicraft production.

The shop culture educational system began to show signs of stress as mechanical engineering became more complicated and as the shops grew in size:

> As the machine shop became like a factory, it lost the uniqueness which gave it its importance as a source of mechanical engineering talent. (Calvert 1967, p. 6)

These developments made it difficult to continue the exclusive reliance on workshop training, and as a result various engineering institutes were founded. At the beginning these schools provided training which differed very little in content from the education received in industry. Shop culture training thus paradoxically continued inside schools. The establishment of schools as a means of providing industry with qualified personnel did not automatically mean that the content of engineering education changed. It did so only in the second half of the nineteenth century, when the curriculum at many schools became increasingly theoretical. School culture entered the American stage with a heavy emphasis on mathematics, textbooks, and experiments. Calvert (p. 65) writes about this trend:

> Technical education could offer potential mechanical engineers professional instructors, who provided students with abstract knowledge of the scientific prin-

ciples of engineering and also (through mechanical engineering laboratories) made it clear how these principles could be applied in practice.

In other words, the difference between school and shop culture education concerns what is taught and how it is taught, not where it is taught.

School culture had its roots on the European continent. American educational reformers were especially influenced by developments which had started in France and Germany earlier in the century. Even though Calvert's concepts were designed for the American case, they apply equally well to these countries. The historian Kees Gispen (1990) has made successful use of Calvert's dichotomy when discussing the German case. Gispen emphasizes what he calls the "segmentalist" and heterogeneous character of the German engineering profession, thereby showing that school culture engineers were frequently educators, while industrialist and consultants represented shop culture. We will below see how Linde personally experienced the upsurge of school culture and its struggle with shop culture.

Linde's Youth

Carl Linde was born in 1842 in Berndorf, a small community in Upper Franconia (Linde 1979, pp. 3 ff.). His father was a vicar, and his mother had worked as a teacher in her youth.[1] Both parents seem to have encouraged intellectual activities. When Carl was seven, the family moved to Kempten, a town in southwestern Bavaria, where his father had gained a higher position within the Protestant Church. A student of the liberal arts secondary school, the *Gymnasium*, Linde nevertheless despised Latin and Greek, finding more comfort in history, French, and mathematics. The mathematics program at Kempten included plane geometry and basic algebra, but the science curriculum was much briefer.[2] Linde's physics course

---

1 Linde's (1979) autobiography first appeared in 1916 and was reprinted in 1979 and 1984 together with some personal letters from his correspondence, 1861-1910. Linde's "From My Life and My Work" will be used for the outlines of his life despite the problematic nature of the autobiographical genre. Linde's statements have been double-checked as far as possible, and my general impression is that it is quite accurate.

2 See the ring binder at the Linde Co. in Höllriegelskreuth in the south of Munich, LAG-H: "Zur Geschichte der Linde AG."

included the study of equilibrium of forces and simple machines, along with the measurement of air pressure and temperature. Mathematics and the classical languages were central at the school, but only minor parts of the natural world were allowed to cross its threshold. This focus fitted well in the concept of *Bildung*, the ideological foundation of most *Gymnasien* (Ringer 1969). Those subjects formed the core of this ideology which aimed at cultivating the personality of the student through disciplined intellectual exercise.

A career in theology was of course close at hand for a young man with Linde's upbringing and education. Much to his father's disillusionment, however, Carl expressed a preference for mechanical engineering. The deep impressions a local spinning mill made on him were instrumental in his decision to study the power of machines instead of that of the Almighty (Linde 1979, pp. 9 f.). At the time there were three Bavarian schools which could fulfill this wish, namely the polytechnics in Munich, Augsburg, and Nuremberg. However, since it was difficult to maintain high quality in as many as three Bavarian *polytechnische Schulen*, none of them gave a very advanced engineering education (Manegold 1970a, p. 43). The typical student entered at the age of fifteen and graduated three years later, and a large percentage ended up in public service rather than in industry (Grüner 1967, pp. 22 f.). There were a few technical schools possessing more of a college (*Hochschule*) character outside Bavaria, and a friend gave Linde the momentous advice to apply to the national Swiss polytechnical school in Zurich, *Die Eidgenössische Polytechnische Schule*. Linde was particularly impressed by the "scientific significance" of the school, followed the advice, and was admitted to its mechanical engineering section in the fall of 1861.

The Swiss Polytechnic

The Polytechnic in Zurich had been founded six years earlier, an event representing the culmination of a fifty-year long debate over Swiss higher education. At the beginning of the century Philipp Albert Stapfer, Secretary for "the arts and sciences," had proposed the creation of a national institution of higher learning (*ADB* 1967-1971, Vol. 15, pp. 451-456). Peter Gyr (1981, pp. 92 f.) argues that "Stapfer's models were the German universities and the Parisian *École Polytechnique* founded in 1794/95." Aspects of both traditions were in fact still alive in 1854, when the Swiss parliament decided to erect a polytechnic institute in Zurich. A majority of the Swiss cantons feared centralism and opposed the simultaneous creation of one large university, but they still voted in favor of the polytechnic, since they understood that creating several regional technical schools would be far too expensive (*100 Jahre* ... 1955, pp. 32 ff.; Geiser 1890, Ch. V). The idea of dividing the polytechnic into a number of departments came from the German educational system, and the emphasis on natural science and mathematics was adopted from the Paris example. The parliamentary committee which had prepared the bill had been particularly influenced by the organization and aims of the Karlsruhe Polytechnic Institute.

The great general impact of the *École Polytechnique* and its scientific approach to engineering is well known (Schnabel 1925; Shinn 1980; Weiss 1982). Since the less well-known *polytechnische Schule* of Karlsruhe was based on this French school (Grüner 1967, pp. 15 f.), some of the former's characteristics and ties with Zurich will be discussed below. Karlsruhe served as a pattern for a number of schools (Ahlström 1982, pp. 29-33; Manegold 1970a, p. 42). The most obvious common denominator for Karlsruhe and Zurich is the division of both schools into six specialized departments, *Fachschulen*. Five of these were identical in both institutes: the departments for civil engineering, mechanical engineering, chemical engineering, forestry, and structural engineering. The only difference was that Karlsruhe had a trade department (Schnabel 1925, pp. 33, 37), which at Zurich was replaced by philosophy and political economy. The *Fachschule* concept had actually emerged in Karlsruhe in 1832 and was subsequently seen as "a new era in the history of higher technical education" (Ahlström 1982, p. 33; Henriques 1917, p. 24). The man behind the 1832 reorganization had been Karl Friedrich Nebenius, the Baden Secretary of the Interior (*ADB* 1967-1971, Vol. 23, pp. 351-355).

There was also a personal connection between the two institutes. One of the co-writers of the bill in the Swiss parliament was Josef Wolfgang von Deschwanden, who had studied at Karlsruhe and would become the first director of the Swiss Polytechnic. His teacher in Karlsruhe had been Ferdinand Redtenbacher (Gyr 1981, p. 97; Schnabel 1925, p. 40), a reformer of mechanical engineering education to whom we will return, since he was of indirect importance to Linde.

The attitudes expressed toward the role of science in engineering are of paramount significance for this study. The Karlsruhe Polytechnic was one of the first in the German-speaking world to give science a positive role. The Grand Duke of Baden wrote in the 1825 edict stipulating that a polytechnic be founded in Karlsruhe that the school should

> take care of the *Bildung* of our dear and faithful bourgeoisie [*Bürgerstand*] and, broadly speaking, of everything that concerns the advanced trades. For that purpose it should pass on necessary basic knowledge, mainly in mathematics and natural science, together with its various, immediate applications pertinent to bourgeois activities.[3]

The aim was thus to educate the middle-class, and it is clear that science should play a fundamental role in this process.

The goal was not expressed so clearly in the Swiss case. Instead of referring to any specific class, the supporters of the Zurich Polytechnic in the early 1850s made extensive use of nationalistic arguments. A Swiss institute of technology would be a means of keeping the federation together, since young men would come from all corners of the republic to study there. Albeit situated in German-speaking Zurich, the school would be bilingual and serve as a bridge between "German and Roman science" (Geiser 1890, pp. 105 ff.). In other words, the reformers—J.H.A. Escher, the President of the national council among them—saw the institute as a way of avoiding the fragmentation of Switzerland and simultaneously of giving this small country an international role. Throughout his career Escher in fact strived to centralize Swiss political and cultural life (*NBG* 1852-1866, Vol. 6, p. 350).

The appearance of science at the Swiss Polytechnic was Janus-like. First of all, basic natural science was to play a central role in the sixth department, philosophy and political economy. This *Fachschule* was virtually a miniature university, including almost everything from botany to law (Dahlbeck 1866, p. 32; Koristka 1863, pp. 13 f.). Its primary goal was the education of secondary school teachers, but it also aimed at giving the Swiss state international prestige: "all of the natural sciences and mathematical disciplines [were] to be represented at their most advanced level ..."

---

3 Quoted in Schnabel (1925, p. 27). The quote has wrongly been interpreted by Ahlström (1982, p. 33) to imply "that this education should basically comprise mathematics and the natural sciences."

(Oechsli 1905, p. 151).[4] This wish, to attract first-class scholars, scientists, and mathematicians and thereby enhance the school's status, did in fact come true. Several renowned personalities were hired at the very beginning: among them the architect Gottfried Semper, the professor of literature Friedrich Theodor Vischer, and the renaissance specialist Jacob Burckhardt (Manegold 1970a, p. 56). Semper and Vischer were still in Zurich when Linde came there. The school board also managed in 1855 to attract the already well-known physicist Rudolf Clausius, whose lectures on thermodynamics were of great significance to Linde. Clausius was responsible for "mathematical and technical physics and for the direction of the physics laboratory" (Ronge 1958, p. 81). The historian Grete Ronge (1958) has argued that Clausius was employed because of the practical importance of thermodynamics to areas like steam engine technology, but an additional reason was probably to give status to the new school.

This array of famous scientists and scholars helped give considerable prestige to Switzerland in general and Zurich in particular. One of the roles played by science at the Swiss Polytechnic was thus a nationalistic one.

The other face of science at the school was more mundane. After all, its chief duty was to educate engineers, for which the different branches of natural science, mathematics, and the modern languages would act as "auxiliary sciences," *Hilfswissenschaften* (Wolf 1880, p. 12). The term appears in the 1854 law which founded the *Eidgenössische* School. The idea that science is an important source of knowledge for technology was explicitly supported by the Swiss Parliament and thus officially sanctioned.

Linde in Zurich

How did the Janus-face of science affect Linde? Or, putting it more precisely, what education did he actually receive at the Swiss Polytechnic, and what role did thermodynamics play for him?

Although his basic knowledge of physics, chemistry, and mathematics was considered insufficient, Linde was admitted to the mechanical engineering department. Gustav Zeuner, the director of this *mechanisch-techni-*

---

4 Cf. the first program of 1855-1856 from the Swiss polytechnic, reprinted in *Festschrift* ... (1894, p. 161), as well as Wolf (1880, pp. 18 ff.).

sche Fachschule, allowed him to begin in October 1861, under the condition that he quickly acquire the necessary experience by taking private lessons. Linde should otherwise have attended the one-year "mathematical preparatory class" according to the regulations, but his father would only pay for a total of three years in Zurich—making it impossible for him to waste one year in this class.[5]

If we assume that Linde attended the prescribed courses at the mechanical engineering department, then it is easy to reconstruct the skeleton of his Zurich education from the course catalogs. It is also possible to get a close-up view of some classes, those marked with asterisks in Figure 6.1, from remaining lecture notes.[6] Each student in any of the five engineering departments could also freely attend lectures at the department of philosophy and political economy (Dahlander 1866, p. 28). Linde (1979, p. 13) took the opportunity to listen to lectures on art history, literature, and history—F.T. Vischer and Wilhelm Lübke being among the lecturers. It should be emphasized that Linde complemented his technical interests throughout his life with a genuine taste for humanistic studies and music. Finally, we can infer from the course catalogs that Linde probably went with his department on study trips to a handful of companies in the machine and textile industry and to one ironworks. Among these companies was the *Maschinenfabrik Gebrüder Sulzer*, Winterthur, which a dozen years later would become one of the chief producers of the Linde ice-machines (*Programm* ... WS 1862-1863, p. 14).

The mechanical engineering students seem to have come into direct contact with industry only through these study tours. At the Zurich Polytechnic there was nothing like sandwich courses, where classes and internships are mixed. All practical training instead took place in workshops and drawing rooms at the college. Figure 6.1 implies that 36% of the classes were devoted to practical machine design, lithography, and drawing. How-

---

5 Cf. Linde (1979, pp. 10 f.) and a letter from Carl to his brother Hans from the fall of 1861, reprinted in Linde (1979).

6 The library of the present Swiss Institute of Technology in Zurich, the *ETH-Bibliothek*, has unpublished lecture notes by Heinrich Berchtold, one of Linde's class-mates, from some of Zeuner's and Clausius' classes; these are Zeuner (1862) and Clausius (1863). There is also one notebook written after Linde had left the school by M. Kussevich; see Zeuner (1869-70). Some lecture notes were even published: Zeuner (1865) and Reuleaux (1865).

ever, the real figure was even higher, since extra time was given to practical design work during the last year of study (*Programm* ... SS 1864).

Subject	Total number of hours*	%	Teacher
Machine design (practice)	640	24	Reuleaux
Differentials and integrals	352	13	Dedekind Durège Christoffel
Machine design (lectures)	320	12	Reuleaux
Machine drawing	256	10	Fritz
Technical mechanics**	256	10	Zeuner
Theoretical mechanical engineering**	240	9	Zeuner
Experimental physics with technical applications**	128	5	Clausius
Mechanical technology	96	4	Kronauer
Experimental chemistry	80	3	Städeler
Descriptive geometry	64	2	Deschwanden
Lithography	64	2	Deschwanden
Large constructions	64	2	Culman
Analytic mechanics	48	2	Durège
Civil engineering	32	1	Gladbach
Metallurgy	32	1	Bolley
Chemistry of construction materials	16	1	Bolley
Total	2,688	101	

* The figures rely on the assumption that there was an average of 16 weeks each semester.

** Lecture notes are available from parts of these subjects.

Figure 6.1. Linde's education at the mechanical engineering department of the Swiss Polytechnic in Zurich; compiled from *Programm* ... (WS 1861/1862 - SS 1864).

Franz Reuleaux was responsible for machine design. Since his lectures and workshop classes amounted to a total of about one thousand hours, Reuleaux can be said to have been Linde's most important teacher, at least quantitatively. Reuleaux' (1865) lectures followed a neat structure very similar to that of his book "The Designer" (1861). The lectures and the book both present different mechanisms and machines in a systematic way, but without elaborate mathematical or scientific formulae. Reuleaux' lectures were divided into seven sections. For example, the first section included block and tackle, cranes, and devices for lacking, winding, and braking; the fourth section dealt with water wheels and turbines; in the seventh section steam engine design was discussed. In each case he explained the general principles and gave some practical examples. We can use the same terminology as in Part I and say that under each heading he explained the pertinent classificatory ideal type and described a number of archetypes or types.

If Reuleaux wanted to give his lectures a more realistic touch, then he could chose from among four hundred items in the collection for machine design at the institute. This "systematically arranged and very pedagogically designed" collection of demonstration models gave the students some idea of how various mechanisms work (Koristka 1863, pp. 14 f.). Since the practical workshops remained in a makeshift state until the Polytechnic moved into a new building in the mid-1860s, Reuleaux' demonstrations must have been quite important to Linde. The scholar Karl-Heinz Manegold (1970a, p. 58) has claimed that Reuleaux never ceased to stress the importance of a "scientific" (*wissenschaftlich*) approach to technology. Similarly, Hans-Joachim Braun (1977, p. 3, 1981) has shown how Reuleaux was one of the central figures in creating a "science of machine design." Both as a teacher and as an administrator Reuleaux followed the path that had been laid out by his teacher in Karlsruhe, Redtenbacher. Franz Schnabel (1925, p. 37) has claimed that

> Redtenbacher's great historical importance [was] his introduction of science [*Wissenschaft*] into the technical workshops and his bringing together of theoretical and technical mechanics.

Both Redtenbacher and Reuleaux emphasized the cultivating and educational effects of science and tried to bridge the theory and practice of mechanical engineering, but it is not clear what their approach really meant. For instance, we have already seen that Reuleaux' lectures were fairly devoid of advanced science and mathematics.

This paradox can be solved by returning to Calvert's school culture concept and by following a thesis put forth by the historian Edwin T. Layton. First, the Swiss Polytechnic has to be regarded with its lectures, textbooks, demonstrations, and experiments as an example of school culture; the same holds for Reuleaux' work (Braun 1981, p. 122). Reuleaux' experimental classes were still held in what was called a workshop, *Werkstatt*, but it was more like a laboratory than an industrial site. There Reuleaux was a teacher and not a master artisan, and as such he needed to present his subject-matter in a systematic manner. Instead of simply treating one machine after another, he endeavored to create a logical classificatory system; instead of teaching the students how to handle a large number of individual machines, he wanted them to understand their underlying, common principles. Layton (1971, 1979) has observed that systems of this kind were often presented in a manner similar to those of scientists. For example, "in the case of the turbine," Layton (1979, p. 88) writes that

> engineers borrowed and adopted the methods and spirit of basic science in order to generate a body of science tailored to the needs of technology.

Layton demonstrates that in the second half of the nineteenth century several branches of technology were modeled on the physical sciences, especially on their systematic and deductive nature. It could be added that teaching techniques were often a crucial factor, overlooked by Layton, in these early attempts to bring engineering closer to science. Reuleaux also later developed a new technological subject with a scientific structure, kinematics (Lang 1905; Reuleaux 1877). Thus when Reuleaux' commentators assign to him a scientific approach, this does not mean that he made physics bear directly on his technology, rather that he tried to systematize this engineering discipline in a way similar to that of science. Thus Reuleaux' work did not constitute a case of scientification as defined in the Introduction.

At least one of Linde's other teachers, Zeuner, worked simultaneously with problems of pedagogy and systematization (Grabow 1984). In 1859 he published the first edition of his "Fundamentals of the Mechanical Theory of Heat," a "textbook made especially for technicians" (Zeuner 1866, p. V), but at the same time a basis for technical thermodynamics, a new *research and development program* around which a *school* of practitioners would gather. We will return to Zeuner's work in the following chapter. Suffice it here to say that the outlines of his lectures were quite close to those of the "Fundamentals." Zeuner's courses were heavily theoretical and mathematical, in contrast to Reuleaux' practically oriented lectures. In fact, it had been Director Zeuner's idea to separate theoretical mechanical engineering (*theoretische Maschinenlehre*) from machine design (*Maschinenbau*) at the Polytechnic (Gabow 1984, p. 13).

I will also discuss further Linde's connections with Clausius in Chapter 7. Unlike Zeuner and Reuleaux, Clausius does not appear to have been particularly inspiring as a teacher (Linde 1979, p. 12). The gap between his published papers (Clausius 1864, 1867) and his lectures was rather wide. While the papers were advanced and had theoretical aims, the lectures were comparatively elementary and had practical goals. The unpublished notes from Clausius' lectures clearly show the "auxiliary" character of the physics course (Clausius 1863). The title of the notebook is in fact "Technical Physics," rather than "Experimental Physics." For Linde and his classmates, science and mathematics were tools for technical ends, not ends in themselves.

At the end of his three years in Zurich, Linde (1979, pp. 15 f.) played an important role in a student strike. As a result he received neither a diploma nor grades. Instead he secretly got two letters of recommendation, one from Zeuner and one from Reuleaux. A copy of Zeuner's letter remains, in which he praises Linde for "his diligence and serious pursuit."[7]

To the Shop and Back to School

With these letters in hand, the twenty-two-year-old man started to look for a job in the machine industry. His initial aim was to acquire manual experience in a machine shop following advice from Reuleaux (Linde 1979, pp. 16 ff.). In other words, he wanted to supplement his school culture education with shop culture training. His first opportunity came at a cotton mill outside Kempten, where he spent the fall months of 1864 at the vise and lathe. Linde soon found this drudgery too limited in scope and went to Berlin in order to look for a more promising position. On Reuleaux' suggestion he called on the Borsig company, the largest locomotive producer in Germany (*Borsig* 1902), where he was once more enrolled without pay and placed at a vise. After a couple of months he moved on to the "more varied" assembly hall (this was before the time of the monotonous

7 Zeuner's letter of recommendation was written on October 3, 1864, and copies can be found in Linde (1979) and at *ETH-Bibliothek*, Zurich.

assembly line), and in August 1865 he got a low-paying position in the drawing office.

Linde was disappointed with the slow promotion system at Borsig and continued to look around for a better job. He soon found one in Munich, where Georg Krauß, a Zurich-based engineer, intended to found a company for the production of locomotives (Linde 1979, pp. 19-27). The Krauß locomotive had been produced by a Zurich machine shop, *Werkstätte Zürich Maschinen*, since 1864 and had in a short time gained a foothold on the market. Linde now offered Krauß his services. The new firm, Krauß & Co., hired Linde in late winter of 1866 after having consulted Zeuner, and made him responsible for the technical arrangements and installations at the new plant, which only one year later employed about 200 workers (*1815 - 1915* ... 1922, pp. 129 f.). Linde became head of the technical office as soon as production had gotten under way, and he after a short while made some important contributions to the design of the transmission mechanism and braking system of the Krauß locomotive. The brakes were steam powered and gave Linde some insights into the design of cylinders, pistons, and steam vessels, an experience that was probably essential to his later compressor designs in the area of refrigeration. It must have been a nice piece of engineering work, since Zeuner referred to it in one of his books (cf. Linde 1979, p. 25), and a description of it was published in both German (Linde 1868) and English.

Linde returned to the academy after only four years in the machine industry. In August 1868 he was appointed assistant professor of theoretical mechanical engineering at the new Munich polytechnic institute. This school had been founded as a result of a wide-scale reform in Bavarian technical education (Grüner 1967, pp. 96 ff.; Kluckhohn 1879, p. 51 f.; Manegold 1970a, p. 73; Riedner 1941, pp. 230 ff.). As was mentioned above, there had been no technical colleges in Bavaria in the early 1860s. This deficiency was remedied by replacing the three low-level polytechnics with one advanced *polytechnische Schule* in Munich. It had the character of an official college (*Hochschule*) from the start in 1868, but it did not actually receive the *technische Hochschule* label until 1877.[8] Six secondary

8 Its *Hochschule* character had already been confirmed by a royal ordinance of April 12, 1868; see *Bericht* ... (1868-1869, p. 1). The new name first appears in *Programm* ... (1877-1878).

schools (*Realgymnasien*), where the emphasis lay on science and modern languages, had been instituted in Bavaria in 1864 to prepare young men for college studies, and a few years later three industry schools opened in Nuremberg and Munich (1868), and in Augsburg (1870). These *Industrieschulen* had originally been designed for people who intended to continue directly to industry and now also began to serve as preparatory schools for the Munich Polytechnic.

The Munich Polytechnic consisted of five departments: a general division, along with one each for civil, structural, mechanical, and chemical engineering. Since the early history and subsequent development of this college have been discussed elsewhere, this need not be done here (Kluckhohn 1879; Riedner 1941; *Technische* ... 1968). It is more important to describe some of the official attitudes toward science and give a short account of Linde's first years there.

We encounter the following passage on the opening page of the first institute catalog:

> The Munich Polytechnic is a technical college granting a complete, theoretical education for the technical profession. It gives the student both a general education [*allgemeine Bildung*] and a specialized education aimed at a discipline based on the exact sciences and the arts of drawing. (*Programm* ... 1868-1869, p. 1)

The first task obviously refers to the general department and the second one to the four specialized *Fachschulen*. A famous speech, held in 1864 by the Karlsruhe professor Franz Grashof, had had considerable influence on the polytechnic founders (Riedner 1941, p. 230). In fact, some of Grashof's formulations were very similar to those adopted in the program of the Munich Polytechnic. Grashof (1864) had said that the technical college ought to give a "scientific education for the technical professions ... which are founded on mathematics, the natural sciences, and the arts of drawing" (in Schnabel 1925, p. 41).

At the inaugural ceremony in Munich the director of the college, C.M. Bauernfeind, fully supported these pro-science ideas. His long speech had actually been announced as dealing primarily with "the influence of the exact sciences on education in general and on technical training in particular" (*Reden* ... 1869, p. 20). Bauernfeind made it clear that the main assignment of any polytechnic was "to teach the exact sciences and their applications to all branches of advanced technology" (p. 22). In this endeavor he was strongly supported by the Bavarian Secretary of Trade, Gustav von Schlör, who was responsible for technical education and stipulated that the task of the Munich institute was "to apply the results of science to practical life in a useful manner" (in Riedner 1941, p. 234).

Grashof, Bauernfeind, and Schlör were all apparently convinced that scientific knowledge would become a very powerful tool if turned to technical aims. Like the Swiss reformers, they called for the scientification of technology—even though none of these men used this term. Such pro-scientification opinions were quite strong among politicians and influential educators in Switzerland and Germany of the 1850s and 1860s. The historian Helmut Albrecht (1987) has shown in a study of the technical college in Braunschweig that this ideology was also strong outside Karlsruhe, Zurich, and Munich. My thesis is that Linde shared a common ideology with these people and that his attempt at scientification of 1870-1871 was a concerted, positive act. With his background as a student at the Zurich and a teacher at the Munich Polytechnic it is hardly surprising that Linde chose a thermodynamic approach for the prize contest sponsored by the Mineral Oil Society of Halle.

Unfortunately, no lecture notes remain from Linde's initial years as a professor, but we know that he made extensive use of material from Zeuner's lectures (Linde 1979, p. 31). The titles of his courses also give us some idea of the areas in which he worked. Among other topics, he dealt during the first year with "thermodynamic machines," steam engines, and "the theory ... of caloric machines" (*Programm* ... 1868-1869, p. 23). In addition to fulfilling a heavy teaching load, he also managed the mechanical technology collection (*Programm* ... 1869-1870, p. 11). Furthermore, in 1870 and 1871 Linde co-edited the "Bavarian Journal of Industry and Trade," for which he wrote a couple of long articles and several shorter items. In his autobiography Linde (1979, p. 29) explains that one of his goals as editor had been to review the literature on applied thermodynamics. His endeavor was carried forward in the aims of the journal, which included

> the communication of the outcome of scientific research and experiments, which show or might have technical applications ... [and] the publication of scientific papers, which give information about mechanical and material laws pertinent to technical work. (*BIGB* 1870, Vol. 2, p. 29)

Since these words appear in the preface to the 1870 volume of the journal, it is likely that Linde had some role in their formulation. They clearly reveal a belief in the power of scientification.

The journal also figured in Linde's response to the Mineral Oil Society: he needed material for the periodical. If he was going to spend time writing articles, he might just as well go for a prize, especially since the award was substantial: 8,750 guldens (*ZVDI* 1870, Vol. 14, p. 394). This was no mean amount, since his ordinary salary as an assistant professor was only 1,000 guldens per year, student fees excluded. Linde (1979, p. 28) had recently married and with two small children was very worried that he would not make ends meet.

Thus the general, institutional background to Linde's initial attempt at the scientification of refrigeration technology has been outlined. In the following chapter we will turn to the more specialized intellectual world of thermodynamics and mechanical engineering.

7. The Intellectual Context: Rationality and the School of Technical Thermodynamics

The Legacy of Linde's Teachers

This chapter will put Linde's contributions to the discipline of theoretical mechanical engineering into their proper context. It will suggest what intellectual tradition Linde belonged to, and how his ideas were received and developed in the 1880s by others within that tradition. The account will focus on questions of technological modes, aims, concepts and methods.

There is a controversy among historians of mechanical engineering about how long it took for the fundamental insights of thermodynamics to diffuse throughout the engineering profession. Lynwood Bryant (1973, p. 157) maintains that this process was very fast and concludes that discussions on thermodynamics "were published widely in the journals in the 1850s and were codified into textbooks in the 1860s, where a practical engineer ... could find them if he wanted to."

However, this begs the question, since we still do not know if the general engineer was interested in these accounts, or if he was able to grasp their content. In an article on the history of "industrial thermodynamics" M.C. Duffy (1983, p. 56) is much more cautious on this point and claims that "[a]wareness of the fundamentals of thermodynamics spread slowly ..." Duffy (p. 52) is more precise when he says that "... thermodynamics only became of major importance after 1890 with the development of internal combustion engines ... and large central electricity-generating stations." The controversy thus includes several issues: when was the mechanical theory of heat available to an engineering audience? When were engineers well enough educated to make use of it? And, when did it really have a decisive impact on their work?

The first of these questions was partly answered for the German-speaking world in the previous chapter. Gerd Grabow (1984, pp. 16 f.) has pointed out that the 1859 edition of Zeuner's "Fundamentals" was the first comprehensive text written directly for engineers; Kurt Mauel (1969) believes that it did indeed influence them. The second question has also partly been addressed; at least some engineering students were being taught the basics of the mechanical theory of heat in the early 1860s, Linde among them. In this chapter we will analyze in more detail how much a

Zurich student like Linde could make of Zeuner's program. However, the third question cannot be addressed for refrigeration technology until the following chapters.

Even though Linde had been a student of Zeuner and Clausius, we cannot therefore conclude that he made use of information from their classes in his refrigeration papers—written almost a decade later. His pioneering articles from 1870-1871 and others written in the 1870s contain only a handful of explicit references to texts dealing with thermodynamics. Moreover, the references are seldom precise.

Linde's (1870, pp. 206 f., 365 f.) first paper on refrigeration cites a speech, "On a Mechanical Proposition Applicable to Heat," given by Clausius in June of that same year. Linde also states that several of his concepts come from journals like *Annales de Chimie et de Physique*. In a speech to the Bavarian Polytechnic Society in November 1869, Linde (1869, p. 329) referred to papers by R. Mayer and J.P. Joule, two of the most famous discoverers—or inventors, if you like—of the first law of thermodynamics. He surely made extensive use of Zeuner's most important work, the "Fundamentals," as a thermodynamically-oriented engineering source. Even if there are no references to this book in the 1870-1871 articles, we can tell from other papers that Linde had quite recently studied it carefully (Linde 1869, 1870a). Linde (1875-1876) published two additional papers on refrigeration in the mid-seventies which were very similar to the first articles. Since these later papers were published in the "Proceedings of the Society for the Advancement of Industrious Life," they were directed to an audience quite similar to that of the earlier articles. The later papers repeatedly cite the second, 1866 edition of the "Fundamentals." Furthermore, by 1870 Linde had consulted some of Clausius' published works and two highly theoretical books by the Frenchman G.-A. Hirn (Clausius 1864; Hirn 1865).

Since Linde, own references are few and vague, his texts should be compared with those written by his former teachers and with lecture notes from their classes. We have already seen that Linde used material from Zeuner's classes in his own teaching.

Linde (1870, p. 206) claims at the outset of this first refrigeration paper that any alteration of the heat of a body depends on changes of at least one of three forces: (1) "the effective force of the heat," keeping the smallest particles of the body in motion; (2) the cohesion between these particles;

and (3) any external forces affecting the body. These three forces correspond exactly to what Zeuner (1866, pp. 24 f.) calls the work of oscillation, of changes in position, and of changes in volume, respectively. However, while Zeuner like Clausius uses the term "disintegration work" to cover any work connected with the numbers 2 and 3, Linde uses the same word only when discussing work affecting internal cohesion.[1] Both Linde and Zeuner obviously and hardly surprisingly adhered to a kinetic theory of heat, understanding heat as the motion of the most minute particles of bodies. Linde's (1870, p. 207) and Zeuner's (1866, p. 12) accounts also rely on the notion of the equivalence of heat and work in accordance with the first law of thermodynamics. Today we call it the law of the conservation of energy, but in the 1850s and 1860s it was common to speak of the preservation of force. Like most of their contemporaries, they used the following units: calories for heat and *Meter-Kilogramm* (corresponding to foot-pounds in British-American units) for work. Conversions were made by means of a constant called the heat equivalent, which had been introduced by Clausius in 1850 (Yagi 1981, pp. 88 f.). We encountered this heat equivalent in the previous chapter as the constant A in Linde's formula for the coefficient of performance.

Linde's short introductory remarks are followed by an account of various closed cyclic processes. Linde (1870, p. 207) defines such a process as one "during which the body [in question] has to return to the same state of heat after equal periods of time." This concept connects Linde's work to a very long tradition with its ultimate roots in practical steam engine design. There the "body" is water, which is being vaporized, superheated, and condensed back to water, so that the cycle can start over. We saw in Chapter 1 that both Sadi Carnot and Clausius studied such processes very closely. Linde's starting point is the Carnot formula, which describes the theoretically perfect steam engine cycle. Linde presents the standard formula along with a reference to Zeuner (1866, p. 61), and tells the reader that it had been given its mathematical form "as early as 1851 by Rankine and Thomson on the basis of the propositions developed by Clausius" (Linde 1870, pp. 208 f.). This wording is strikingly close to a sentence in one

1 The German word is *Disgregationsarbeit*; cf. Linde (1870, p. 206) and Zeuner (1866, pp. 11, 26). Cardwell (1971, p. 269) uses "disgregation" in English when discussing Clausius' papers, but it seems to me that "disintegration" is a clearer term.

of Clausius' papers and indicates Linde's familiarity with his works. Clausius (1864, p. 167) had written in reference to the common formula that

> [it was] already deduced earlier by W. Thomson and Rankine from my version of Carnot's proposition and from the proposition concerning the equivalence of heat and work.

Linde distinguishes between two cases in his discussion of the perfect refrigeration cycle: (1) the refrigerant remains a "permanent" gas throughout the cycle; (2) it is partly liquid, partly vapor. Linde (1875, p. 362) refers to Zeuner's "Fundamentals" (1866, pp. 125, 135) when dealing with the non-condensing gases, but Linde undoubtedly had already encountered the pertinent formulae in Zurich. These basic expressions concerning the isothermal (constant temperature) and adiabatic (no heat being communicated with the surroundings) changes of gases can be found in unprinted lecture notes from both Clausius' and Zeuner's classes.[2] The same conclusion holds also for the second case, where the formulae are more complicated, since they have to take into account the behavior of both liquid and vapor. Nevertheless, both teachers had thought it worthwhile to include the formulae in their standard courses.[3] When first introducing the expression for the relationship between the amount of vapor and temperature, Linde (1870, p. 321) assumes that it is well known to the reader, and omits all references. In contrast, Zeuner (1865, p. 159) had said in one of his lectures that Clausius was the first person to use this formula.[4]

Linde's debt to his former teachers is also suggested by certain parts of his theoretical analysis of ice-machines. For instance, when dealing with the Windhausen cycle, Linde (1870, p. 265) has to introduce expressions for the expansion at constant pressure and the compression at constant volume of a gas; compare Figure 5.2. These formulae are identical with those described by Zeuner (1866, pp. 138 ff.) in the "Fundamentals," the only difference being that Zeuner presents them both as differential equations

---

2 Compare Linde (1870, p. 322) with Clausius (1863, pp. 199-205) and Zeuner (1865, pp. 142-152).

3 Compare, e.g., Linde's (1870, p. 321) formula for the amount of vapor with those given by Zeuner (1865, p. 159, 1866, p. 323) and Clausius (1863, p. 220, 1864, p. 174).

4 The formula is $x_1 = [xr/T_2 - c\ \ln(T_1/T_2)]T_1/r_1$, where x_1 = the amount of vapor, x = the amount of liquid, r = heat of vaporization, c = heat capacity, T_2 & T_1 = temperatures as in Figure 5.1.

(e.g., $dQ = c\,dT$) and as differences ($Q = c\,(t-t')$), whereas Linde only uses the latter form. However, they merely represent a general knowledge of thermodynamics and do not necessarily prove Linde's ties to Zeuner. These links are better illustrated in Linde's (1870, p. 266) account of the Siebe process. Here, Linde uses a concept from Zeuner: "the internal latent heat" of a vapor, defined by Zeuner (1866, p. 271):

> the excess amount of heat which one unit of weight of vapor at the temperature t acquires when compared to one unit of liquid weight at the same temperature.

Linde adopts not only the concept; he also uses exactly the same notation as Zeuner.

Technological Modes of Presentation

Linde's work was firmly grounded in the thermodynamics of his time. However, there was a striking difference in *style* between the engineer Linde and the scientist Clausius. Whereas Clausius made extensive use of differentials and integrals, Linde stuck to simple arithmetic, in addition to powers and natural logarithms. Presumably, Linde chose to avoid higher mathematics because there were a large number of engineers and entrepreneurs without extensive schooling among the readers of the "Bavarian Journal of Industry and Trade." The use of differences instead of differentials helped such readers to move easily from formula to practical problem. Terms like "T_1-T_2" seem closer to real experience than the infinitely small "dT." It is clear that Clausius and Linde directed themselves to different groups. Whereas Clausius (1864, p. 244) addressed "the scientific audience," Linde (1869, p. 328) spoke to an "industrial and ... technical audience."

The latter quotation comes from a speech Linde held one year before he became involved in refrigeration, but in the 1870-1871 papers he also repeatedly mentions *Techniker* as his most important peer group. However, there are also similarities between Linde and Clausius, for example their taste for deductive reasoning. In Chapter 5 we learned how Linde presented some of his theoretical and practical ideas in a deductive manner. He may well have been directly influenced by Clausius on this score. One of Clausius' Zurich pupils describes his lectures: "The rigorous unfolding based on a few premises predominated over the crucial experiment and the clear description."[5]

Zeuner falls between Linde and Clausius in this connection. Zeuner wanted to make his readers and pupils well acquainted with basic scientific concepts, methods, and results. Gerd Grabow (1984, p. 18) claims in his biography of Zeuner that the "Fundamentals" only requires "very slight" knowledge of mathematics. But such a conclusion is valid only if the reader is interested in the simplified rules of the book, not in the complete deductions. One definitely has to master calculus to appreciate his texts fully. The rules were important to Zeuner (1866, p. 449): "In the *first* place, the practical man requires that theory presents him with rules and *propositions* ..." Hence, his mathematically heavy sections usually ended with simple formulae or rules. Zeuner (p. V) wanted his "Fundamentals" to be an "aid" (*Hülfsmittel*) for the "mechanic" (*Mechaniker*) who could make use of the main results of thermodynamics. He wished to combine "simplicity and clarity" (p. VI) with a scientific base. Zeuner's views on the auxiliary role of science no doubt accorded with the official ideology of the Zurich Polytechnic Institute.

The question about style, or, more accurately in this case, *modes of presentation*, was in fact debated seriously at the time. Clausius published in 1864 a short paper in which he attacked some passages in the first edition of the "Fundamentals." Clausius (1864, p. 237 f.) admits that:

> in order to make the mechanical theory of heat useful for practical mechanics, it is necessary to facilitate their use of the theory by computing tables and setting-up of approximative formulae as simple as possible.

However, he believes that Zeuner has gone too far in this direction. Clausius claims that there are cases where Zeuner's recommended approximations lead to variations as large as 40%. Clausius concludes that such uncertainties undermine Zeuner's whole project: making thermodynamics attractive to engineers. What would the technicians think about the usefulness of the mechanical theory of heat, if such approximations abounded? We can determine with hindsight that Clausius' fear was exaggerated, since both Zeuner and Linde were successful in bringing thermodynamic methods and results to a wide audience. Both men belonged to a techno-

5 Quotation from an anonymous person studying in Zurich around 1860. His short memorandum can be found in *Festschrift* ... (1894, pp. 131-145), and the quote appears on pp. 134 f.

logical school which Zeuner had christened *technische Thermodynamik* and which has attracted considerable scholarly interest (Grabow 1984, pp. 14-21; Krug 1981; Lohmann 1981; Pawlowitsch 1978). Linde took one step closer to engineering practice, whereas Zeuner remained in academic circles all his life. R. Mollier has tellingly noted in Zeuner's obituary that the latter probably never understood how large the gulf was between his writings and engineering practice (*ZVDI* 1908, Vol. 52, p. 1223). The following chapters will demonstrate that Linde seems to have been better at bridging theory and practice.

The concept "technical thermodynamics" is more or less self-explanatory. We have seen that Zeuner wanted it to be an area of mechanical engineering with a firm base in the new mechanical theory of heat. He spread his gospel to a German-speaking audience from three platforms: the lecture hall—first in Zurich, later in Dresden; the journal *Der Civilingenieur*—of which he had been a co-founder (Lohmann 1981, p. 64); and his book the "Fundamentals"—in fact titled *Technische Thermodynamik* from the third edition onward. This textbook had its counterparts in this field both in French and English. The French had G.-A. Hirn's "Mechanical Theory of Heat" (1865) and the British had W.J.M. Rankine's *Manual of the Steam Engine* (1859) (Cardwell & Hills 1976 p. 15; Schröter 1910, p. 15). These authors' quest was for a *scientification* of the technology concerned with energy conversions. Like Hirn and Rankine, Zeuner did not aim at constructing a science, but to reform a technology. He was a *translator*, mediating the scientific and technological structures of knowledge. The ultimate goals of technical thermodynamics were technological and productive. For instance, Zeuner (1866, p. 522) hoped when discussing the steam engine cycle that his book will make it possible "to change it, so that it approaches the perfect [cyclic] process prescribed by theory." This is exactly what Linde hoped to achieve with his scientification project in the area of refrigeration technology. Linde's work should thus be considered within the context of the rise of technological thermodynamics as a research and development program.

Several commentators have investigated Zeuner's activity as a writer, a teacher, and an institutional organizer. A. Pawlowitsch (1978) has depicted Zeuner as a very inspiring lecturer and an enthusiastic college reformer. Linde's (1979, p. 12) autobiography describes Zeuner's classes as "vivid and clear." At the prime of his career Zeuner was instrumental in the transformation of the Dresden Polytechnic into a *Hochschule*. K. Krug has argued that Zeuner managed to turn technical thermodynamics into a "scientific school" (*wissenschaftliche Schule*), Linde being one of its central members. Since Zeuner's and Linde's goals were technical, I believe "technological school" would be a more appropriate term.[6]

Technology is an institutional and social, as well as an intellectual and practical activity. Thus one way to interpret Linde work would be to say that he was a member of Zeuner's technological school and chose to use and develop Zeuner's research and development program in his work. Unlike the term "technological community," suggested by Edward Constant (1980, 1987) to delimit a heterogeneous body of practitioners working with similar problems, "school" is used here to designate a more closely knit group. Members of a technological school can be directly tied to one another in vertical chains, like teacher-pupil or master-journeyman, or in horizontal chains, like fellow students or close colleagues. A school is more homogeneous than a community in Constant's sense. The program, in turn, contains the concepts, values, styles, modes, methods, and strategies which members of the school utilize in their engineering work. However, the program is more open than the school, and it is also possible for non-school members to adopt parts of the program.[7]

Hans-Dieter Lohmann (1981, p. 67) has summarized Zeuner's "method of working" in six imperatives (here slightly paraphrased):

1. To take into account the results of physics.
2. To develop mathematical expressions that are easily applied to practical problems.
3. To compute useful diagrams and tables.
4. To develop theoretical expressions which might help to solve future problems.
5. To make all presentations intelligible and clear.
6. To publish important results promptly and professionally.

---

6 For the definitions of *Wissenschaft* and *science* in the 19th century, cf. Liedman (1986).

7 Compared with what Dierkes (1989) and Knie (1989) have called "design tradition" (*Konstruktionstradition*) and "style of research and design" (*Forschungs- und Konstruktionsstil*), the terms "school" and "program" designate a more homogeneous group of practitioners and more formalized working prescriptions.

Such programmatic statements could of course be used in any technological area. We have to consider the theoretical basis and practical aims which were specifically tied to thermodynamics in order to get a complete view of the Zeuner-Linde program. An example from the "Fundamentals" will demonstrate this need. Zeuner (1866, p. V) writes in the introduction to the second edition that one of his chief goals is "to judge the true characteristics of our steam engines, the degree of perfection of their cycles, and the cycle of a theoretically perfect steam engine." If we substitute the word ice-machine for steam engine, then this statement describes exactly what Linde did in his 1870-1871 papers (and if we use the word heat engine, then it also fits Rudolf Diesel's early dreams). Linde's articles meet most of the six requirements above. In short, Linde was raised in the school of technical thermodynamics, worked within its program, and carried it on to new generations (like Diesel's).

Zeuner's Contributions

We shall see in Chapter 8 that Linde's early papers arouse some economic interest, but no one seems to have developed Linde's theoretical ideas any further during the 1870s.[8] Linde (1875-1876) himself published two papers in the mid-seventies, but they did not contribute much to refrigeration theory. The main difference between them and the earlier papers is that they contain a survey of as many as twenty-one refrigeration systems. In January 1874 Linde spoke before the Polytechnic Society in Munich on the topic of refrigeration machinery; the speech was subsequently published, but it does not contain any theoretical novelties (Linde 1874). Not until 1881 did someone follow up on Linde's results concerning vapor compression refrigeration in a comprehensive paper. This person was in fact Zeuner.

Let us look more closely at Zeuner' s (1881) paper, which was published after Linde had taken the step from theory to practice. The central parts of the paper deal with the theory of an ideal machine along with the theory and design of existing machines. The whole essay focuses on the

---

8 Ledoux (1878) was published in French, but this author apparently did not know Linde's work. However, he does have a reference to Zeuner (p. 172).

vapor compression principle, which is considered theoretically superior to the cold air system. Zeuner (1881, pp. 450 ff.) is not as categorical as Linde when comparing vapor compression with absorption; Zeuner's motive for leaving absorption aside is the lack of pertinent test data for such machinery, not the assumption that it would defy a thermodynamical analysis. Since he chose vapor compression, Zeuner (p. 455) was able to claim that his primary task boiled down to the creation of a theory of refrigeration which would be the exact reverse of steam engine theory. A vapor compression refrigeration machine, unlike an absorption or a cold air device, can be more or less treated as a steam engine run backward. For example, identical formulae for the behavior of liquid-vapor mixtures can be used in both cases.

Indeed, the theoretical similarity between steam and vapor compression is an important clue for why this refrigeration principle was preferred by Linde and Zeuner. The science of thermodynamics had been developed to a great extent on the basis of steam engine studies, not only in Carnot's work; Zeuner had penetrated this prime mover in minute detail and worked out a set of analytic tools for it in his "Fundamentals." It must have been relatively easy for anyone educated in the school of technical thermodynamics to adapt these tools to vapor compression refrigeration.

Zeuner's (1881, pp. 455-458) idea for how the heart of a theoretically perfect compression system should be designed includes a novel device: a compressor to replace the throttle valve. Figure 2.3 above, which depicts the ideal type of vapor compression, illustrates that the refrigerant is usually led back to the evaporator exclusively through this valve. Zeuner has been influenced by steam engine design and now suggests that the valve be replaced by a compressor that corresponds to the feeder pump of a steam engine. He claims that considerable work is thereby gained as the expanding vapor, coming from the condenser, moves the piston. Zeuner (pp. 466 ff.) shows both algebraically and graphically that the introduction of a feeder pump would enhance the degree of efficiency. In fact, attempts were soon made to introduce such a feeder pump in actual designs, but they were not successful in this period (Linde 1893, p. 1423).

Zeuner ends his paper by showing that the reversed Carnot cycle is the most efficient one, theoretically speaking. Unlike Linde, who in 1870-1871 had treated this as an axiom, Zeuner (1881, pp. 460-463) arrives at the Carnot cycle along a path concerned with heat of vaporization and the relationship between vapor and steam. However, Zeuner just like Linde emphasizes that the temperature difference between evaporator and condenser ought to be as small as possible, and that one ought to choose a refrigerant with a high value for its heat of vaporization. Up to this point, Zeuner's account rests on a couple of idealizations. He assumes that the temperature of the cylinder walls remains constant throughout the cycle, and that there is no clearance volume in the cylinder. The clearance volume is that part of the cylinder where the piston does not reach at the end of the compression stage.

Zeuner has practical considerations in mind and does not only supply his readers with formulae based on idealizations. Instead he goes on to develop expressions for the machine which by that time had become the most common: the ammonia machine working on a wet cycle (Zeuner 1881, pp. 466-471). This machine works with a mixture of vapor and liquid throughout the cycle. The opposite is a dry cycle, where the vapor is superheated at the end of the compression stage; the pressure and temperature are so high at this point that the refrigerant cannot exist as a liquid (Beckman 1976, p. 115). The ideal, superheated process is best described by the so-called Clausius-Rankine cycle, not by the Carnot cycle, which is primarily applicable for the wet process. In other words, Zeuner, like steam engine theorists at this time (Duffy 1983, p. 56), wanted to replace the Carnot cycle with the Clausius-Rankine cycle as a *Leitbild* for mechanical refrigeration design. Zeuner's results show that a perfect ammonia machine, without a feeder pump and working on a wet cycle, would be 10% less efficient than the theoretically perfect one. We will see in the following chapter that these results supported the path which Linde had chosen after he had given up dimethyl ether in 1874.

Zeuner (1881, pp. 472-477) would not have been true to the methods of technical thermodynamics had he not included a couple of pages bridging theory and practice. His paper ends with two sections describing useful approximative formulae and discussing the detrimental effects of the clearance volume, and is followed by an appendix discussing a number of physical constants relevant to the analysis of ammonia refrigeration systems. Zeuner uses information from a Linde machine to claim that even if the clearance volume is only 1% of the total cylinder volume, the degree of efficiency is noticeably lowered. Zeuner thus showed that considerable accuracy is very important in practical ice-machine construction, but he

(p. 472) also acknowledged that Linde's system belonged to the most "carefully designed" machines on the market around 1880. In other words, Linde's step from theory to design had been quite successful. The following chapters will describe how and why this transition took place, and also how Linde, unlike Zeuner, even gave up his academic career to continue as an entrepreneur in the economic realm.

The scientification of refrigeration technology began with Linde and Zeuner. Zeuner (1887-1890) included a chapter on cold production in the third edition of his now famous book; Linde (1893, 1894, 1895, 1902) continued to publish articles in this area. A number of other people also began to contribute to the scientific treatment of the field, but these developments will lead us to far into the details of theory (Behrend 1883, 1898; Heimpel 1894; Richmond 1892-1893). Trade journals also began to publish thermodynamically inspired articles in this period. It should be mentioned, however, that in the 1890s the dry process began to receive further theoretical treatment, and the temperature-entropy diagram appeared as a useful tool—complementing the common pressure-volume indicator diagram. Donald S.L. Cardwell and Richard L. Hills (1976, p. 15) show in their discussion of the temperature-entropy diagram which entered most areas of thermodynamic technology at the end of the century that Linde had used it in his teaching as early as in the 1870s. An American, George Richmond (1892-1893, pp. 210, 234 f.), discusses both features and concludes that the dry-superheated process is theoretically more efficient than the wet one, and he also gives an extensive interpretation of the refrigeration cycle based on the temperature-entropy diagram. Richmond also states that the biggest advantage of this diagram is that it directly addresses the question of the relationships between steam, superheated steam, and liquid at all points along the refrigeration cycle.

The process of the scientification of refrigeration technology, which Linde had started two decades earlier, continued. It was an open-ended research and development program to which others could and did contribute.

The Unfolding of Theoretical and Formal Rationality

The Introduction presented the central thesis of the present study: the translation of scientific information into the realms of technology and business can be interpreted by means of Max Weber's concepts of rationality and rationalization; the scientification process can be treated as a part of the overall rationalization of the West, thus implying an increasing use of theoretical, formal, and practical rationality. We have primarily followed the spread of theoretical and formal rationality in this part of the study, whereas practical rationality will be discussed more in Part III.

We should not turn directly to Weber's discussions of the adoption of science in industry in order to do justice to his thesis about the Western process of intellectual rationalization, rather must begin with his studies of religion. Of course, this means that we can neither avoid the famous *Protestant Ethic and the Rise of Capitalism*, nor "The Social Psychology of the World Religions," to which Stephen Kalberg (1980) has already drawn our attention. Other parts of Weber's (1920, 1958c, 1965) sociology of religion also have to be considered.

Weber's discussion of the "disenchantment of the world," or more precisely, the removal of all magic forces from this world is central to his analysis of theoretical and formal rationality. This process, to which "science belongs as a link and motive force" (Weber 1958d, p. 139), has a very long tradition in Western culture. Even though in recent times this kind of rationalization has gone so far to have pushed religion "into the irrational realm" of society (Weber 1958e, p. 281), its historical roots are to be found in the area of religion:

> That great historic process in the development of religions, the elimination of *magic* from the world which had begun with the old Jewish prophets and, in conjunction with Hellenistic scientific thought, had repudiated all magical means to salvation as superstition and sin, came [with Calvinism and Puritanism] to its logical conclusion. (Weber 1930, p. 105)

Prophets and priests, from Moses to Calvin, have considered magicians their most important enemies, since the latter claimed to be able to exercise personal power over spirits and demons. All power rests in the hands of God in monotheistic religions like Judaism and Christianity—He is, quite literally, the Almighty. This idea reaches its peak in Calvin's doctrine of Predestination: a human being cannot influence his own redemption;

everything depends on God's will. While magicians adopt various "irrational means" to reach eternity, the priest develops "special knowledge, fixed doctrine, and vocational qualifications" to try to understand the ways of the Lord and the roads toward redemption (Weber 1965, p. 29; cf. Schluchter 1980, p. 16). Priests are educated through "rational training" (Weber 1965, p. 29), where the transfer of formalized and general rules are crucial. The classic set of such rules is the Ten Commandments, which demonstrate every sign of what Weber (*ibid.*) defines as a doctrine:

> ... the outstanding marks of doctrine are the development of a rational system of religious concepts and ... the development of a systematic and distinctively religious ethic based upon a consistent and stable doctrine which purports to be a "revelation."

The tradition of Moses includes the intellectual construction of rational systems, its goal being "to systematize and rationalize the way of life" (Weber 1958c, p. 327).

Since the removal of magic from the world makes it accessible to reason, intellectual activities become increasingly important:

> Religious interpretations of the world and ethics of religions created by intellectuals and meant to be rational have been strongly exposed to the imperative of consistency. The effect of the *ratio*, especially of a teleological deduction of practical postulates, is in some way, and often very strongly, noticeable among all religious ethics. (Weber 1958c, p. 324)

We could adopt a concept previously discussed and say that the social carriers of disenchantment are intellectuals, for whom rational discourse, systematic elaboration, and deductive reasoning are significant. Unlike magicians, whose powers are subjectively held, intellectuals form a learned group, whose insights are collectively shared. However, this does not imply that these insights are accessible to everyone without education. Just like the modern community of scientific practitioners, traditional priesthood is a closed social system:

> ... science, in the name of "intellectual integrity," has come forward with the claim of representing the only possible form of a reasoned view of the world. The intellect, like all culture values, has created an aristocracy based on the possession of rational culture and independent of all personal ethical qualities of man. (*ibid.*, p. 355)

Science attempts both intellectually and socially to replace organized religion. In other words, if we want to understand Weber's position on the emergence of modern science—an "affair of an intellectual aristocracy" (Weber 1958d, p. 134), then we have to turn to the history of religious thinking. Nowadays, the ideals of intersubjectivity, reason, system, and deduction, are to be found in science, but originally they were intimately tied to the needs of the church to present an authoritative and comprehensive ethical system:

> ... prophetic as well as priestly religions have repeatedly stood in intimate relation with rational intellectualism. The less magic or merely contemplative mysticism and the more "doctrine" a religion contains, the greater is its need of rational apologetics. (Weber 1958c, p. 351)

Thus, Weber concluded that the scientist has replaced not only the magician, but also the priest.

The traditional roles of religious doctrines were to create order in this and the coming world and to give meaning (*Sinn*) to life. This process of making the world intelligible has over time usually led to the formulation of ever more "internally consistent constellations of values, or world views (*Weltbilder*)" (Kalberg 1980, p. 1153). Wolfgang Schluchter (1980, Ch. 1) has pointed out that in the Judaic and Christian traditions this intellectual and formally rational activity of understanding the world has also led to a wish to rule the world; that is, it has partly developed into practical rationality.

This adoption of rationally defined concepts and rationally organized systems in order to control the world is no doubt obvious in much technological and scientific work, not least in the activities of the engineers and educators who we have encountered in this and the previous two chapters. Linde tried to "disenchant" mechanical refrigeration by introducing unequivocal definitions of the nature of heat and temperature and by analyzing various refrigeration processes in a systematic manner; he stuck to an approach that was just as rational as that of any Puritan preacher by relying on the "doctrine" or *Weltbild* of thermodynamics and applying the remorseless energy principle to technological problems in a deductive way. Instead of addressing the problem of the Halle Mineral Oil Society by building an ice-machine, Linde approached it theoretically. His first two papers illustrate well Kalberg's (1980, p. 1152) definition that "abstract cognitive processes, in all their expansive active forms, denote theoretical rationality."

Linde, Zeuner, and others within the school of technical thermodynamics tried to understand nature better, ultimately in order to control it by technical means. Engineering students would be able to remove any spells from their surroundings with textbooks like Zeuner's "Fundamentals" in their hands. They could find there technological knowledge presented in a systematic manner and codified in formalized rules and methods. Zeuner's formulae simplified the work of any mechanical engineer—just like the Ten Commandments simplified the lives of the devout Jews.

A significant feature of technical thermodynamics as a research and development program was its emphasis on calculation. The heated controversy between Clausius and Zeuner about the limits of meaningful approximation show that the use of mathematical formulae was a central concern. This paramount importance of calculation comes out clearly in one of Weber's (1958d, p. 139) discussions about theoretical rationality:

> The increasing intellectualization and rationalization ... mean that principally there are no mysterious incalculable powers that come into play, but rather that one can, in principle, master [*beherrschen*] all things by calculation [*berechnen*]. This means that the world is disenchanted. One need no longer have recourse to magical means in order to master or implore the spirits, as did the savage, for whom such mysterious powers existed. Technical means and calculations perform the service. This above all is what intellectualization means.

This above all is what the coming of school culture and technical thermodynamics meant.

8. The Response: The Brewing and Machine Industries Support Invention

The Enrollment of the Scientist-Engineer

Linde had outlined a novel research and development program in the area of technical thermodynamics with his papers of 1870-1871, but he did not immediately continue with it. Not until some brewers approached him did he seriously consider turning from ideas to inventions. We will in this chapter see how two large brewing companies strongly encouraged Linde's first steps on the road toward innovation. The chapter will complement Bruno Latour's (1987) analyses of how scientist-engineers "enroll" politicians, financiers, and others in their search for support by showing how Linde, a typical scientist-engineer, was himself enrolled. While we saw in Chapter 6 how Linde was enlisted by the nascent oil industry, he will here be approached by representatives of the brewing industry.

Even though the "Bavarian Journal of Industry and Trade" was "not the most appropriate" periodical in which to publish theoretically advanced papers, the word about Linde's ideas spread outside Bavaria (Linde 1979, p. 36). It reached among others August Deiglmayr, the director of the largest Austrian brewing company, the Dreher Breweries (*Die Dreherschen Brauereien*). Emil Erlenmeyer, a chemistry professor and one of Linde's colleagues at the Munich Polytechnic, was instrumental in this transmission of information. Together with a Viennese machine manufacturer, Deiglmayr subsequently approached Linde and suggested that he design a refrigeration system for the Dreher brewery in Trieste on the Adriatic Sea—at this time an Austrian city. Linde's experience with the Krauß locomotive firm had made him aware of the slowness of experimental work. Linde therefore declared that he would only embark on this project, if he could do so in Munich. A Munich brewer, Gabriel Sedlmayr (Deiglmayr's uncle), was then asked if Linde could make the necessary experiments at his *Spatenbrauerei* (Sedlmayr 1951, pp. 181 ff.). Sedlmayr's deep interest in the technical aspects of brewing prompted him not only to allow Linde to work on his premises, but even to pay all his expenses.

The financial basis was thus quickly established for the first experiments. Interestingly enough, Linde does not seem to have considered continuing his work on refrigeration before he had been encouraged by Deiglmayr. Both Sedlmayr and Deiglmayr acted as catalysts for Linde's transition from paper to practice. Linde might well have taken the step without them, but under other circumstances and perhaps much later. Thus his research and development program was continued under the auspices of two of the largest brewing companies in the world. We will see in Part III that this connection between scientific ice-machine design and large-scale brewing was no coincidence. The Dreher firm produced 62 million liters (530,000 barrels) of beer yearly in the early 1870s, the Spaten brewery roughly 28 million liters (240,000 barrels).[1] It can be noted for comparison that the largest brewery in the U.S., George Ehret of New York City, produced 140,000 barrels in 1877 (Baron 1962, p. 258). Dreher's production took place in four different breweries, the largest one being the huge Klein-Schwechat plant in Vienna. The Trieste brewery was the firm's smallest and newest one, producing in 1877 less than 5 million liters (26,000 barrels) per year (*Bierbrauer* 1878, Vol. 9 (n.s.), pp. 334, 369 f.). The Dreher company had bought a closed-down brewery there in 1869, but soon met with severe problems because of the local humidity and heat. Spaten was at the time the biggest brewery in Germany (*Bayerischer Bierbrauer* 1874, Vol. 9, p. 130).

The available sources do not reveal exactly when Deiglmayr contacted Linde, or when Sedlmayr entered the picture. These events must have taken place sometimes in 1871-1872 (Linde 1979, pp. 30 f.). Linde's exhausting labors during these years brought on a nervous break-down, forcing him to take a leave-of-absence. Despite this crisis he was made full professor of theoretical mechanical engineering at the Munich Polytechnic in December of 1872, his income increasing overnight by 150% to 2,500 Guldens.[2] He was also able to carry out the initial refrigeration experiments at Spaten.

In January 1873 Linde took the first formal step toward an innovation by applying for his first refrigeration patent together with Sedlmayr. They

---

1 The Dreher figure appears in the *Bierbrauer* (1873, Vol. 4 (n.s.), p. 339) and the Spaten information comes from the Fritz Sedlmayr files at the Munich city archives (SM-NS), boxes No. 1 & 4. Conversions to modern standard have been made with the aid of *Ingenieurs Taschenbuch* (1870, pp. 764 ff.) and *Encyclopaedia Britannica* (1969, Vol. 4, p. 164): 1 beer barrel = 31 U.S. gallons = 117 liters.

2 A copy of the royal decree is in the archives of Linde AG, Höllriegelskreuth (LAG-H), ring binder "Erste Konzepte für TVT Geschichte."

were soon granted a two-year "trade privilege" for a "refrigeration- and ice-machine" by the Bavarian king.[3] Linde's patent application consisted of a description and a drawing of a system including an evaporator (left in Figure 8.1), a single-acting compressor-pump (second left), and a condenser (first & second right). The description exists in two versions, one signed by Sedlmayr and the other, extended with a few lines, by Linde (MAN-HA, 3.37). The brewer apparently showed an active interest in Linde's project and did more than just finance it.

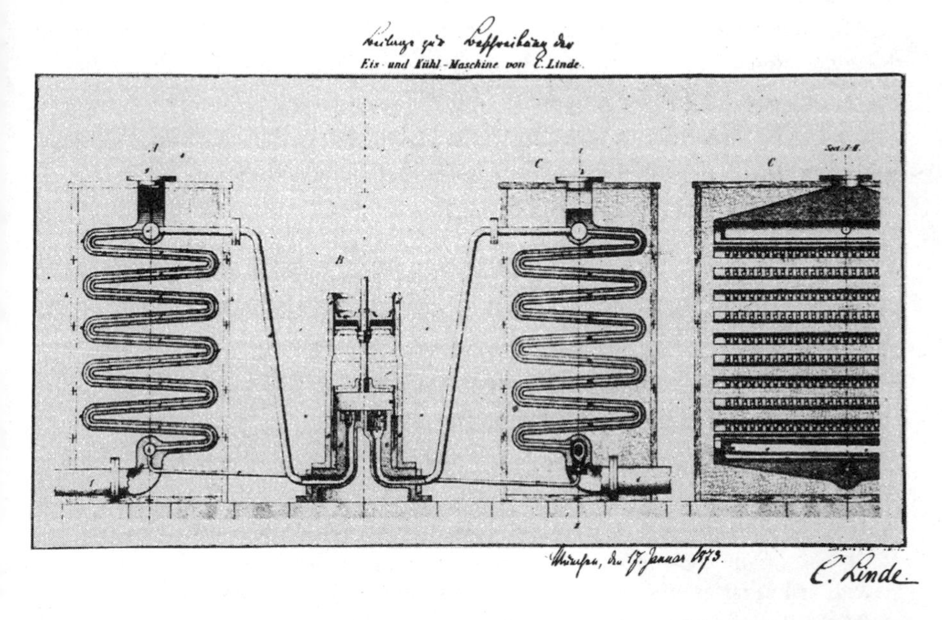

Figure 8.1. Linde's drawing of the main parts of a refrigeration machine system, taken from his first refrigeration patent application of January 1873; courtesy *Historisches Archiv MAN AG*, Augsburg

Linde and Sedlmayr emphasize novelties in compressor design and the use of dimethyl ether in their application, though they also explain how the evaporators and condensers work. The novelties correspond by and large to Linde's 1871 paper, but there is one deviation. Instead of recommending a

3 A copy of the royal letter is in the historical archives at MAN AG, Augsburg (MAN-HA), box 3.37.

slow-moving and large compressor without the risk of explosion, they now describe a small device which works at ordinary speed. It is not stated, but the obvious reason for this change of direction between 1871 and 1873 must have been the wish to keep material costs low. They were also silent about the danger of explosion which comes with high pressures. Linde and Sedlmayr write that

> ... the dimensions and ... amount of work consumed [by the compressor] appear *considerably* smaller and lower than in the case of previously known machines which serve the same purpose.

The patent application is exclusively technical. The thermodynamic reasons for the choice of dimethyl ether are not mentioned, nor is the character of the cycle described. Linde and Sedlmayr merely say that dimethyl ether is "very volatile," hardly a scientific observation. Every refrigeration technician already knew that a working fluid had to be highly volatile. A patent application was not the place to furnish scientific accounts.

When Linde was given the opportunity to speak about the shortcomings of absorption and cold air machinery to the heads of the brewing world in June 1873, science was again absent. Only parts of this talk at the International Conference of Brewers in Vienna remain, but these excerpts suggest that Linde adhered to the practical-analytic and prescriptive aspects of his 1871 paper (*Bierbrauer* 1873, Vol. 4 (n.s.), p. 183; MAN-HA, 3.37). His critique of the cold air system, like two years earlier, focused on its enormous dimensions; absorption was denounced for being hopelessly inefficient. Linde still acknowledged the present superiority of the Carré machinery, but he now went somewhat further, believing that:

> [it] has already come quite close to the reachable maximum of the absorption system, and as far as efficiency goes does not stand any chance of being considerably perfected (*ibid.*).

Linde thus believed that the ideal type of absorption had hit the ceiling and could hardly be further improved. He consequently wanted to break away from the dominant line of development and recommended a change of direction by pointing to the dormant potential of vapor compression.

Linde's point of view was not left unchallenged in Vienna. Advocates of the other classificatory ideal types also gave presentations, including Franz Windhausen, a very respected name in cold air machinery, and Dr. Paersch, an American defending the Carré system (*Bayerischer Bierbrauer* 1873, Vol. 8, pp. 97 f.). The brewing conference lasted six days, and one-

and-a-half of them was devoted to refrigeration. This problem was obviously a central concern of the brewing industry in the early 1870s.

Linde's ideas also began to materialize in 1873, but to be able to take this step Linde had to start enrolling others in the project. He needed assistance from outside Spaten to test his thoughts in practice, and to this end he began to build a network of supporting agents around him. Friedrich Schipper, one of his students at the Munich Polytechnic, helped Linde at the drawing board, the Augsburg Machine Co., *Maschinenfabrik Augsburg*, took care of the hardware aspects of the design, and Erlenmayr helped Linde with the cumbersome production and storage of dimethyl ether (Linde 1979, pp. 37 f.). The Augsburg machine company was one of the best known in Bavaria, specializing in printing presses, water turbines, and steam engines; in 1898 it was going to fuse with a Nuremburg firm, forming the still famous *Maschinenfabrik Augsburg-Nürnberg*, M.A.N. (Büchner 1940). In 1873 the Augsburg firm employed six hundred workers and had gross receipts of two million marks. This firm illustrates Rosenberg's (1976) convergence thesis about the flexibility of the machine industry, for it could draw on its experience with steam engine design when constructing refrigeration machinery. Its background in compressor manufacturing was of particular importance; the design of refrigeration compressors bears a number of similarities to that of steam engine compressors. These similarities go a long way, I believe, toward explaining the relative ease with which *Maschinenfabrik Augsburg* took up the manufacturing of ice-machines. As Knie (1989, 1991) has shown, the company made an almost identical transition two decades later, when they began to manufacture diesel engines—a technology which has also been heavily influenced by steam engine engineering.

We know from a letter written by Gabriel Sedlmayr on November 11, 1873 that the Augsburg Machine Co. had already delivered the first Linde-Schipper prototype to Spaten in mid-November of that year.[4] This machine had two single-acting compressor pumps and weighed over four tons—evaporator and condenser included. A letter by Johann Sedlmayr, one of Gabriel's sons who would soon take over the family business (Sedlmayr 1951, p. 371), reports that Linde had estimated that the machine required

---

4 Fritz Sedlmayr refers to this letter, in a letter to *Maschinenfabrik Augsburg-Nürnberg* of Dec. 17, 1946 (MAN-HA, 3.37).

an energy supply of about eight horse-powers.[5] Linde's (1979, p. 38) autobiography claims that "it reached a degree of efficiency at least twice that of the machine which previously had been considered the best one." The historians K. Krug (1981, p. 91) and Hans-Dieter Lohmann (1972, p. 13) have swallowed this statement uncritically, but I believe it should be taken with a pinch of salt. The figure is vague and corresponds exactly to what Linde had deemed practically possible in his 1871 paper—a degree of efficiency of 30%. Furthermore, as we will see in Chapter 10, Linde's commercial machines did not reach such a level of performance even at the end of the 1880s.

In any case, Linde soon found that good fuel economy is not enough to make a refrigerating system practical and economically feasible. This first prototype worked too slowly and needed too much supervision (Linde 1979, p. 38). Linde admitted in a patent application a couple of years later that "... the operation of this machine turned out to be so difficult that an ordinary mechanic could not be trusted with it" (MAN-HA, 3.37). A contemporary eyewitness, a trainee at Spaten, also tells us that the intricate sealing system did not function satisfactorily. It did not prevent the dimethyl ether from escaping into the air, which meant that the efficiency of the machine decreased and it became a hazard. The trainee, Christian Weymar, writes:

> An explosion occurred through the carelessness of a workman, who one evening had gone into the ice-machine room with a light in order to retrieve some forgotten tools. This incident was apparently the actual reason for cancelling all further experiments with [dimethyl] ether. (in Sedlmayr 1951, p. 370)

Linde does not mention this event in his autobiography.

The failure of the original design must have been a serious blow to the team. Neither of the two main features, which had been particularly emphasized in the patent application, stood up to a practical test—despite its knowledgeable and financially strong social carriers. Both the mercury sealing system and dimethyl ether were abandoned.

---

5 Date of delivery, price, weight, and number of pumps appear in the Augsburg Co. sales records (MAN-HA, 3.37). Johann's letter is from July 2, 1873 (SM-NS, F8).

The Promises of the Second Prototype

Linde and Schipper were forced back to the drawing board, where they came up with a second design, a model of which is shown in Figure 8.2. They removed the mercury, let the glycerine take care of all the sealing, and they replaced dimethyl ether with the more volatile ammonia.

Figure 8.2. A model of Linde's second compressor design, patented in Bavaria in 1876. It applies two vertical compressors and a vertical air vessel containing sealing fluid (foreground), in addition to evaporator and condenser (background); courtesy *Deutsches Museum*, Munich

The latter was a risky choice since Carré, who had used ammonia for several years, had received severe criticism for the toxicity and explosiveness of this refrigerant. The explosion at Spaten and the problems he had with the dimethyl ether supply presumably led Linde to the decision that he might just as well choose ammonia, which was easily accessible and already belonged to the *Stand der Technik* of mechanical refrigeration. In fact, a French refrigeration engineer, Charles Tellier, had experimented with both refrigerants in the 1860s in connection with vapor compression, although there are no signs that Linde knew about these experiments. Like Linde, Tellier had had problems in producing dimethyl ether, but unlike Linde he had preferred this refrigerant because he found that ammonia affected lubrication oils and glycerine negatively (Tellier 1910, pp. 16 ff., 41-50).

Linde and Schipper also managed to simplify the crank movements by eliminating the horizontally moving piston, thus enabling higher speeds and, consequently, smaller dimensions. The first machine of this second design, which the Augsburg Machine Co. delivered in May 1875, weighed two tons and cost about 2,000 guldens—which means that it weighed and cost roughly half as much as the first prototype.[6] It was erected at Spaten, but Linde (1979, 39) insisted on defraying the expenses this time—even though the price was almost equivalent to his annual salary as a full professor. Perhaps he felt slightly embarrassed by the first fiasco and thus did not want to risk more of Sedlmayr's money. According to his own account, he now met "with complete success," whatever that means.[7] It certainly did not mean that the goal of 30% efficiency had been reached, since in April 1875 Linde reported that his machine under construction promised a coal

---

6 According to the Augsburg Co. sales records, the first machine cost 5,041 guldens and weighed 4,150 kg, and the first copy of the second design cost 1,933 guldens and weighed 2,275 kg (MAN-HA, 3.37). However, the price for the first machine is not certain, since the Spaten records only refer to a payment of 3,993 guldens (SM-NS, 20).
Sedlmayr (1951, p. 369) believes that the delivery took place in May 1874, but the archives indicate that May 1875 is the correct date (MAN-HA, 3.37). Furthermore, five months between the first and second design seem to be too short a time, and Linde's application of Jan. 1875 for the extension of his 1873 patent makes no mention of a new design.

7 The description is in a patent application from Linde of Feb. 27, 1876 (MAN-HA, 3.37).

consumption of roughly 70 kg per ton of ice produced.[8] Since, according to Linde's own estimates, a theoretically perfect machine would require 10 kg of coal to produce one ton of ice (in Sedlmayr 1951, p. 368), these 70 kg mean that a degree of efficiency of only 15% had been reached. Nonetheless, the second prototype worked satisfactorily, and Spaten promptly ordered a full-scale system.

Some people around Linde were quite soon convinced that this design had the potential to match natural ice. Georg Krauß, the locomotive manufacturer and Linde's former employer, proposed that Krauß himself should form a syndicate together with Gabriel Sedlmayr and Heinrich Buz, the director of the Augsburg Machine Co., in order to exploit Linde's patents commercially. Krauß' idea was soon agreed upon, and Linde thereby traded his existing and future (up to 1881) patent rights for financial and institutional support. Without such assistance it would have been much more difficult for him to develop a commercially attractive program, and without Linde's knowledge the syndicate members could not have embarked on this promising project. The syndicate was formed shortly before Linde was granted a ten-year Bavarian patent in March 1876 for his second design (*BIGB* 1876, Vol. 8, p. 158; MAN-HA, 3.37). Only four months later the *Maschinenfabrik* issued an impressive prospectus advertising machines of seven different sizes. Orders began to arrive during the fall, and in January 1877 a machine for air cooling and ice production could be installed at the Dreher brewery in Trieste, where it would serve for more than thirty years. It produced the equivalent of 0.67 tons of ice per hour and was delivered together with a steam engine as prime mover (MAN-HA, 3.37, 3.37/2). Five years had elapsed since Deiglmayr had asked Linde to construct a first refrigeration system.

Such a time span between idea and innovation might seem long, but it was actually a remarkable achievement. Linde had also a full teaching job and a fragile constitution to take care of; Schipper had only worked full-time on the project since the summer of 1874; and refrigeration was a new area of engineering for the Augsburg Machine Co. The success was the result of several interacting circumstances, such as Deiglmayr's initiative, Sedlmayr's and Krauß' support, Linde's and Schipper's engineering skills,

---

8 *BIGB* (1875, Vol. 7, p. 248); the figures have been translated into the modern standard.

and the Augsburg manufacturing resources. A number of general factors lay behind these specific conditions, like the expansion and increasing mechanization of the brewing industry, the improvement of engineering education, and advances in the machine industry.

Profits, Science, and Weberian Status Groups

Why should Deiglmayr and Sedlmayr have chosen to support Linde in the early 1870s, whose invention only existed on paper? What motives did they have not to continue relying on natural ice, or not to turn to any of the firms already producing ice-machines?

Let us first consider economically rational reasons in order to answer these questions. In February 1869 Gabriel Sedlmayr had written a report which stated that, "in ordinary winters," the Spaten brewery paid an average of 1.5 gulden per ton of natural ice (*Bayerischer Bierbrauer* 1869, Vol. 4, pp. 25 f.). When the weather turned out to be less favorable, the ice had to be harvested in the Alps, leading to a price of 3-10 guldens per ton. Since the brewery used around 25,000 tons each year, their expenses for ice must have ranged from under 40,000 to as much as 250,000 guldens per year. Unfortunately, Sedlmayr did not compare the natural ice prices with the price of mechanically produced ice. Comparisons are also hard to make because of the shortcomings of the available sources, but we learn from Linde that even the very best machine on the market in 1875 produced ice for as much as 20 guldens per ton, interest and amortization included (*BIGB* 1875, Vol. 7, p. 248). Linde here declares that this figure concerns a Carré machine, whereas ice from an air expansion machine costs 30, and from a Siebe device as much as 60 guldens per ton. Since 20 guldens was well above the highest Munich natural ice prices, Sedlmayr's wait-and-see policy in 1869 appears to have been an economically rational one.

Linde had already claimed in his paper of 1871 that his design would both cut coal consumption in half when compared with existing ones, and be cheaper to manufacture. If this promise had come true, then artificial ice would have been on its way to costing less than 10 guldens per ton. Furthermore, since natural ice prices were probably higher in Trieste than in Munich, it was economically rational for Deiglmayr to show an interest in Linde's ideas. Once Linde had started his experiments, he became even more optimistic. We learn from a letter which Johann Sedlmayr wrote in January 1873 that Linde now believed that he would be able to produce one ton of ice for 4 guldens (in Sedlmayr 1951, pp. 367 ff.). That price would have been most welcome during years with mild winters.

Hence, we can conclude from a pure cost-benefit point of view that Linde's plans must have been promising, but we ought to take a further dimension into account. Remember that at this point in time Linde had not yet built a full-scale machine. When Deiglmayr approached Linde, nothing but nice-looking figures, drawings, and formulae existed. Deiglmayr and Sedlmayr ought to have been aware as industrialists that most technical projects end up more expensive than initially calculated. Thus we have to explain why Linde's case was so persuasive.

In order to address this problem, we may inquire into the *organizational cultures* of the Spaten and Dreher companies (Kenngott 1990). Meinolf Dierkes (1988, p. 54) wants us to use this concept to highlight the "perceptions, values, and symbols, as well as certain basic assumptions about strategies and behavior" that govern the actions of firms and other institutions. Like Weberian bureaucracies, all organizations need certain standard routines to survive (Weber 1958a). Over time, these routines develop into traditions which form an organizational culture (Dierkes and Knie 1989).

Science had become pivotal in the Spaten and Dreher cultures. Chapter 14 will explicate further these firms' very long tradition of applying new technology and scientifically inspired instruments and methods. When Sedlmayr and Anton Dreher had taken a study and espionage trip around Europe in the early 1830s to absorb the latest brewing techniques, they brought home from England a revolutionary tool for the measurement of the alcohol content (Sedlmayr 1934, pp. 314-327). In the 1840s Spaten was among the first in Germany to install a new cooling devise and a steam engine (*ibid.*, p. 393; Sedlmayr 1880, p. 19). The official history of the Spaten firm describes the correspondence between Sedlmayr and Dreher as full of "references to newly appeared written works and to important discoveries and publications in the area of science" (Sedlmayr 1951, p. 181). I would like to argue that Sedlmayr's and Deiglmayr's enrollment of Linde was a concerted act, well in line with the organizational cultures of their companies. Their firms were unusually open to novelties, apart from being gigantic ice consumers. Thus their active interest in mechanical refrigeration was not particularly surprising. In fact, Sedlmayr had already deliberated the purchase of a Carré ice-machine in late 1863, but he dropped the notion when the weather suddenly turned bitter cold and furnished plenty of cheap natural ice (Sedlmayr 1951, p. 331).

However, Deiglmayr's and Sedlmayr's recorded interest in scientific matters does not explain why they believed Linde's claim that his method was a scientific one. After all, why would they put so much faith in his account, without being able to judge its allegedly scientific qualities? In order to answer this question, we have to turn to social issues. Important keys were Linde's positions both as a professor at an advanced technical college and as an editor of an esteemed technical and industrial journal. Both positions brought with them intellectual and social prestige, as well as important personal connections. An ideological key may also have been the pro-scientific attitude of the German-speaking world described in previous chapters.

We may turn to Weber's sociology of domination for a better understanding of the issue of social prestige. In *Economy and Society* Weber (1922a, pp. 177-180, 631-640, 1958b, 1964, pp. 424-429) distinguishes three social categories which may serve as a basis for the execution of power and influence: class, status group (*Stand*), and party or pressure group (cf. Collins 1990a). Whereas the power of the first group is defined in economic and of the last group in political terms, the question of social "honor" (*Ehre*) is central to a status group:

> A status group is a plurality of individuals who, within a community [*Verband*], enjoy a particular kind and level of prestige [*Schätzung*] by virtue of their position and possibly also claim certain special monopolies. Status groups may emerge ... through the development of a peculiar style of life including, particularly, the type of occupation pursued. (Weber 1922a, p. 180)[9]

All occupations cannot be treated as status groups. In our society, plumbers do not form one, whereas medical doctors certainly do. Doctors have successfully monopolized their profession by means of certificates; their incomes have traditionally ensured them a certain standard of living; most people acknowledge that they have some special skills and knowledge and usually show them a fairly high degree of honor. Taken together, these factors give medical doctors no mean prestige in our society.

---

9 The English translation in Weber (1964, pp. 428 f.) is not particularly clear and has thus been modified here.

Robert J. Holton and Bryan S. Turner (1989, p. 137) have aptly pointed out that Pierre Bourdieu's analysis of social status and cultural privilege in his book *Distinction* (1984) shows several similarities with Weber's discussions of *Stand*. Bourdieu's (1988) discussion of the "academic human being" may be even more interesting for the present study, in that it explicitly analyzes the status group of university and college professors. I will, however, stay with Weber, rather than expanding on Bourdieu.

Linde was enrolled and supported by representatives of the brewing and machine industries, in part because he belonged to the status group of college professors. This group might not be particularly impressive to a modern reader, but in Bavaria of the 1870s, professors were scarce, and they received their positions through royal decrees. They fitted well as a group into what Holton and Turner (1989, p. 141) write about status groups in general:

> [They] are organized communally both for the defence and expansion of their entitlement. Status groups aim to achieve legal recognition of their privileges in order to intensify the closedness of their ranks against outsiders.

In short, Linde's professor title presumably made his scientification program more convincing to the non-specialist.

However, Linde's position did not only give him honor and status. It also came with a social network which was crucial to the rapid and successful development of the project. In the first place, Deiglmayr learned about Linde's papers through Erlenmeyer, also a college professor. This chemist would later help Linde (1979, pp. 36 ff.) with the difficult production of dimethyl ether. There were obvious advantages of having access to the equipment of a technical college, but we also must not forget the contributions of at least one of Linde's pupils. Well before his exam, Schipper labored faithfully at the drawing board, and for decades to come he would remain with Linde. School culture thus backed up Linde in a very literal sense by means of social status, material support, advanced assistance, and influential connections.

As a Munich professor, Linde had also been offered and accepted the opportunity to co-edit the "Bavarian Journal of Industry and Trade." Since this journal was published by the Bavarian Polytechnic Society, and since Sedlmayr had been a member of the central committee of this society for more than forty years, it is very likely that Sedlmayr had met Linde before the rapprochement with Deiglmayr. For instance, in 1869 Linde had given a speech on thermodynamics at one of the society's meetings, and Sedlmayr might well have been in the audience. In any case, as a co-editor of its journal, Linde belonged to the same social circle as Sedlmayr, a most important factor if we want to explain why his so-called scientific approach gained such immediate support.

We saw in Chapters 5 and 7 how scientification furnished refrigeration technology with new tools and directions. I have shown in the present chapter how Linde's invocation of science gave his program a healthy aura of promise which attracted brewers and manufacturers. Like the politicians and educators we encountered in Chapter 6, these industrialists appear to have seen a powerful link between the natural sciences and technological development. I shall investigate further in Part III how the Dreher and Spaten breweries had made use of chemistry from early on. The conscious aim of Director Buz was always to keep the Augsburg Machine Co. at the cutting edge of new technology, an attitude that he retained twenty years later, when Rudolf Diesel presented his famous book "Theory and Design of a Rational Heat Engine" (1893) (Büchner 1940, p. 46; Diesel 1983, pp. 144-51).[10] Science was regarded as a useful tool for staying at this edge.

10 There are several parallels between Linde's and Diesel's projects. Both can be seen as scientification attempts and both took the ideal Carnot cycle as a point of departure. Diesel was in fact Linde's pupil at the Munich Polytechnic. The engineer Jonas Hesselman (1948, p. 184) has written about the adoption of Diesel's ideas in Sweden and also observed the persuasive power of science: "Thermodynamic calculations ... were probably necessary in order to obtain support from the men of practice."

9. The Expansion: The Linde Co. Supports Innovation and Diffusion

The Stabilization of the Technical Core

We saw in Chapter 5 how Linde encountered his problem and presented his original solution on paper, and we learned in Chapter 8 how he completed the inventive phase by designing his first cooling machine. Since it did not work satisfactorily, considerable changes had to be made, resulting in the second prototype running safely and not requiring constant supervision. Next, we will follow the processes whereby the transition from invention to innovation was completed through the construction and marketing of a third, stable design. This transition meant that Linde's research and development program had to face a commercial test, and that Linde had to decide whether to continue as a college teacher or become an entrepreneur.

When we left the narrative of Linde's endeavors, he had just received a Bavarian patent for his second design along with the first orders. In 1876 he patented this machine in Great Britain as well, and in the following year he was granted his first patent rights for the whole German nation. It had previously been impossible to receive one patent for all of Germany, because before July 1877 the German states had all had their own patent laws. The new law in fact replaced as many as twenty-nine local laws (*BIGB* 1877, Vol. 9, pp. 177-182). The German *Reich* had been founded in 1871, and the creation of a central Patent Office in Berlin fit well with Bismarck's unification plan, as did the currency law of 1873, the trademark protection law of 1874, and the copyright law of 1876 (Beer 1959, p. 56; Sartorius 1920, pp. 251, 260). But patent legislation was also an important concern for engineers and capitalists; the Society of German Engineers, in cooperation with the Central Association of German Industrialists, had long supported a new patent law, and there was even a German Association for Patent Protection, having been founded by the famous engineer and industrialist Werner von Siemens (Beer 1959, pp. 103 ff.; Scholl 1981, pp. 39-49). Linde himself had actually been a member of the committee which prepared the national patent law at the trade and communications department (*Bericht* ... 1875-1876, p. 12).

Linde's first national patent covered basically the same twin-cylinder, single-acting design which he had patented in Bavaria in March 1876, the first prototype of which had been erected at Dreher's brewery (LAG-H; MAN-HA 3.37). In the *Reich* application Linde particularly emphasizes the intricate lubricating and sealing system applying glycerine, the distillation vessel for supplying the "volatile liquid" (that is, ammonia), and a rotating ice generator. Hence, the patent covers a complete ice-machine system, not only a compressor.

Since this apparatus seems to have worked satisfactorily in Trieste, one might have expected the design to become a "black box" and thus remain stable (Hård 1992; Latour 1987), but Linde and the syndicate wanted to reduce manufacturing costs by making a less complicated machine and reduce ice-production costs by making it more compact (Linde 1979, pp. 39 f.). After a short period of innovative work they introduced a new compressor to the market in 1877, a model of which can be seen in Figure 9.1. Since it exhibited more similarities to the familiar steam engine, the Augsburg Machine Co. could make more use of its collective experience from the production of such machines when turning, more and more, to ice-machine production. The new machine was a horizontal, double-acting design with an ingenious stuffing box. Glycerine had the dual duty of both sealing and lubricating like in the previous engine, and ammonia was used as a refrigerant. Interestingly enough, this third design was never patented. The compressor was apparently too similar to ordinary pumps, and the main features of the stuffing box had already been included in the patent described above. The main novelty with the sealing system is that the glycerine-filled cavity is connected to the low pressure side of the evaporator rather than to the high pressure side of the condenser.

The Augsburg Machine Co. delivered the first machine of this design to the Dietrich Brewery of Dusseldorf in May 1877 (MAN-HA, 3.37). With this design Linde and his team had arrived at an innovation which would remain an influential archetype for decades to come. The engineering professor Max Jacob (1917, p. 419) referred to Linde's autobiography, and in apparent agreement with it noted forty years later that

> The horizontal, double-acting, ammonia compression machine with this kind of packing has become the typical form of the modern refrigerating machine in Europe.

An engineering encyclopedia of 1925 similarly stated that the contrivances of the third design "are still fully modern" (*Uppfinningarnas bok* 1925, Vol. 2, p. 1004). It is obvious from contemporary sales catalogs that this design had established itself also in the United States by the turn of the century (Wolf 1900).[1]

Figure 9.1. Model of Linde's third compressor design from 1877. The vertical compressor is seen between the steam engine cylinder in the foreground and the evaporator and condenser in the background; courtesy *Historisches Archiv MAN AG*, Augsburg

Two questions can be asked at this point: why did the third compressor type become such a powerful *Vorbild* for other firms? Why did the Linde team not go on to develop a fourth one? While the first question will be addressed in Chapter 10, the second one may be discussed here. The problem is, put in a less counterfactual way, why stabilization and closure occurred. Modern sociology of technology has rightly emphasized that such cases cannot be explained by reference to technological factors only

1 For the sake of completeness, it should be noted that, today, the single-acting compressor has usually replaced the double-acting one, since the former is easier to make tight (Trott 1981, p. 32).

(Pinch and Bijker 1987). Kanehira Maruo (1992) has adopted a network approach in his analysis of the establishment of the three-way catalyst, according to which closure is seen as the outcome of consensus among the most powerful actors in the automobile area. I have elsewhere argued in a study of diesel engine design that the creation of stable "black boxes" is a prerequisite for designers to be able to cope with a messy world; if everything is open for negotiation, then design work becomes virtually impossible to handle (Hård 1992). Andreas Knie, Regina Buhr, and Marion Hass (1992) have shown how the defining power of the Underwood company forced typewriter design into a narrow corridor.

Closure appears in the terminology of this study when an artifact meets the requirements of the majority of powerful concerned parties—financiers, manufacturers, designers, repairmen, and users. In our story the Augsburg Machine Co., the syndicate's salesmen, and their repairmen benefitted from technical stability. By keeping to one and the same archetypical compressor, they did not need to learn new manufacturing procedures, they could stick to their standard models in their familiar sales catalogs, and they did not have to receive continuous updates about technical novelties. Given the fairly slow means of communication at the time, the transfer of information to salesmen and repairmen became a serious problem as the business spread over Europe and the United States. Since ice-machines were complicated devices that needed close supervision, stability was also beneficial to users. If a brewer decided to buy a larger version of a standard model, then it was fairly simple for the mechanics to understand how the new machine worked. It is not enough only to discuss the demand put forth by manufacturers and designers when explaining why a certain artifact is stabilized; the needs of repairmen and users also have to be taken into account (Mack 1990).

Linde intended to leave the commercial arena after having designed the third compressor and devote all his time to college duties (Linde 1979, p. 44). Throughout the inventive and innovative periods he had taught at the Munich Polytechnic, where in 1875 he founded the laboratory for theoretical mechanical engineering (p. 32). This organizational innovation was one of the first of its kind and fitted beautifully into the ideology of school culture. Its task was threefold:

> It partly served purely scientific [*rein wissenschaftlich*] purposes, partly answered questions of a technical-practical nature, and partly trained mature students to carry

out investigations of thermodynamic processes and procedures. (*Bericht* ... 1877-1878, p. 11)

Figure 9.2. The laboratory of theoretical mechanical engineering at the Munich Polytechnic, founded by Linde in 1875; courtesy *Linde AG*, Höllriegelskreuth

Activities in the laboratory primarily centered around the steam engine (*ibid.*, 1875-1876, pp. 31 f., 1876-1877, p. 19). Two essential features distinguished this school culture institution from the mechanical workshop. Firstly, the laboratory was a place for research and education, not for production; see Figure 9.2. Linde wrote that: "The students should be given the opportunity to make their own experiments, discuss them, and compare them with theory ..." (in Manegold 1969, p. 176). Secondly, the student in the laboratory was taught how to analyze a machine, while a shop apprentice would learn how to operate it. Calvert (1967, p. 71) argues that the proponents of school culture often used "terms such as 'laboratory' in descriptions of practical machine experience offered in the schools." Linde was one of the pioneers of such technological laboratories; others were set up by, for example, at Cornell University in Ithaca, New York, by Henry Thurston and in Berlin by Reuleaux (Braun 1981, p. 123). Laboratory practice was an integral part of these educators' *professional culture*.

Since Linde had invested such efforts at the Munich Polytechnic, it is hardly surprising that he wanted to be able to continue what he had begun at the college, but instead toward the end of the 1870s he found himself increasingly involved in the refrigeration business. If Linde had believed that the advanced engineering work was completed when the innovation was made, then he was severely mistaken. The hard job of adapting the machine to different circumstances and applying it to various needs had merely started. If we use H. Ulrich's (1970) terminology, then we would say that Linde and his partners had entered the long "application phase." Linde had to decide which of his two creations—the commercial or the educational one—he should continue to guide. He chose the former. In his sometimes heroic autobiography Linde (1979, p. 46) claims that he left teaching because he "felt" engineering practice to be more of a "calling." However, pecuniary expectations arguably played a substantial role. Since eleven orders for refrigeration systems (for ice production, water cooling, and air cooling, respectively) had arrived during 1877 and 1878, there was a promise of a bright future (MAN-HA, 3.37/2).

The Inventor Becomes an Entrepreneur

An ice-machine includes much more than the compressor. Even though this core had been stabilized locally in the Linde setting, several other parts of the system remained *in flux* (Hård 1992). Linde and the syndicate decided to found a joint-stock company in order to raise money for further research and development. In June 1879 the *Gesellschaft für Linde's Eismaschinen* (Linde Co.) was founded in Wiesbaden with a capital stock of 200,000 marks (117,000 guldens). Its purposes were

> on the one hand to utilize the Linde patents for refrigerating and ice machines and to utilize and advertise possible new patents; on the other hand to erect refrigeration plants and ice factories on the account of both the company and others.[2]

---

2 From the Linde Co. statutes, printed in 1886 (LAG-H, "Versch. Notizen zur Werkshistorie 1879-1964").

Thus a corporate body had been set up to take care of continuous innovation, application, and marketing. The board of directors included highly influential representatives of the machine industry (Director Buz of the Augsburg Machine Co., Director Krauß, and the railroad constructor Carl Lang) and the brewing industry (Carl Sedlmayr of Spaten and Director Gustav Jung of the Mainz Brewing Co.).[3] Linde, who had already moved to Wiesbaden, was made chairman of the board.

With his move from the college in Munich to the business in Wiesbaden Linde ceased to be a "scientist-engineer" and became an "inventor-entrepreneur." He became more interested as such in the production of ice-machines and the reproduction of the stock-holders, investments than in the production of technological knowledge and the reproduction of engineering students. The historian of technology Thomas P. Hughes (1971, p. 63) has written about this type of person in his book about Elmer Sperry, the American electrical engineer:

> As an inventor-entrepreneur, Sperry presided over the process of invention, development, and innovation; he had to be, therefore, intimately acquainted with the state of technological development in his field and he had to identify a market for particular inventions made possible by the state of the art. His concern, in other words, was the transformation of an idea into a practical device that could perform well in a competitive environment.

This description of Sperry's tasks applies neatly to Linde's work. The main difference between Linde and Sperry was that Linde took an active part in management and business—two activities that, since Schumpeter's days, are usually connected to entrepreneurial work.

Throughout the 1880s the Linde Co. remained a knowledge-intensive engineering and marketing firm. It designed and installed refrigeration systems in close cooperation with the machine industry, but it never undertook to manufacture them. Linde (1979, p. 52) uses the following words to describe its activity: "drafting ... calculating ... inspecting ... erecting ... installing ... and communicating with customers ... and machine firms." The manufacturing rights were sold to several machine companies which divided the world market between them, a strategy that had already started under the syndicate and was now expanded to the United States, for example (Linde 1979, p. 44; Goosman 1925, Vol. 68, p. 414). The Augsburg Machine Co. acquired the rights for Germany, and the Sulzer

3 A copy of the founding document is at *ibid*.

Brothers of Zurich for Switzerland, Spain, and Italy. The Augsburg firm, which in the mid-1870s had lived through some years of hardship, welcomed refrigeration production as a promising area of expansion (Büchner 1940, p. 47). In 1877 the company assigned an engineer to work especially with refrigeration problems (Krumper 1916, pp. 7 f.). The division of production in different countries led to some problems. The Augsburg and Sulzer firms soon took care of France and Belgium as well, whereas other firms were responsible for Great Britain and North America (Linde 1979, pp. 51, 62 ff.). This fairly decentralized system spread knowledge thinly over a large area, where the Linde Co. representatives played an essential communicating role. Some of its engineers were stationed in foreign countries and made responsible for the installation of new refrigeration systems after having received some training in Wiesbaden. The most famous of them was Rudolf Diesel, who represented the Linde Co. in France and Belgium throughout the 1880s; a lively account of this hectic work can be found in Eugene Diesel's (1983, Ch. V) biography of his father.

Diesel had been Linde's student at the Munich Technical College, like several other men who were hired by the Linde Co. We have already met Schipper, the first member of this group. The close contacts with this college continued even after Linde gave up his teaching position there. His successor to the chair, Moritz Schröter, went on to supply the company with bright, young engineers. The official Linde Co. history of 1929 lists seven "collaborators" who started to work with Linde in the 1870s and 1880s; *all* of them were graduates of the Munich school: Friedrich Schipper (who started to work with Linde in 1873), Robert Banfield (1877), Karl Heimpel (1879), Rudolf Diesel (1880), Hermann Reuter (1881), August Krebs (1882), and Alexius Negele (1886) (*50 Jahre* ... 1929, pp. 17 ff.). However, the Linde Co. was not the only firm to attract these men to refrigeration jobs. For example, when the Augsburg Machine Co. in 1888 founded a special department for refrigeration, Linde's former student, Lucian Vogel, became its director.[4] Linde could now reap the fruits

4 Cf. a manuscript for a talk, "Erzeugnisse der M.A.N. Werk Augsburg - Bedeutende Männer," by Georg Strössner (MAN-HA, 3.37). A personal account of refrigeration work at the Augsburg works is given by Krumper (1916) who was employed as an engineer by this company in 1875.

of what he had helped to create at the Munich college—a theoretically advanced mechanical engineering education combined with laboratory practice. Its graduates had broad problem-solving abilities enabling them to not only deal with steam engines, but also to enter such esoteric fields as refrigeration technology. In this manner, school culture directly supported Linde's project. It should be noted that in Munich no courses were given in mechanical refrigeration until after the turn of the century, and that no ice-machines were analyzed during Linde's years in the laboratory for theoretical mechanical engineering.[5]

Before we look closer at what kind of application work the Linde Co. undertook, some figures concerning sales and profits up to the early 1890s will be presented. The delivery lists of the Augsburg Machine Co., the largest producer of Linde equipment, show that slightly less than ten refrigeration systems were sold within Germany each year during the late 1870s (MAN-HA, 3.37/2). Sales soared to roughly fifty systems per year during the first three years of the following decade; they then stabilized for three years before jumping to twice that figure; after 1890 there was a marked downward trend, probably in part as a result of saturation and because Linde's basic patent rights became invalid in 1891. The periods of rapid expansion were 1881-83 and 1887-89. The Augsburg figures correspond closely to the dividends granted by the Linde Co., which peaked in 1884 and 1889 (*50 Jahre* ... 1929, p. 176). In the former year, the company actually gave more than 100% return on investment. Clearly, the 1880s was a profitable decade for the Linde Co. and its shareholders.

By the end of 1890 the Augsburg Machine Co. had sold more than seven hundred machine systems, of which four fifths went to breweries (Linde 1979, appendix, p. V; MAN-HA, 3.37/2); the core parts of two of them can be seen in Figure 9.3. Warehouses and ships which needed to preserve food-stuffs, and factories producing and selling ice made up the next largest group of customers. In accord with its founding goals, the Linde Co. also erected its own ice-factories in a number of cities, Paris, Dusseldorf, Munich, and Strasbourg among them (Linde 1979, pp. 49 f.).

---

5 The reader who is interested in the professionalization of refrigeration engineering around the turn of the century can consult Thévenot (1978, pp. 158-164). There (p. 161) it is claimed (without references) that Linde gave refrigeration courses already in 1873. However, in the *Programm* ... of the Munich Polytechnic no such courses are scheduled before 1902-1903.

They not only sold ice profitably to local firms which could not afford their own ice-machines, but also advertised vividly the potentials of the Linde machinery.

Figure 9.3. Two identical Linde refrigeration machines of the third design installed at the *Franziskaner-Keller* brewery of Josef Sedlmayr in Munich are at the center of this picture from 1894; courtesy *Historisches Archiv MAN AG*, Augsburg

The Development of Complete Machine Systems

The technical account has so far focused on the various Linde compressors. However, the Linde Co. well understood that its customers needed a complete refrigeration machine system—the term "machine system" is here understood in a narrow, technical sense (cf. Hughes 1987). It was more or less necessary that the Linde Co. and its collaborating machine firms could deliver and install compressor, ice generator, evaporator, condenser, steam engine, and other paraphernalia. It would not have been enough merely to produce a thermodynamically sound compressor. However, like most other German ice-machine firms, the Linde Co. focused on the perfection of single machines, not the development of large, geographically extended systems that included producers, retailers, and customers. Such "cooling chains" emerged in the United States (Dienel 1991).

The customers of the Linde Co. and the Augsburg Machine Co. often expressed very different demands, thus making stabilization more difficult. Some industrial establishments wanted brine cooling connected to an elaborated network of refrigeration pipes; others wanted to manufacture ice; others still wanted a system for the cooling and drying of air. This diversity had already been obvious in the mid-1870s. Spaten's first full-sized machine had been installed for brine cooling, whereas the Dreher machine in Trieste had had the dual purpose of ice production and air cooling.

The Linde Co. after having arrived at stable compressor design developed three different apparatuses for the making of can-formed ice in order to meet various demands. The goal was not fuel-efficiency, but to facilitate the handling of machinery and ice:

> It appeared commercially important that we design an ice generator which would reduce manual work as much as possible in large firms. (Linde 1979, p. 42)

This search for a labor-saving device led to a semi-automatic machine which produced can-formed ice continuously; compare Figure 9.4. Two methods were developed for the purpose of making crystal-clear ice, one rotary and one horizontal. The latter system was first used at Linde Co.'s iceworks in Elberfeld-Barmen in 1880-1881, but it was not patented until July 1883 (Linde 1979, pp. 58 f.). Apart from ice-generators, the company developed systems for room cooling. In many breweries fermentation and storage areas were equipped with refrigeration pipes close to the ceiling. Since the Linde Co. never patented such systems, it can be assumed that they belonged to a common stock of technological knowledge at the time, so to speak to its *Stand der Technik*. More interesting is the company's devices for the cooling and humidifying of air; air conditioning systems of this kind were patented in 1883 and became particularly popular with the meat trade (pp. 57 f.).

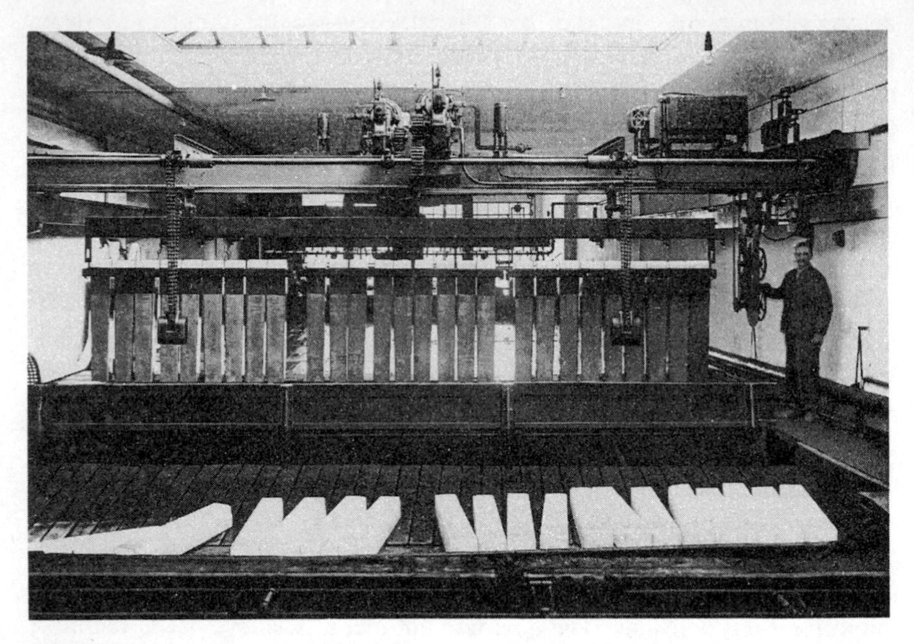

Figure 9.4. Semi-automatic, continuously working ice-generator, installed at the *Löwenbrauerei* in Munich; courtesy *IHK-Wirtschaftsarchiv für München und Oberbayern*, Munich

Our story has now gone far beyond the fundamentals of thermodynamics. However, as we will see in the following chapter, Linde continued to find support in science—not least for reasons of public relations. Early in the 1870s Linde had acted as a translator of thermodynamics into refrigeration technology, and the syndicate had subsequently made the invention marketable. In other words, the syndicate had acted as a translator between the technological and economic spheres. All three spheres—the scientific, the technological, and the economic ones—were put under one roof by the creation of the Linde Co. In this house an increasing number of businessmen and college-trained engineers collected, interpreted, and translated information. The company could focus on continuous innovation and development by licensing the production rights to existing machine firms. The rapid success of the Linde Co. was due largely to its ability to process information and communicate special knowledge. These are certainly anachronistic terms, but the activity of the Linde Co. actually appears fairly modern. With his college background Linde represented a new brand of entrepreneur in the machine industry. The historian Ernst Barth (1973, pp. 98 f., 195) mentions that in 1914 the Linde Co. probably had the highest ratio of technicians of all German machine firms. The company's emphasis on innovation and design represented a new path, where research and development work was separated from manufacturing. If we compare it with the famous firm Siemens & Halske, then we could say that the Linde Co. undertook what this electrotechnical company did at its technical and design offices, as well as in its laboratory (Kocka 1969, pp. 136 ff.).

10. The Final Word: The Scientification of the Marketplace

Linde Versus Carré Absorption

The previous chapters might have given the impression that the success of the Linde Co. was a fairly straightforward affair. Its rapid growth must have been a shock to other ice-machine manufacturers, but they certainly did not give up without a fight. One firm copied the Linde design and another put forth—in Linde's eyes—unfair claims about its own machines. In this chapter we shall see how the Linde Co. reacted to these threats by invoking the patent law and calling for unassailable machine tests. Linde did not believe that a totally free marketplace could handle the introduction of new technology. In particular, his belief that a scientific approach could be used to guide potential customers will be emphasized below. However, we shall first see how well the Linde design compared with other machines in the early 1880s.

We saw in the preceding chapter how the Augsburg Machine Co.'s sales of Linde's machines constantly grew during the first half of the 1880s. They stabilized for two years after a peak following the very mild winter and disastrous ice harvest of 1883-1884 (Linde 1979, p. 56; Thévenot 1978, p. 79). Before the peak was reached the success of the Linde Co. had been noted in the trade literature. The contemporary engineer Gottlieb Behrend (1883, p. 18) related it in part to the large vaporization heat of the refrigerant which the company used, and wrote that "... the Linde ammonia machines have made an extremely rapid entry, while the others ... have shown more inferior results." Behrend's book, "Ice and Refrigerating Machines," has over one hundred and fifty pages and furnishes a comprehensive account of the state of the art at this time. Among other things, it enables us to compare the Carré absorption and the Linde vapor compression systems, which were then the main antagonists on the market. Together with some further sources, Behrend's account makes it possible to give a reasonably accurate evaluation of the practical contribution of Linde's scientification program to refrigeration technology. We will see that subsequent commentators have often greatly exaggerated the performance of Linde's early machines. For example, Goosman (1925, Vol. 68, p. 137) suggests that Linde's work "in a short time" led to machines which reached 50% of the theoretical maximum, a claim that will be challenged.

Behrend (1883, pp. 65-85) compiled his figures from sales catalogs of four German companies. The Carré absorption system was represented by Vaaß & Littmann, Halle a.S., and Oscar Kropff, Nordhausen; the Linde compression system by Osenbrück & Co., Bremen, together with, of course, the Linde Co.

Behrend presents a host of figures for each system, but he never explicitly compares them. The following "deconstructive" comparison, which Behrend himself did not make, assumes that the firms did not dare present their customers with greatly distorted information which could result in litigation. It is also necessary to standardize the expenses for labor, coal, and lighting in order to make just comparisons; depreciation and interest rates totaled 15% a year.[1] All figures apply to the first year of usage and concern an average-size ice-machine, running two hundred days a year. Working around the clock it would produce twelve tons of ice a day, or 2,400 tons per year.

The result of this comparative exercise is presented in Figure 10.1: a Linde machine would have been roughly 16% cheaper to use in the first year than a Vaaß & Littmann device. If both machines required the same amount of repair, then this figure would have increased with time, since the variable costs were 31% lower for the Linde design. We remember from Chapter 5 that Linde had consciously aimed at two things. First, he had wanted to reduce fixed costs by introducing a refrigerant with a large heat of vaporization, since a machine using ammonia or dimethyl ether would be considerably smaller than one applying diethyl ether. So far he succeeded but, as the Figure shows, he did not manage to bring down the total fixed costs under the level of Carré's systems. The purchase price of absorption machinery remained the lowest. Linde's second goal had been the lowering of variable costs by improving the refrigeration cycle and some technical details. He surely succeeded in this case.

1 Since the companies give different figures for the unit price of labor and coal, these figures have been standardized. The daily wages of a mechanic have been set at 4 marks, of a boilerman at 3.50, and of a day-laborer at 2.50; the price of coal at 20 marks per ton. The price for oil and lighting has been put at 2.70 marks; 1 mark equals 0.58 guldens. 5% interest rates and 10% depreciation were used throughout by all companies.

	Vaaß & Littmann	Oscar Kropff	Linde & Augsburg	Osenbrück & Co.
Depriciation and interest (15% of purchase price)	30.00	32.06	32.62	34.12
Labor (standardized)	16.50	15.00	12.50	12.50
Coal (standardized)	30.00	30.00	17.28	21.60
Other running costs	6.00	7.00	6.56	3.50
Sum	82.50	84.06	68.96	71.72
Price per ton of ice produced	6.88	7.00	5.75	5.98
Kg of coal required per ton of ice produced	125.0	125.0	71.9	90.1

Figure 10.1. Daily costs (marks) for the running of various ice-machines producing 12 tons of ice per day, 200 days in a year; compiled from Behrend (1883)

If we only look at the figures for coal consumption, then the superior performance of the Linde-Augsburg machine is even more striking. Of course, such comparisons assume that all firms used steam engines with similar degrees of efficiency. Compared with the Vaaß & Littmann and Kropff systems, Linde's device gave three-fourths more ice per energy unit, definitely showing the advantages of ammonia compression with respect to fuel economy. This fact is further emphasized by the performance of the Osenbrück ammonia compression design, which produced 39% more ice than the Carré replicas. The difference in performance between Linde-Augsburg and Osenbrück can probably be attributed to the engineering skill of the former companies, a factor which has been especially noted by the British engineer J.A. Ewing (1923, p. 86).

The obvious conclusion is that any customer in the early and mid-1880s could adduce weighty arguments for choosing a Linde machine. Even if the Linde Co. might have underestimated the number of hands required (one mechanic, one boilerman, and two day-laborers), the running costs of its machine was definitely the lowest. However, Figure 10.1 does not give us the whole picture. Compared with the Carré design, Linde's was fairly new on the market. No-one knew if it would last during the whole period of depreciation, one decade. Furthermore, since an absorption machine requires less mechanical work than a vapor compression one, it might well be that a customer could have used an already existing steam engine. The purchase of a vapor compression machine would in most cases also have required the acquisition of a new steam engine. If the customer bought an absorption system, then his or her fixed costs would have decreased up to 16%, according to the Vaaß & Littmann figures. If the customer also could use the excess steam from his old engine to heat the ammonia-water mixture instead of merely disposing of it, the coal expenses would turn out considerably lower than in the table. Even though arguments of this kind are not discussed by Behrend, it is still clear that potential customers did not focus only on how many kilograms of coal were required to manufacture one ton of ice. The success of the Linde Co. did cause a tremendous growth in the popularity of ammonia compression, but it did not mean that absorption disappeared during our period. In 1898 Behrend (1898, pp. 14 f.) reluctantly has to admit that absorption remains on the market, despite several technical drawbacks—even though compression had the upper hand. Both absorption and vapor compression remained technical options, and none of them had established itself as a ruling standard in mechanical refrigeration engineering.

The Osenbrück design was very similar to Linde's. Behrend (1883, p. 35) describes the Osenbrück machine as follows: "The only difference lies in the compressor pump, which applies oil as a sealing fluid instead of glycerine, which Linde uses." In fact, the Bremen firm had copied Linde's design so closely that Linde (1979, pp. 68 f.) threatened to take Osenbrück to court for patent infringement. Osenbrück was obviously afraid of losing such a case, agreed in 1884 to pay a licence fee to Linde, and was thus able to remain in business. Linde's contributions in the mid-1870s to a national patent law thus proved to have been worthwhile. This law protected the Linde Co. and helped it reach and retain a strong position.

Another threat also appeared in the first half of the 1880s when a competitor, Rudloff-Grübs & Co. of Berlin, claimed to sell the most efficient ice-machine on the market. This firm manufactured the Raoul Pictet design for Germany which supposedly defied the second law of thermodynamics. Such a claim—neither the first nor the last one in the history of technology—simply could not be ignored by the Linde Co., but this time the patent law was of no aid (Linde 1979, pp. 69-72).

A graduate of the *École Polytechnique* and a physics professor in Geneva, Raoul Pictet had a firm scientific background similar to Linde's (*Pictet* ... 1878; Thévenot 1978, pp. 56, 481). In the mid-1870s he had introduced a vapor compression machine which applied sulfur dioxide and allegedly produced small amounts of liquid oxygen (Gillet 1876; *Om fabrikationen* ... 1881; *Om framställandet* ... 1881). Whereas the last feat has subsequently been questioned, there is no doubt that his refrigeration business thrived.[2] As many as forty-four systems were sold to European brewers and a foothold was gained on the American market during its first two years. The controversy with Linde did not start until the first half of the 1880s, when Pictet launched a new refrigerant, the so-called *liquide Pictet*. This mixture of sulfur dioxide and carbon dioxide was advertised as a product with extraordinary qualities, outdoing even the efficiency of the reversed Carnot cycle. Such a statement was a menace to the entrepreneur Linde, since it threatened his business, but it was also a menace to the scientifically educated engineer Linde, in that it threatened the status of thermodynamics.

Since several customers swallowed Pictet-Grübs' claims, Linde found that the customers in the market obviously needed guidance. In 1884 he wrote a letter to the permanent committee of the Bavarian Polytechnic Society, suggesting that it "appoint a commission of experts who are willing to carry out thorough and scientifically exact tests with various refrigeration machines."[3]

---

2 Goosman (1925, Vol. 68, p. 135), maintains that Pictet's liquefaction was fake, but a later writer, Mendelssohn (1977), does not support this view.

3 Quoted from a letter of March 22, 1884, in the archives of the Bavarian Polytechnic (hereafter abbreviated ABPTV), presently in the special collection of the Deutsches

He also declared that the Linde Co. was ready to pay at least three thousand marks for this purpose. The society responded positively by appointing a small group under the chairmanship of professor Moritz Schröter, who commenced his investigations in 1884 and published the first results three years later.[4] The other members of the investigation committee were Ernst Voigt, a physics professor at the Munich Technical College, W. Gyssling, engineer and director of the Bavarian Society for the Investigation of Steam Engines, and Dr. Bunte, Secretary General of the German Association of Gas and Water Engineers and a chemistry professor at the Karlsruhe Polytechnic (ABPTV, 175 [-]). We know from Chapter 8 that Linde had been an active member of the society since his time in Munich and knew its influential members. Since Schröter was moreover Linde's successor for the Munich college chair, the job of supplying the market with "unbiased" results stayed within a circle of associates (Schröter 1887, p. 1). Schröter shared several pro-scientific values with Linde and declared that the comparative experiments were based, as far as possible, on "scientific principles" (*wissenschaftliche Grundsätze*) (*ibid.*).

Nevertheless, the outcome of Schröter's work was not exactly what Linde had wanted it to be. The results did indicate that the Linde design was the most efficient ice-machine of the six investigated brands, but the experiments had methodological problems that made interpretation quite difficult (Schröter 1887, pp. 167-171). The tests had been conducted in different companies under different circumstances, and the only conclusion Schröter dared draw was that vapor compression machines appeared considerably more efficient than representatives of the other ideal types. Of course, such a result did not make it possible to distinguish the Linde from the Pictet system, since both belonged to the vapor compression group. Some of Schröter's figures indicated that Pictet's machine was not particularly efficient, but the results were not conclusive. Largely because of

---

Museum (ABPTV, 175 [-]); those parts of the archives dealing with mechanical refrigeration do not seem to have been analyzed at depth before; cf. also *1815-1915 ...* (1922, pp. 234 f.).

4 They were published as Schröter (1887). The most recent comprehensive history of refrigeration, Thévenot (1978), is quite confusing on this score; on p. 56 it says that the society got involved in 1887, whereas according to p. 59 the same event should have taken place in 1875. Schröter (1887, p. 170) makes it clear that work started in March 1884 and continued on and off for three years.

incomparable testing conditions, the controversy between Pictet and Linde continued.

The Refrigeration Testing Station as a Closure Mechanism

In order to achieve a clearer denunciation of Pictet's claims and hence close the controversy, Linde wrote once more to the Polytechnic Society committee in June of 1888, this time suggesting the foundation of a specially equipped refrigeration testing station (Goosman 1925, Vol. 68, p. 479; Linde 1979, pp. 70 ff.; Schröter 1890; *1815-1915* ... 1922, pp. 235 ff.). His letter regretted the incompleteness of the previous investigations and declared that the Linde Co., together with the Augsburg Machine Co., was willing to finance the proposed establishment (ABPTV, 175 [-]). He pointed out that only in such a *Versuchs-Station für Kältemaschinen* would it be possible to create conditions ensuring "unquestionable comparisons of the efficiency of various machine systems." Linde suggested that the experiments be supervised by a commission with renowned "representatives from both science and industry" to guarantee "exactness and credibility."

Like they had done four years earlier, the society promptly complied with most of Linde's suggestions. It appointed a commission, with Schröter as its chairman, and adopted some general guidelines for its work. Five of the nine members of the commission were technical college professors, among them Zeuner, and the others came from the brewing and machine industries (ABPTV, 175 [3]; Schröter 1890, p. 7). Twenty-two German companies producing refrigeration systems were invited to take part in the tests, but only three of them were ready to accept the challenge; positive replies came from A. Neubecker of Offenbach a.M., the *Maschinenfabrik und Eisengießerei* of Halle, and Rudloff-Grübs & Co. (ABPTV, 176 [1]). The wide hesitation resulted probably from the Linde Co.'s involvement in the arrangement of the earlier Schröter tests. The firms might have expected that the experiments would not be quite correct, or maybe they were afraid of any direct comparisons with the Linde or other systems. Their reaction may also have stemmed from ideological objections to the substitution of so-called scientific tests for free competition.

Most of all, Linde had wanted an affirmative reply from the Rudloff-Grübs & Co., and this he got. Pictet himself was present at the first official meeting of the commission in August 1888—as was Linde (ABPTV, 177 [1]). Both Grübs and Pictet appeared convinced that their machinery would be able to match Linde's. Grübs later explained somewhat indignantly that their motives for taking part in the experiments had been to "prove to the public that a certain competitor has acted wrongfully when claiming that its machines are more efficient than ours" (ABPTV, 177 [1]).

Since Pictet had earlier been involved in scientific work, it is not overly surprising that he welcomed Linde's initiative, believing that their struggle could be settled unambiguously and unequivocally by intersubjective means. A prerequisite was, of course, that Pictet and Grübs should help plan and conduct the tests.

The Linde Co. acquired a Munich site for the erection of the station during the summer of 1888, and some members of the commission prepared detailed directions for the experiments. These directions were finally accepted on August 29, 1888, in a "special program." Since several of its formulations are adopted *verbatim* from a paper issued by Rudloff-Grübs & Co., it is clear that Pictet and Grübs did exert some influence on the planning process (ABPTV, 175 [9], 175 [3]). The three most important variables to correlate would concern the production of cold, the consumption of coal, and the need for cooling water. In order to create equal conditions the same prime mover would be used throughout the tests. The temperatures of brine and cooling water were standardized. To ensure a high degree of accuracy all tests would be repeated once and reserve instruments would be mounted at the most crucial points.

In the fall the committee contracted firms for the erection of the station building and for the construction and installation of two steam engines (ABPTV, 176 [2], 177 [1]). Linde played an active part in both matters, and an engineer from the Linde Co., Alexius Negele, acted as an on-site supervisor.[5] Work proceeded slower than expected, and the steam engines could not be installed until April the next year. The station was quite large. The main building was almost one hundred feet long and could house four machines. Despite this fact, only the Rudloff-Grübs and Linde companies participated in the initial test series. The two firms drew up a treaty supplementing the conditions outlined by the commission; it was signed in April

5 See letters from Linde to the society (ABPTV, 175 [2], 180 [1]) and a letter of attorney for Negele (*ibid.*, 176 [4]).

1889 (ABPTV, 176 [3]). Among other things, they agreed to allow representatives of the competing firm to oversee all tests for the purpose of intersubjective correctness. An interesting paragraph of the treaty stated that the Linde Co. was to pay twenty-five thousand marks if its machine was not at least 20% more efficient than that of its adversary; most of the money was to be given to brewers' widows and children. The company's outlays to the builder, Carl Del Bondio of Munich, and the steam engine manufacturer, Siller & Jamart of Barmer-Rittershausen, for the erection and equipping of the station amounted to sixty-odd thousand marks. This sum can be compared to the forty-odd thousand marks that an average-size Linde machine cost. Such items as the wages of the committee members and a mechanic, as well as all the extra work performed by Linde Co. employees, should also be added to the firm's expense account. Furthermore, the thermometers must have been rather expensive, since they were extremely precise.

After considerable delay, testing could finally start in mid-November of 1889. A dozen people were involved, repeatedly recording more than forty different variables in accordance with a detailed "Test Program" and an "Execution Program" (ABPTV, 179 [1], 180 [1]). Nothing had been left to chance. Indicators and manometers had been checked at the Munich Technical College, and thermometers at the *Physikalisch-technische Reichsanstalt* in Berlin (Schröter 1890). A special arbitration jury, with Schröter as its chairman, had been appointed in order to settle any disputes between the competing firms.

Despite the meticulous planning, there were a couple of hitches; a steam engine failed, for example. Nevertheless, they were able to finish the test series within two months. The main result was well in accordance with Linde's hopes and wishes. It showed that the Linde-Augsburg system produced, on average, 32% more ice per energy unit than that of Pictet-Grübs. The difference between the systems was particularly large at very low temperatures, making the average figure somewhat unfair. Of more practical interest was the figure concerning the most commonly used, "normal," temperature (-5°C [23°F]). It showed that the Linde machine made 25% more ice per kg of coal. Strangely enough, Schröter does not explicitly provide the readers of his report with these figures, but they can be easily computed (Schröter 1890, p. 84).

The winners could now assert that the superiority of Linde's design had been decisively proven by scientific methods. The final word had been uttered. In this case, scientific primarily meant the creation of uniform conditions, the recording of quantified data, the systematic variation of parameters, and the drawing of conclusions based on thermodynamic theory. It is hard to judge completely the fairness of the tests, but it has to be admitted that Linde gave his competitors full oversight of the planning and executing of the experiments. They could have withdrawn, had they felt something was not correctly done. Rudloff-Grübs & Co. also had its own representatives both on the test committee and on the arbitration jury. Both Pictet and Linde were present at the first meeting of the jury. Still, Linde's word certainly carried the greatest weight; he worked out the calculation formulae, and, on his initiative, it was decided that the compressors be run at the same speed throughout the whole test series.[6] True, Grübs was granted the right to have another machine tested later, this time a device constructed for non-variable speed, but this was really a sham offer, since everybody knew that the first test series would be the important one. Since Pictet's machine had been constructed to run at different speeds at different temperatures, this decision was certainly a drawback for Pictet-Grübs.

Despite these reservations, on the whole the tests were probably equitable. The project was later criticized for methodological errors. For instance, Gustav Döderlein (1903) criticized the way in which the Schröter group read off the pressures, but the criticisms did not affect the comparisons between the machines. Two American engineers also disapproved of some aspect of the tests, but their doubt appears to have been caused by misunderstandings.[7] Their general judgement of the Schröter tests still was that "these were made in the most skilful and scientific manner."[8] Although the figure of 32% is somewhat too high, it is nonetheless beyond doubt that Linde's design required considerably less energy than Pictet's.

---

6 See the minutes of the commission from November 19, 1889 (ABPTV, 177 [1]).

7 The critique, furnished by Denton and Jacobins in the *Transactions of the American Society of Mechanical Engineers* (1892, Vol. 13), concerns the amount of cooling water being used. The issue is debated by Jacobins and Linde in *ibid.* (1893, Vol 14, pp. 1431 f., 1434-39).

8 The judgment is Jacobins'; see *ibid.* (1893, Vol. 14, p. 1436).

However, it has to be remembered that the results did not take into consideration any differences due to other running costs, purchase price, quality, or durability. Grübs lamented these shortcomings already before the tests had started, but in vain (ABPTV, 176 [3]).

Grübs had felt early on that things were not going his way. The whole affair suddenly took a strange turn. Two months before the tests began, he actually disposed of the ice-machine department of his firm to, in fact, the Linde Co. (ABPTV, 180 [1]). As Grübs wrote in a letter two months after the deal had been announced, the issue had developed into a matter of the "business honor" of his firm and the "scientific honor" of Pictet (ABPTV, 176 [3]). Of course, the tests also retained their economic significance for Pictet, who still had crucial business interests to look after in countries other than Germany. Since the foreign market was important to Linde as well, *his* interest in completing the test series hardly diminished after his firm had acquired Pictet's German patent rights. Thus, in addition to paying for the printing of the ninety-page German test report (2,000 copies!), the Linde Co. supported, together with its representatives in Paris, *La Société anonyme Cail*, the translation of the report into French (ABPTV, 175 [4]).

Since considerable sums had been invested in the station, the Linde Co. soon decided that arranging a second test series might be worthwhile. The Schröter commission was happy to continue its work, and its chairman mailed new invitations. After two Bavarian firms accepted the offer to participate, new experiments started late in 1891 (ABPTV, 176 [1]). The brave challengers, who now had to pay all expenses themselves, were the *L. Seyboth Bureau für Eismaschinen & Kühlanlagen* in Munich and the *Maschinenbau-Aktiengesellschaft* in Nuremberg, whose ammonia compression machines were tested during the following year. In order to guarantee a just comparison, the Linde Co.'s system was tested once more in 1893. The results, which were published continuously in the "Bavarian Journal of Industry and Trade," were very flattering to the Linde Co. They showed that on average its machine made as much as 32% more ice per energy unit than the Nuremberg one, and 27% more at "normal" temperature. The corresponding figures for the comparison with Seyboth's machine were 20 and 21%, respectively. No wonder that Seyboth complained loudly, when it came to paying his share of the running costs for the tests (ABPTV, 176 [5]).

The Linde Co.'s machine was no doubt among the most efficient ones on the market. Its advantageous coal consumption figures clearly contributed to the upsurge in the 1880s of ammonia compression in general, and of the Linde design in particular. However, the above comparisons have only indicated the relative strength of Linde-Augsburg when compared with other systems. It remains for us to judge how close Linde actually came to his *Leitbild*, the theoretically perfect machine. Linde had hoped in 1871 that it would be possible to construct a machine that followed the reversed Carnot cycle and had a degree of efficiency of 30%. In 1873 he had even claimed that his first dimethyl ether machine had already reached this figure.

The Carnot ideal cycle played a crucial role in Linde's scientific approach. In 1871 he had criticized Windhausen's air expansion and Siebe's vapor compression machines for being hopelessly far from the theoretical ideal. However, Zeuner had demonstrated that it is more or less impossible to follow the Carnot cycle unless a second compressor is installed between the condenser and evaporator, and Linde's systems did not include such a compressor. When the pressure-volume diagrams in Schröter's (1890) second report are compared with the Siebe-Harrison cycle of Figure 5.3, Linde's cycle does not appear to have been closer to the Carnot ideal. The expansion work of the refrigerant was not being used in any of the machines. In other words, the Carnot cycle had had more of a symbolic and rhetoric than a practical function.

It is not possible to use the value in Figure 10.1 of 72 kg of coal per ton of ice in order to compare the fuel-efficiency of Linde's design with the optimum. The efficiency of the steam engine is not known. What we need is, for example, a figure for the amount of ice produced per horsepower and hour (hph). From Chapter 5 we recall that Linde arrived at a figure just below 100 kg of ice per hph at common temperatures. Behrend's (1883, p. 77) book informs us that an average-size Linde machine required 18 hph in order to manufacture 500 kg of ice; that is a degree of efficiency of about 28%. Furthermore, exactly the same value can be computed from Schröter's (1890, p. 84) second investigation. One of his chief results was that the Linde machine produced 3.2 million calories of cold per hour if it was supplied with one horsepower. It follows from the fact that one horsepower equals 0.633 million calories per hour that the tested machine reached 28% of the theoretical optimum for the temperatures in question. Hence, in this case Linde appears in the 1880s to have come quite close to his original goals. The Linde-Augsburg machine almost reached a degree of efficiency of 30% and was nearly twice as efficient as the Carré design. This was surely a great achievement. However, it is hard to believe that Linde had already reached these goals with his first dimethyl ether machine, as Krug (1981) and Lohmann (1972) have suggested. Furthermore, J.C. Goosman (1925) must have been wrong in claiming that Linde reached a degree of efficiency of 50%.

The outcome of the two test series at the station effectively killed any interest from other firms in participating. The institute instead became a place for the Linde Co. to test novel designs—an asset for its development department (ABPTV, 175 [3]). The station had fulfilled its task of supplying potential customers with test data indicating the superiority of the Linde design. However, the tests still did not manage to remove all competition. Despite the results, several buyers still preferred other machines —a fact which the inventor-entrepreneur and businessman Linde was forced to accept. The original hope of the scientist-engineer Linde had been that it would be possible to guide the actors on the market by means of scientific adjudication. This indicated to him that ultimately economic problems could be conclusively solved by unimpeachable comparisons based on intersubjective data that everyone would accept. Linde referred to experiments concerning the characteristics of the Pictet liquid when he declared in 1887 that they "deal with an important technical-industrial question which can only be conclusively answered by scientific means" (ABPTV, 175 [-]). In anachronistic terms, we could say that Linde's hope had been that the refrigeration testing station would contribute to the *closure* of the controversy between him and Pictet (Engelhardt and Caplan 1987), and that the tests might even lead to the establishment of the Linde system as the ruling standard of mechanical refrigeration technology. Just as we have earlier seen Linde wish to make the ideals of science—accuracy, intersubjectivity, calculation—bear on technology, in this chapter we have seen him want it to influence economic matters. If you like, we could say that he tried to defend the *Leitbild* of "the scientific marketplace." Just as computer companies have formulated the *Leitbild* of "the paperfree office" in order to foster their own business (Marz and Dierkes 1992),

Linde strived for the scientification of the marketplace in order to defend his own position in the refrigeration business.

Of paradigmatic importance to this endeavor—like to the scientification of refrigeration technology and the academization of mechanical engineering education—was what Weber (1930, p. 24) has called the "exact and rational experiment." This experiment combines careful observation and an empirical approach with mathematical methods based on quantification of data and therefore is, in Weber's grand historical scheme, a distinctly Western phenomenon. For instance, the invention in China of the compass and book printing did not result from systematic investigations and were "technically highly primitive" (Weber 1920, Vol. I, p. 440 f.), and the sciences of India "though well developed in observation, lacked the method of experiment" (Weber 1930, p. 13). Only in the Occident did the formally rational experiment emerge, and it did so in the arts:

> With its mathematical basis, the natural science of the Occident is a combination of rational thinking and the technical "experiment," the latter being the characteristically modern element of all natural science disciplines. While rational thinking dates back to the period of ancient philosophy, the roots of the experiment is to be found in the "experimental" higher arts of the Renaissance. [...] Later, the economic and technical interests of the northern European trades helped scholars to carry the experiment over into natural science. The needs of mining were especially important in this process. (Weber 1920, Vol. I, p. 439; cf. Weber 1981, p. 368)

The experimental method, including the systematic variation of parameters, is an important part of the Western rationalization process (Münch 1981, p. 139).

Chapter 14 will discuss further how this scientific approach turns the world into an object that can be manipulated at will. More important to the present analysis is its tendency to reduce all factors to quantifiable and controllable data. In the Weberian view, this emphasis on calculation and predictability must be seen against the background that modern, experimental science and technology are so intimately tied to capitalism. Calculation is predominant in this economic system. Like the rational experiment, capital accounting—being indispensable to the capitalist firm—arose in the Renaissance, and "... capitalistic accounting presupposes rational technology, that is, one reduced to calculation to the largest possible degree ..." (Weber 1981, p. 277). Thus, the activities of the refrigeration testing station can be interpreted as an attempt to serve the capitalist firms on the market with readily calculable data.

Linde founded an experimental laboratory at the Munich Polytechnic in order that his students systematically learn how various machine characteristics could be measured; he built the refrigeration testing station for the purpose of teaching the public what ice-machine to buy. In both cases, the underlying wish was to reach indisputable conclusions that could not be contested by any rational person. This is the technocratic wish which has been analyzed, much in the Weberian tradition, by Herbert Marcuse in his famous book *One-Dimensional Man* (1964).

Since all customers did not choose his machine, Linde had to realize that fuel economy and other testable factors were not the only important ones. In a paper from 1893 he reluctantly noted that all systems have their benefits and drawbacks, and that "an attempt to challenge a final decision on the respective merits is well-nigh impossible" (Linde 1893, p. 1415). Linde admits that there will always be features the judgement of which depends on "differences of opinion," but he nevertheless goes on to maintain that there are indeed factors which can be unequivocally determined—"for instance, the question of efficiency" (*ibid.*). In other words, Linde was aware of customers' attention to things other than efficiency tests, but he remained convinced of the importance of calculable test data.

The 1893 paper had originally been presented at the Mechanical Engineering Section B of the World's Engineering Congress in Chicago. One of Linde's chief objectives was to suggest to this international audience the establishment of "standard testing rules" (Linde 1893, p. 1427). In the paper he listed the variables that ought to be measured, and described a typical test report. The paper and the subsequent discussion persuaded the American Society of Mechanical Engineers to appoint a committee for the determination of standard rules. Linde's ideas, and not only his machines, had begun to spread over the world.

11. Linde Refrigeration: Social Carriers, Translators, and Agency Networks

The events described in this part will below be briefly analyzed by means of the social carrier concept. I will argue that the success of the Linde machine system was, in large part, the result of organizational factors, not only technical and cognitive. Furthermore, some alternative interpretations will be discussed.

I have already discussed the six characteristics of a social carrier of any technology. In order to be able to implement the technology in question the carrier must be motivated, be organized properly, have enough power, be informed about the situation, have the resources to acquire or develop the technology, and have the skill to operate and maintain it. To become a social carrier, an agent has to fulfill every requirement, unless it is able to unite with another agent to meet the conditions. The Linde case is a clear example for the necessary creation of such a combined social carrier.

Figure 11.1 illustrates which conditions were met by various agents carrying the Linde system in the 1870s and 1880s. When our story began, the Halle Mineral Oil Society was the only motivated actor, actively pushing the development of a new ice-machine. At this time, Linde was not yet motivated to embark on so large an enterprise, but he was well informed about the technological and scientific spheres pertinent to refrigeration. He had the resources to do some research as a college professor, in addition to the social status to be taken seriously.

Deiglmayr was particularly motivated by his problematic Dreher brewery in Trieste to support an economically sound refrigeration system, and he thus initiated the second period. With this encouragement and given some economic and logistic support by Sedlmayr and Spaten, Linde and Schipper could undertake some initial development and design work. These actors were able to construct a couple of prototypes together with the Augsburg Machine Co. However, they still lacked an organization that could provide long-term investments and comprehensive information about possible demand. These requirements had to be met, if the design should be turned into marketable innovations. Hence, the syndicate was founded in 1876.

	1870-1871	1872-1875	1876-1878	1879-1893
Halle Mineral Oil Society	1			
Deiglmayr/Dreher		1	5d	
Carl Linde	3e, 4a, 5e	3e, 4a, 5fg	3e, 4a	
Sedlmayr/Spaten		3d, 5d	5d	
The Augsburg Machine Co.		5h	5h	5h
The Syndicate			1, 2, 3d, 4b	
Polytechnic Engineers		5gh	5fg, 6	
The Linde Co.				1, 2, 3bd, 4ab, 5bcefg, 6
Brewing companies			5d	5d

Key:

1. Motivation
2. Organization
3. Power
   a. Traditional
   b. Legal
   c. Charismatic
   d. Economic
   e. Social status
   f. Political
4. Information
   a. Technology/Science
   b. Economy
5. Resources
   a. Adaptation
   b. Diffusion
   c. Marketing
   d. Purchase
   e. Research
   f. Development
   g. Design
   h. Manufacturing
6. Skills

Figure 11.1. The social carriers of Linde refrigeration machinery, 1870-1893

The syndicate with Buz, Krauß, and Sedlmayr at the fore provided the project with information from both the machine and brewing industries, along with capital to ensure stability. The syndicate also hired skillful engineers, not only to develop new designs, but also to guarantee that its machines were properly installed and maintained. Neither Linde nor the syndicate was able to introduce the novel refrigeration technology alone, but together with the Augsburg Machine Co. they could act as a combined social carrier. The manufacturing resources of this machine firm were essential to the success of the project. Even though Figure 11.2 is from a later period, it gives us some idea of the intricacies of ice-machine compressor manufacturing; it was not a task that any backyard firm could undertake. Purchasing resources came from Dreher, Spaten, and other breweries.

Figure 11.2. The manufacture of a Linde refrigeration compressor at the Augsburg Machine Co. in 1908; courtesy *Historisches Archiv MAN AG*, Augsburg

We have now followed the process of social carriage from research and design to the manufacturing of a machine, whose central parts would become an archetype or *Vorbild* within its field. The stabilization of the third compressor model did not mean that development ceased, only that focus shifted to other parts of the machine system. When the number of customers simultaneously began to grow, more venture capital and a more united organization were needed. A company was formed in 1879 for this purpose, an act which brought the syndicate members, its engineers, and Linde into one organizational body. The Linde Co. was a highly motivated and well-informed organization with skilled employees, both in Wiesbaden and in various corners of Europe. Its economic power as a joint-stock company was greater than the syndicate's had been; with an esteemed, former professor as its director, it enjoyed considerable social status. The company also had resources for marketing (even though rather small amounts were spent on such activities), but it lacked production resources. While these were supplied by the Augsburg Machine Co. and other machine firms in other parts of the world, the primary purchasing resources came from the brewing industry. The largest brewing firms were particularly important as social carriers on the consumer side. In summary, the Linde refrigeration system was introduced by *Gesellschaft für Linde's Eismaschinen, Maschinenfabrik Augsburg*, and large-scale breweries, forming a combined social carrier.

Three concepts have been used in this study to analyze processes of technological change and adoption on an agency level. *Translators* and *concerned parties* have been employed in addition to *social carriers*, and it is now time that their relations be discussed.

The carrier concept is limited to the agents who actively and purposefully drive technology into a certain direction or transfer it from one area to another—and in this sense it includes what Ariane Berthoin Antal (1992) has called *champions* and *supporters*. In the literal sense of the word, social carriers carry a technology into existence or carry it into a new setting and therefore need information. Since virtually all carriage processes involve the transfer of such information between the spheres of technology and economy (and sometimes also between these spheres and the scientific one), a social carrier also has to be a translator. It was shown above how scientist-engineers like Zeuner, Clausius, Reuleaux, and Linde translated information between the areas of science and technology, and how Linde went further than any of the other three men by becoming an inventor-entrepreneur. He thereby also acted as a translator between the technological and the economic spheres, a function that he shared first with the syndicate and later on with the Linde Co. This company was an engineering firm whose success was dependent on its well-educated and well-informed personnel. Linde's success as a direct, unmediated translator between science and business was not that great, however. Despite his work with the refrigeration testing station, Linde never managed to persuade all agents in the marketplace that the superiority of the Linde machine system had been proven.

Figure 11.1 makes obvious that successful social carriage requires more than mere fulfillment of the translation function. Translation is usually a necessary condition, but never a sufficient one; all social carriers have to be translators, but a translator does not need to be a carrier. In a similar way, we can say that all social carriers are concerned parties, but a concerned party does not need to be a carrier. "Concerned party" is a more comprehensive term than "social carrier," and "social carrier" is wider than "translator." In the Linde story we have mostly met agents who were both carriers and concerned parties, two exceptions being Pictet and Grübs. They were hardly carriers of the Linde system, but they were certainly concerned parties and had much at stake in the struggle with the Linde Co. We will meet a number of carriers and other concerned parties in the brewing industry in the next part of this study.

Another way to analyze Linde's work from the mid-1870s onward is to map the agents he enrolled to make his project thrive. Even though Linde himself had initially been enrolled by Deiglmayr to build a ice-machine, Linde began enrolling a number of others as soon as he had become motivated enough to get onto the path of innovation. It was clear to Linde from the very outset that he could not carry out all tasks himself; he needed a machine firm to build prototypes and an assistant to make drawings and perform tests. Later on, it also became obvious that financiers, salesmen, and repairmen were required. In short, he needed an *agency network* to support him. Unlike Michel Callon's (1987) *actor network* and John Law's (1987) *heterogeneous network*, which also include non-social entities like electrons and winds, the agency network includes only purposefully acting individuals and groups. The agency network remains on the level of social entities whose acts are based on certain motives in line with Weber's definition of sociology as a science that tries to understand meaningful human behavior.

Figure 11.3 depicts some of the most important agents in the network around Linde, each agent being connected to a specific function in the overall project. This particular kind of agency network is similar to what

Andreas Knie (1991, p. 215) has called a "support network" (*Unterstützer-Netzwerk*)—that is, an agency network supporting Linde's work. Manufacture was taken care of by the Augsburg Machine Co., here symbolized by its Director Heinrich Buz, who welcomed the opportunity for his firm to move into a new, promising area of production. Georg Krauß was one of the central figures when it came to the raising of venture capital and was certainly driven by profit motives. Gabriel Sedlmayr expected the production process of his brewery to become more reliable with mechanical refrigeration, and therefore supported Linde in various ways, initially by allowing him to experiment on the Spaten premises and later by purchasing several ice-machine systems. In the latter function, he can be said to represent the whole brewing industry, Linde's largest group of customers. Engineers were involved in many parts of the project: Friedrich Schipper—responsible for much design and development work—was one of them, Rudolf Diesel—responsible for repair and maintenance in Paris—another one. However, as the project expanded, new engineers had to be employed; that is, reproduction had to be ensured. Moritz Schröter turned out to be instrumental in that process as the head of the mechanical engineering department at the Munich Technical College.

Of course, Figure 11.3 is incomplete since it only shows a few agents and tasks; it is also an idealization, since most agents served also other functions. The term "function" is here chosen only to describe the various tasks that certain agents actually fulfilled in the Linde project and should not be taken to imply a functionalist view of technological change in general; the figure is not meant to suggest that the Linde project was a self-regulating system behaving like an organism (Checkland 1981; Emery and Trist 1960).

The development of the Linde refrigeration system has been interpreted in terms of social agents. Behind the concepts of social carrier, translator, and agency network lies a number of structures, the existence of which has been more or less tacitly assumed. Among these were the political, educational, productive, and distributive structures which are to be found in Germany at the time, in addition to bodies of scientific theory, technological know-how, and engineering skills.

Georg Krauß
finance

Heinrich Buz
manufacture

Gabriel Sedlmayr
purchase

Carl Linde
coordination

Moritz Schröter
reproduction

Friedrich Schipper
design and develop-
ment

Rudolf Diesel
repair and maintenance

Figure 11.3. An agency network depicting some of the central individuals and their assigned tasks within the Linde project of the 1880s; courtesy *Deutsche Staatsbibliothek*, Berlin (Sedlmayr); *Deutsches Museum*, Munich (Buz, Diesel, Krauß, Linde, Schröter); and *Linde AG*, Höllriegelskreuth (Schipper)

Furthermore, agents generally do not participate only against the background of structures, but simultaneously alter them. Accordingly, Linde introduced machine laboratory education and contributed to the elaboration of Zeuner's technical thermodynamics; the Augsburg Machine Co. advanced compressor technology; the Linde Co. contributed in several ways to the technology of refrigeration; breweries altered their production methods. In the following part of the study, we will focus on the last of these processes.

III. The Rationalization of the Brewing Industry

No monograph in the history of technology is complete without an account of the user side. Trevor Pinch and Wiebe Bijker (1987) have convincingly shown in their unorthodox history of the bicycle that it often becomes impossible to understand why a technology has been shaped in a certain way, if only design and production are discussed.

We have already briefly encountered some representatives of various user groups—brewers, meat packers, and paraffin manufacturers, among them. Traditional home consumers do not enter into the history of refrigeration until shortly before the First World War (Cowan 1983); at the turn of the century roughly half of all refrigeration machines manufactured in Germany were sold to breweries (*Wirtschaftliche* ... 1908, p. 14). We have seen how Linde's research and development work was carried out in close cooperation with two breweries, and how three fourths of his machines were initially sold to the brewing industry. It thus seems justified to pay particular attention to the role of refrigeration technology in this business, especially since many brewers appear to have been particularly attracted by scientific solutions to their problems. Roger Thévenot (1978, p. 77) writes that:

> Most of the very first refrigerating machines, invented by the great pioneers around 1860-1870, were installed in breweries, and, quite interestingly, brewing refrigeration played a decisive role in the rational and scientific development of compression refrigeration ...

Why did some agents in the brewing industry turn first to natural ice and later to mechanical refrigeration. How did these transitions come about? Why were they more pronounced in Germany than in Britain and more among large breweries than among small ones? What consequences did the introduction of mechanical refrigeration have on the business as a whole? These questions will primarily be answered on a macro level, but familiar individuals, like Sedlmayr and Deiglmayr, will also reappear. In this connection we will return to the question why Linde's scientific approach received particular support from these agents.

The mechanization of brewing refrigeration will be discussed in Chapter 13 which is the core of Part III. This process will be linked to other developments in the brewing industry. In short, we shall see that mechanical refrigeration was commonly connected to large-scale, factory-organized breweries which applied scientifically-rooted instruments and methods in order to control their production processes and to standardize their products. The central thesis is that the mechanization of brewing refrigeration can only be understood if it is tied to the scientification and academization of this industry. This thesis may be seen as a corollary of the main thesis of this study, further elaborated in the Conclusion, that all of these processes may be seen as rationalization in den Weberian sense.

12. The History of the Brewing Industry: Craft and Factory

Max Weber's Anti-Evolutionism

The scholarly debate about the radical or gradual character of technological development was briefly reviewed in the first section of Chapter 3. The establishment of an archetype belonging to a new ideal type can be defined as a revolutionary change, whereas the emergence of a new type can be seen as an evolutionary step. Such changes are regarded as complementary in the present study.

A similar debate can be found where in economic history and organization theory focus is on how the organization of work and industry has developed, how production processes change, and what implications such changes have on technological choice. Controversies in these fields of scholarship concern, for instance, whether the introduction of automatic spinning machines made the textile industry instantly independent of skilled workers (Bolin-Hort 1990; Lazonick 1985), whether the introduction of computers into the manufacturing industry will enable workers to radically change their tasks (Kern and Schumann 1984), and whether or not manufacturing in the Japanese automobility industry is really radically different from traditional, Western, assembly-line production or not (Berggren 1990).

There is another issue in these disciplines, going back to Karl Marx' (1982) analysis of the history of production. It is well known that Marx vigorously attacked the capitalist industry of his time for having reduced workers to the level of machines. The mechanization of production had made industry increasingly independent of the workers' traditional skills, thus alienating the laborers from their own work. However, Marx' critique was not directed toward all kinds of production, but primarily to *factory (Fabrik)* production, where machines played an important role. He contrasted this with *craft (Hantwerk)* production, where the workers controlled their own activities and were acquainted with the whole production process. Between these systems of production Marx placed the *manufactory (Manufaktur)* system where work was centralized under one roof, but where machines were rare, and individual skills were still required. The issue that concerns us here is whether the passages from craft via manufacture to factory were gradual or radical processes.

In his *General Economic History* Weber brings up this topic in two ways. First, Weber (1981, p. 163) criticizes Marx' division between manufactory and factory for being "casuistical and of doubtful value." Weber does not see any reason for distinguishing between them, at least not from an economic point of view. Instead, he emphasizes that in our society both are capitalist establishments: "The crucial fact is that the entrepreneur operates with fixed capital, in which connection capital accounting is indispensable" (*ibid.*). The only difference is that a factory may embody more fixed capital—in the form of machines—than a manufactory. Following Weber, the present study will not make use of the term "manufactory."

Second, Weber (1981, p. 173) criticizes the evolutionary stage model implicit in Marx' work:

> ... the factory did not develop out of hand [i.e., craft] work or at the expense of the latter but to begin with alongside of and in addition to it. [...] As little as out of craft work did the factories develop out of the domestic [i.e., putting-out] system, rather they grew up alongside the latter. As between the domestic system and the factory the volume of fixed capital was decisive.

In other words, even if Weber distinguished between the craft, the putting-out *(Verlag)*, and the factory systems, he strongly argued that they do not make up an evolutionary sequence. Even though factories emerged later in history, they did not develop from craft establishments in a continuous manner, but represent a discontinuous leap. For Weber the history of industrial organization is a history of revolutions.

One reason for this anti-evolutionary stance is Weber's method. Since he treats industrial production systems as ideal types, he cannot regard the passage from one system to another as a gradual shift. Another reason is his economic focus. Even though Weber (1981, p. 116) defines craft work as "the case in which skilled labor is carried on to any extent in specialized form," it is obvious that it is the economic dimension that is conclusive. Factories may include skilled workers performing specialized tasks, but a factory is led by an entrepreneur who hires labor on a free market and makes large capital investments. Craft production is, in the first place, associated with the traditional guild system, whereas factory production is necessarily run along rational, capitalist lines.

In Weber's (1981, p. 115) terminology all systems mentioned in the previous paragraphs belong to industry *(Gewerbe)*, a concept which "embraces all those economic activities which are not to be viewed as agricultural, trading, or transportation operations." Thus craft work is also industrial work.

Most industrial sites are also workshops *(Werkstätten)*. In Weber's (1981, p. 162) schema, this category is opposed to home production and the putting-out system. The decisive distinction is that workshop production is physically removed from the home and economically separated from the household. Thus a large, modern factory is also a workshop.

I will use this Weberian approach when analyzing the development of the brewing industry in the nineteenth century. In particular, the introduction of mechanical refrigeration and the scientification of the brewing process will be seen to have been carried by the economically rationally behaving factory owners, not the traditionally-oriented craft or household brewers.

Brewing: A Technology Based on Temperature Control

Before we get into the historical development of the brewing industry, it is appropriate to describe briefly the basic principles of brewing, especially highlighting its reliance on fairly exact temperatures (*Encyclopaedia Britannica* 1969, Vol. 4, pp. 164-167; *Encyclopedia Americana* 1945, Vol. 4, pp. 475-485).

Since time immemorial the basic brewing ingredients have been malt, water, and yeast. From the sixteenth century until very recently, the use of other materials in beers sold in Bavaria has even been illegal—with the exception of hops (Bring 1935; Lintner 1906, pp. 233 f.). In other countries brewers have often applied substitutes like corn or rice, additives like sugar, and preservatives like ascorbic acid.

Before brewing can begin, grain—usually barley—has to be turned into malt. This malting process consists of three steps: steeping, germination, and drying. In the initial phase the grain is immersed in water for a couple of days. The seeds have now been activated, and germination starts as the water is removed. During a period lasting up to a fortnight, the grain has to be provided with moist air of roughly 15°C (60°F). Simply put, germination means the breaking down of starch and proteins with the aid of different enzymes, and this process is checked by drying or kilning the malt at temperatures above 40°C (100°F). Properly stored, this malt can be kept for years.

We have now come to the brewing process proper. It can be divided into the following parts: crushing, mashing, boiling, cooling, fermentation, and storing.

The purpose of crushing or grinding the malt is to separate the important germ from the insoluble husk. Undesirable material is simultaneously removed, and the remaining grist is moved to a masher. There are two main mashing techniques, infusion and decoction, both aiming at the decomposition of the starch into fermentable sugars like maltose. Infusion mashing is simply the mixing of the ground malt with water of about 65°C (150°F), a temperature at which some of the important enzymes are most viable. In order to activate other kinds of enzymes as well, the decoction procedure involves mashing at a number of temperatures. After mashing, the husks are filtered away. The remaining sugar solution, called wort, is boiled for a couple of hours, during which the enzyme action is halted, some proteins are made to coagulate, and hops are added. Hopping the wort has three objectives: to support the precipitation of proteins and to make the beer bitter as well as more durable. Both hops and proteins are removed after boiling.

The wort is now hot and sterile, but before yeast can be added and the alcohol fermentation starts, it has to be chilled to +7 or 15°C (45 or 60°F), depending on what sort of beer is desired. The lower temperature is required for bottom fermented beers of the Bavarian kind, whereas top fermentation takes place at the higher temperature, resulting in British style beers. In both cases, the temperature is allowed to increase some 5°C (10°F) during fermentation. Top fermentation takes place at the surface of the liquid, whereas in the Bavarian system the yeast slowly falls to the bottom of the wort. For our purpose, the most interesting thing to notice is the temperature difference between the processes. If making British beer often requires no refrigeration, this technology is almost indispensable for bottom fermentation. After eight days at 7-13°C (45-55°F) the second phase of bottom fermentation starts, in which the temperature has to be kept just above the freezing point of water. Hence, it is not surprising that, for many centuries, brewing was not allowed from late April till late September in Bavaria (Lintner 1906, p. 234).

Bavarian style beers need more than a colder environment during fermentation and storage; they are also stored much longer than British ones. A synonym for bottom-fermented Bavarian beer is lager, which is the German word for storage. Lagers require up to a couple of months at about 1°C (34°F), as opposed to less than a week at roughly 7°C (45°F) for British beers. The main purposes of storing, which takes place in huge casks, are maturing, carbonation, and clarification. At last, the beer can be distributed to customers in kegs, cans, or bottles.

The identification of Bavarian beers with bottom fermentation is mainly a historical one. Top fermented beers, such as *Weißbier*, are also brewed in Bavaria, and bottom fermentation has spread to most other countries, including Austria, France, and the United States—a diffusion process that started in the 1820s (Sedlmayr 1951, Ch. 17). Britain remains a stronghold of top fermented beers, and classes like ale, porter, and stout come under this heading.

While the principles of brewing have remained basically the same throughout the centuries, the economic and technological aspects of brewing have undergone considerable changes. In the following chapters focus will be on England, where a true brewing industry emerged in the late eighteenth century and where the thermometer was first employed, and on Germany, where the adoption of mechanical refrigeration was most rapid.

Pioneers: The British Porter Factories

For many centuries comparatively large breweries have coexisted with very small ones. We find brewers in the mid-1500s employing more than one dozen laborers and producing "many hundreds of barrels" annually (Mathias 1959, p. 5). Unlike these specialized factory owners, the average brewer was simultaneously a bar-owner or a baker with a small circle of customers; traditionally, many of them were women (Monckton 1966, p. 62). Weber (1981, p. 167) has observed that a third kind of breweries was also common: the communal town brewery where any citizen could brew his or her beer for home consumption. Technologically, the difference between these three breweries was quantitative rather than qualitative; their mode of production was always manual. Tools rather than machines were used: rakes, pokers, oars, axes, and shovels, for instance. Wood supplied the heat for boiling, and horses were sometimes used for pumping, milling, and distribution (Monckton 1966, p. 77).

The trend toward factory brewing began in London at the turn of the eighteenth century, where the number of thirsty customers constantly grew. Since beer is perishable, the brewer had to make sure that it was correctly handled during production, distribution, and storage. The brewing bar-owner or inn-keeper had a considerable advantage in this regard, because he could control his ale more closely and serve it more quickly. The large breweries, however, needed a more durable type of beer, and this they found in porter (Mathias 1959, pp. 12-27, 551 f.). Porter is extremely rich in hops, keeps much longer than ale, and does not require the best raw materials or fine temperature control. A less sensitive beer than ale was a prerequisite for brewing on a large scale at a time when no ice-machines and thermometers were used. The historian Peter Mathias (p. 13) summarizes that: "Porter, in brief, seems to have been the first beer technically suited for mass-production at contemporary standards of control ... "

Brewing first became a large-scale and capital-intensive industry in the porter business (Mathias 1959, Chs. II-III). In 1815 the largest London porter brewery turned out ten times more than the biggest ale brewer. However, factory production is not only a question of sheer size, but also concerns how much capital is applied and how production is organized. Instead of taking apprentices, the factory-owner hired unskilled laborers and such specialized craftsmen as coopers, and above them he placed a number of clerks and one or two chief brewers (female brewers had disappeared with the coming of capitalistically organized firms). Altogether, a large brewery could employ about one hundred people, all of whom the brewer had found on a free labor market—one of the chief elements of the modern, capitalist system in Weber's (1981) scheme. The owner had usually acquired his brewery either through inheritance or by raising a substantial amount of capital. He was often uninterested in the brewing processes as such, but chose to rely on salaried brewers. This state of affairs is illustrated by the London Tradesman of 1747:

> The Brewer in London ... seldom takes Apprentices; his work is carried on by Labourers who have acquired their Knowledge by Experience, and those who intend to set up Business have either been acquainted with it, by being Son or Relation to some Man in the Trade, or take their chance by depending on the Skill and Honesty of the Clerks and Servants. (in Mathias 1959, p. 23)

In other words, the master-apprentice relationship of the craft tradition had begun to give way to the capitalist-employee relationship of capitalist industry.

On the technical side, the porter industry pioneered the mechanization of brewing. The large firms introduced a semi-continuous process requiring substantial amounts of energy. Almost like the chemical industry of later days, brewing water was first pumped up to the mash-tuns at the top of the building, and after mashing, the wort was piped to boilers and coolers by means of gravity. Consequently, the fermentation vats were placed underneath the cooling devices. The storage area was often situated in the basement. This system simplified the moving of the product through the plant, and it was the first step toward continuous flow production. Manual work was reduced to a minimum in such large breweries. People primarily assumed controlling and regulating functions during the brewing process proper. Physical labor mostly appeared at other stages along the production chain, especially during mashing and distribution; many hands were also needed for loading and cleaning. But the overall trend was toward an increasing degree of mechanization.

Naturally, the application of machinery required a considerable energy supply. For a long time, the brewer received heat from wood or coal and mechanical energy from humans or horses. The steam engine did not enter the London brewing business until 1784, after the Boulton & Watt Co. had introduced their famous transmission system which enabled the steam engine to perform rotative work. Now, the horses walking in endless circles could be replaced directly by a steam engine. Once installed, it was soon given new tasks like mashing. Mathias (1959, p. 96) writes that: "By 1800, therefore, thanks to the engine, virtually all the operations of brewing had been mechanized." It should be noted that this statement is only valid for a handful of London breweries, the very largest ones which could afford investing in expensive steam engines. Hence, the steam engine (like the ice-machine later on) should not be regarded as a prerequisite, but as a reinforcement of the trend toward large-scale mass-production.

In small-scale craft the master brewer is able to oversee the whole production process by himself. Years of experience has taught him how to judge factors like temperature and fermentation time. In a factory brewery such personal knowledge is, of course, much more scarce. Out of one hundred employees in a typical late eighteenth-century porter brewery, only the chief brewers—usually one or two—possessed this broad, subjective experience. In order to ensure a high quality product, the owner had to rely on simple rules-of-thumb and intersubjective indicators, which were easy to interpret by all workers. Two instruments in particular fitted these purposes very well: the thermometer and the saccharometer. They began to spread in the second half of the eighteenth century.

The manner in which these two tools were adopted by factory brewers illustrates the diffusion of information from other spheres of human action. The thermometer had been used in the scientific sphere long before Michael Combrune, a British brewer, showed its usefulness to his peers in the mid-1700s. Unlike most brewers, who tried to keep their manufacturing secrets to themselves, Combrune chose to publish important aspects of his own knowledge (Monckton 1959, p. 161). His much-read *Essay on Brewing* (1758) marked the beginning of accurate temperature gauging in the brewing industry. The story of the saccharometer is similar. This device was developed from the hydrometer—an instrument that measures the density of a liquid. The hydrometer had been used much earlier, but it was not adapted to brewing until the 1770s, where its purpose was to measure the strength of beer and to control the proportions of various ingredients. By measuring the density of the wort before and after fermentation, a figure for the alcohol content can be computed; the stronger a beer, the more its density has fallen during fermentation (Otto 1865, p. 178). Higher sugar content means higher density, hence the name saccharometer. John Richardson made it popular among brewers and he also coined the term saccharometer in his book *The Philosophical Principles of the Science of Brewing* (1784).

The introduction of the thermometer and the saccharometer was clear a case of the scientification of brewing, but, as Mathias (1959, pp. 42, 72) has noted, it was also an attempt to increase the control of the production process. A further step along these lines was the later adoption of alarm thermometers that automatically signaled when the temperature became too high or too low. Such alarms were first used in the British porter industry, but after some time they spread to other countries. Their impact was probably even stronger where the more sensitive, bottom-fermented beers were made.

Several large-scale brewers in Germany and Austria-Hungary found these tools extremely helpful; Gabriel Sedlmayr and Anton Dreher were two of the most important ones. The pioneering character of their Spaten and Dreher breweries in bringing British brewing technology to the European Continent is in fact borne out by most commentators (Feuchtmayr 1921-1922, p. 25; Mansfeld 1913, pp. 10 f.; Struve 1893, pp. 51 ff.). They made a study trip around Britain in the 1830s, picking up techniques concerning malting, mashing, and machinery. They were deeply impressed by the application of the saccharometer, a discovery which Sedlmayr later described as seeing "the light of the rising sun" (in Lintner 1906, p. 236). Since Sigismund Hermbstädt (1826), one of their former teachers, had written about the saccharometer, they had presumably learned about this instrument earlier, but not until they saw it in practice did they understand its potential.[1] Back home, their British experience enabled them to continue transforming their breweries into mass-producing establishments. Of course, the thermometer, which had been introduced into Bavaria by the 1820s, also played a crucial role in this transition from craft to factory (Deuringer 1861; Sedlmayr 1880, p. 18; Struve 1893, pp. 85 f.).

However, the coming of factory brewing was not caused solely by technical factors. A prerequisite was the liberalization of trade and the removal of age-old privileges and restrictions. In the spirit of Adam Smith, and in fact against the will of the majority of brewers, the Bavarian government in 1799 and 1805 issued laws which brought the brewing business closer to free competition and took away considerable power from the guilds (Feuchtmayr 1921-1922, p. 39; Struve 1893, pp. 27 f.). Earlier, so-called "force laws" had regulated the relationships between farmer, maltster, brewer, and victualler, and various privileges had protected the brewers from undue competition (Hartl 1912, pp. 1-50). Weber (1981, p. 166) has also commented on this phenomenon, tying its emergence partly to technical factors:

> With the technical progress in the manufacture of beer, the addition of hops and the preparation of 'thick beer' by stronger brewing, the brewery right became specialized, different types falling to different individual patrician burghers.

---

1 I am indebted to Dr. Mikulas Teich for this interpretation.

This old system had been geared toward stability and security for the producers. However, the new laws, also supported by rural nobles who wanted the privileges of town brewers removed, did not fundamentally change this state of affairs. Their main thrust was to move control from the guilds to town and state authorities who checked the quality of the beers, set prices, and gave concessions to brew. Thus, a certain level of security was maintained, even though the guilds could no longer prevent a victualler from importing beer from the countryside or from other towns or states. The legal obstacles to large-scale production had now been removed, and the aggressive brewer could expand into new distant markets and mechanize as he saw fit. However, this was easier said than done; since the fixed price system made it impossible to compete with lower prices, it was hard for newcomers to get a foothold on the market.

The Sedlmayr family firm was among the first to grasp these opportunities. In 1818 it was the first Bavarian brewery to install a "British malt dryer," which used hot air instead of smoke, along with a steam engine (though the latter turned out unsuccessful) (Struve 1893, p. 46). This was the path of rationalization on which young Gabriel continued. His adoption of the saccharometer, his successful installation of a steam engine in 1846, and his later support of Linde fitted well into the pro-mechanical organizational culture at Spaten that had begun early in the century.

Spaten was not the only firm to invest in new machinery, although it was certainly at the cutting edge. The Zacherl brewery had tried to install a steam engine in 1840, but Sedlmayr's was the first one in Bavaria which was not merely used for pumping water (Lintner 1906, p. 237; Sedlmayr 1880, p. 19). Attempts to spread information about the steam engine to a German audience had been made even earlier, for instance by Kasperowski in his book "The Steam Brewery or the Art of Brewing Beer by Means of Steam" (1834). By the time the last price and concession regulations were removed in the 1860s, capital-intensive factory brewing had begun to establish itself in Bavaria (Holzner 1893, p. 7; Mansfeld 1913, p. 11). Theodor Vetter (1921, p. 12) summarizes the technical aspects of this change and mentions the introduction of British malt drying, of the thermometer and the saccharometer, of the steam engine, of hoisting and pumping machinery, and of ice-cooled storage cellars. However, this is only one side of the coin. Factors like expanding markets have to be taken into account in order to appreciate fully the drive toward mechanization.

The town-based breweries profited mostly from the growing demand, and Munich became the center of large-scale Bavarian brewing. In the 1860s the average Munich brewery produced almost fifty times more than the average Bavarian competitor (Struve 1893, pp. 70-77). However, a growing population and *per capita* consumption meant that the countryside brewers could grow as well (Tillmann 1972, p. 87; Vetter 1921, p. 20). Total production almost doubled during the two decades preceding 1865. Because of the growing popularity of Bavarian *Lager* and the coming of the railroad in the mid-century, the value of Bavarian beer exports simultaneously rose by more than four hundred percent, even though it was quantitatively still marginal (Struve 1893, pp. 65, 81). We recall from Chapter 1 that Munich had excellent railroad connections by 1860, a factor which has been especially emphasized by the economist Franz Feuchtmayr (1921-1922, pp. 34 f.).

Large-scale factory brewing thus relied on free labor, advanced technology, expanding markets, and substantial amounts of capital, factors which have all been regarded by Weber as paramount for modern, capitalist establishments. Many brewers turned their firms into joint-stock companies as a result of these developments, an arrangement which was particularly popular among export-oriented firms; typically, the first joint-stock company in Bavaria was the *Exportbrauerei* of Ludwigshafen am Rhein, which took this step in 1859 (Struve 1893, p. 94).[2] The capital enabled them to mechanize and control the chain of production more closely, but it also forced them to increase turnover and profits.

Since the brewing industry's enrollment of Linde dates from the early 1870s, it is particularly interesting to note that the brewing figures soared during these *Gründerjahre*, but also that expansion suddenly stopped in the middle of the decade. Bavarian beer production increased by almost two thirds in the period 1870-76, but during the following four years production fell by 4% (Struve 1893, 95, 129; Tillmann 1972, p. 108). During the boom several middle-range breweries chose to follow the large ones, investing heavily in new machinery, and when the heydays were over in

---

2 An interesting exception is the Spaten brewery which remained in the hands of the Sedlmayr family.

1876 they found themselves in big trouble.[3] The small brewers, often bar-owners, did comparatively better.[4] With less machinery, they had less interest to pay off; they had no middlemen; they did not rely exclusively on the proceeds of their beer production. The result was a bifurcation of the trade (Struve 1893, pp. 178 f.; Vetter 1921, p. 15). Even today, a number of small breweries remain in Bavaria.

Nevertheless, the 1880s became the decade of the big companies. The very largest breweries raised their share of total production more than five times between 1883 and 1889 (Feuchtmayr 1921-1922, Table IV). At the end of the decade joint-stock companies constituted only 1% of the total number of breweries in Bavaria, but its production made up more than 17% of the total. Exports more than trebled between 1879 and 1891 (Struve 1893, pp. 150, 154). The large firms profited the most from increased exports, whereas locally oriented craft brewers had to struggle with a weak domestic demand. *Per capita* beer consumption did not again reach the 1876 peak until 1897, and total Bavarian consumption did so in the late 1880s (Tillmann 1972, p. 87; Holzner 1893, p. 9).

Thus large-scale factory brewing had gained a firm foothold in Bavaria by 1890, even though the craft tradition still remained. I will show in the following chapter that the brewing factory became the locus for mechanical refrigeration.

---

3 A middle-range brewery was defined as one with a malt consumption of 0.1-1 million liters (2,800-28,000 bushels) a year (Hartl 1912, p. 72).

4 Between 1878 and 1881 the number of middle-range breweries decreased by 7%, whereas the number of large and small breweries actually continued to rise; computed from Feuchtmayr (1921-1922, Table III) and Tillmann (1972, p. 98).

13. The Mechanization of Brewing Refrigeration

Max Weber's Anti-Determinism

This chapter makes a critical assessment of some commentators' conclusions concerning the relationship between the spread of mechanical refrigeration and some structural changes of the brewing business, in addition to furnishing a descriptive account of various refrigeration apparatuses. On the one hand, it will favorably assess Franz Feuchtmayr's (1921-1922, p. 27) conclusion that the introduction of mechanical refrigeration fostered the trend toward economic concentration of this trade. On the other hand, it will critically discuss the validity of H.F. Tillmann's (1972, p. 41) statement, that "the small-scale craft breweries developed into large firms because of the introduction of artificial cooling." The latter statement smacks of technological determinism and may be questioned on both theoretical and empirical grounds. As I argued in Chapter 1, it cannot be assumed that economic changes are uniquely caused by technological factors. This objection to technological determinism follows Weber's (1981, p. 174) claim that:

> the modern factory was not in the first instance called into being by machines but rather there is a correlation between the two. [...] The specialization of work and labor discipline within the workshop ... formed a predisposing condition, even an impetus toward the increased application and improvement of machines.

Or, in Collins' (1986, p. 25) concise words: "In Weber's scheme, technology is essentially a dependent variable."

In fact, Weber directly addressed the relationship between technological and economic change in a speech at the sociology conference in Frankfurt in 1910. He there criticized contemporary engineers for viewing technology as the driving force of modern culture, as well as Marx' infamous words that the handmill gives you a feudal lord, whereas the steam plant gives you a capitalist. Weber (1924, p. 451) said: "Neither does ... a certain technology bring a certain economic system, nor is the opposite the case." In other words, Weber opposed technological and economic determinism alike—and went on to criticize all kinds of reductionist explanations in history:

> I would like to lodge a protest against ... the notion that something—be it technology or economy—can be the 'last' or 'final' or 'true' cause of anything. When we

> analyze a causal chain, we always find that it runs first from technical to economic and political things and then from political to religious and economic things. Nowhere do we find a point of rest. (p. 456)

Wolfgang Schluchter (1989, p. 386) observed in an analysis of this speech that Weber's irreductionist stance of course did not mean that he found technology of no great importance in modern society; quite the contrary.

Schluchter is not the only scholar to comment on Weber's attempts to avoid any one-side explanations in the social sciences and humanities. For instance, Gert Schmidt (1981, p. 174) has noted that when Weber (1924, pp. 8 ff.) discusses business and labor research, he emphasizes that the complex relationship between labor skills, technical solutions, and capital requirements must always be kept in mind; Pietro Rossi (1986, pp. 43 ff.) has discussed the methodological problems that may follow from so multidimensional an approach to the writing of history as Weber's; in a discussion about the mistakenly idealistic readings of Weber's *Protestant Ethic and the Rise of Capitalism* Günter Abramowski (1966, p. 21) has declared, that Weber was, "on principle, an opponent to all 'dogmatic' attempts to explain historical phenomenon in a one-sided way." Hence, a Weberian explanation of the emergence of the capitalist factory system would not refer only to Protestantism or only to the steam engine (cf. Cohen 1981, pp. LXII ff.)

In line with Weber's method of history this chapter argues that the coming of factory brewing was not an outcome of mechanization. Rather, it shows that the very largest breweries were, on the user side, the main social carriers of mechanical refrigeration, and that this technology allowed them to grow even bigger. During our period, a craft brewer could not even afford an ice-machine. Unlike Tillmann, I suggest that the mechanization of refrigeration was an integral part of the coming of factory brewing in Germany rather than the cause of this process.

The following account has, primarily, been based on contemporary brewing periodicals, as well as textbooks and other reference works—all of which were seriously concerned with the problems of temperature control.[1]

---

1 Periodicals include *Allgemeine Zeitschrift für Bierbrauerei und Malzfabrikation, Bayerischer Bierbrauer* [later: *Zeitschrift für das gesammte Brauwesen*], *Bierbrauer, Deutsche Brauindustrie*, and *Ice and Refrigeration*. Central books are Balling (1865), Fasbender (1881-1885), Habich (1869, 1883), Heiss (1875), Lintner (1877-1878), Michel (1880), Otto (1865), Possanner (1894), Thausing (1882, 1893), and Wagner (1870).

Because there is little modern literature on this topic, the discussion relies on secondary sources from the early part of the twentieth century.[2]

Non-Mechanical Cooling

We saw in the previous chapter that temperature control is required at several points throughout the brewing process. Large and fairly quick temperature reductions are needed after both mashing and wort boiling. Fermentation and storage require continuous temperature regulation, particularly in the case of bottom fermentation. When mechanical refrigeration was adopted by the lager breweries, it was initially applied to storage. The following account treats technologies which were used before mechanical refrigeration had entered the brewery. The various ways in which cool air, cold well or stream water, and natural ice were being applied to the brewing process will be discussed (Arnold and Penman 1933, pp. 91 f.; Balling 1865, pp. 159-180; Otto 1865, pp. 162-174; Wagner 1870, pp. 308-322). The division air—water—ice—machine can also be read as a chronological sequence to a certain extent, although it is not the case that one type of cooling was merely replaced by another. At the end of our period, in fact, all four methods were used for various purposes.

One of the oldest cooling contrivances, which remained in the breweries long after mechanical refrigeration had been introduced, was the surface cooler. Its German name, *Kühlschiff* (cooling ship), might give the reader a better idea of its appearance. It is a shallow vat, very wide and made of wood or iron. The hot mash or wort was piped onto the surface cooler, remaining there until it has reached roughly 10°C (50°F). Since the liquid gives off its heat to the surrounding air, it might be impossible to reach this temperature in the summer-time. The larger the surface area of the liquid, the faster the cooling took place. Wood was the common material at first, but in the 1820s iron came into use in Britain. Not unexpectedly, Gabriel Sedlmayr had an iron version installed at Spaten in 1843, and two years later he also published in the "Bavarian Journal of Arts and Trade"

---

2 Andorfer (1929), Attman (1961), Arnold and Penman (1933), Baron (1962), *Illustriertes Brauer-Lexikon* (1910), Feuchtmayr (1921-1922), Fraenkel (1897), Hartl (1912), Michel (1906-1907), Olson (1935), Rossi (1893-1894), Sedlmayr (1951), Stetefeld (1911), Struve (1893), Tillmann (1972), and Vetter (1921).

an article on the iron surface cooler (Sedlmayr 1951, pp. 221, 238). Iron is both easier to clean and a better heat conductor; using iron instead of wood reduced the cooling time by about one third (Balling 1865, p. 164). Other implements which were applied to speed up cooling were stirrers, fans, and ventilators. By keeping the liquid or air agitated, all three devices helped increase the evaporation, and thus the degree of cooling, of the mash or wort. The surface cooler was effective in the initial stage of the refrigeration process, but as the temperature was lowered the cooling-down became slower and the risk of infection increased. In order to avoid these problems, brewers in the nineteenth century began to use counterflow devices: warm mash or wort flowed through a pipe in one direction and cold water in another pipe in the opposite direction.

One ideal type of mash or wort cooler was the so-called Baudelot cooler, the first one being installed in a French brewery in the late 1850s (Sedlmayr 1951, p. 238). This refrigerator, one version of which can be seen in Figure 13.1 (K), consisted of several layers of horizontal pipes through which flows cold water, hot wort trickling down on the outside of the pipes. Heat was thus conducted to the air and water simultaneously. Of course, leaving the wort open to the atmosphere increased the risk of infection, but this apparatus was easier to clean than the counterflow pipes. The temperature also had to be regulated after the cool wort had been led to the fermentation vats in the basement. Since heat develops during fermentation, various means of keeping the temperature of the wort within correct limits were designed. Figure 13.1 shows that this was commonly done by immersing into the wort a system of tubes through which cold water was pumped. These so-called attemperators were available in a number of shapes and sizes.

Storing was probably the worst problem for the lager brewer. Recall that brewing had not been allowed during the summer months in Bavaria for centuries. In the absence of ice or artificial refrigeration, the brewer had been forced to fit up rock caves or dig deep cellars. Several of the most successful Bavarian brewers were traditionally found in the mountain regions, and in the United States some firms constructed gigantic underground cellars (Baron 1962, pp. 230 ff.; Struve 1893, pp. 55 f.)

The storage problems became less acute with the growing use of natural ice (Baron 1962, pp. 230-234; Otto 1865, pp. 171 f., 257-262; Rossi 1894, pp. 110, 167; Tillmann 1972, pp. 18-25). It was a significant step

Vollständige Kühlanlage mit Eiswasser.

(A. Neubecker, Offenbach a. M.)

Figure 13.1. A complete cooling system at the A. Neubecker brewery in Offenbach a.M. Here, no ice-machine is used, but ice-cool water is pumped through a system of pipes by means of a steam engine; from Possanner (1894, p. 159)

toward reducing the dependence on sudden weather fluctuations. Together with the thermometer and the saccharometer, natural ice was seen as the decisive difference between early and late nineteenth-century brewing (Struve 1893, p. 50). Ice and thermometers enabled brewers to control their product more closely and to prolong the brewing season, even though it certainly did not mean that they became independent of the climate, as we have heard brewers like Sedlmayr complain. But the Bavarian government was nevertheless able in 1850 to remove the old law forbidding summer brewing.

Natural ice brought radical novelties into the brewery in some instances, whereas in other cases it only meant a slight change in the daily brewing practice. The adoption of natural ice in the lager breweries was most revolutionary in regard to storage. It removed the need for rock caves or underground cellars and made the brewer less dependent on the topography. In Bavaria it simplified the expansion of Munich brewing at the expense of the mountain regions. Ice was harvested in or around the town or, during mild winters, transported there on rail from far away. Initially, the delivered ice was merely placed around the beer vats, creating a cool but moist and unhealthy atmosphere. The second step was to put the ice in a room below the beer. This solution made it easier to collect the melting water and reduce humidity, but the placement of the ice made the circulation of the air quite ineffective. It was left to Gabriel Sedlmayr to suggest in 1844 that the ice be placed above the storage room instead (*Gabriel* ... 1911, p. 6; Sedlmayr 1951, p. 230).[3] Because cold air is heavier than warm air, this arrangement allowed the air to circulate more or less naturally. An intermediary solution was to erect an ice-room alongside the storage area, whereby reasonably good circulation was maintained. By the 1870s the Sedlmayr solution had been accepted as the most efficient one (*Bierbrauer* 1875, Vol. 6 (n.s.), pp. 104 ff.). By the mid-sixties it had become the ruling standard of ice storage, at least among the larger breweries. Interestingly enough, it was also called "the most rational method" by a contemporary commentator (Balling 1865, p. 348).

Even though the Sedlmayr principal solution emerged in Germany, the most sophisticated ice-house designs came from the United States. Since the American natural ice business had developed into what Hans-Luidger

---

3 Tillmann (1972, p. 24) wrongly states that this event took place in 1842.

Dienel (1991) has regarded as a large "technological system," more methods for taking better care of the ice was designed in the United States than in Europe (Baron 1962, p. 233). Whereas American ice-machines owed much to Europe, the opposite was the case in ice-house construction. One American example was the Brainard system (*Bierbrauer* 1875, Vol. 6 (n.s.), pp. 104 ff.). Its significant feature was a zigzag-shaped metal ceiling between the storage cellar and the ice-room, the purpose of which was to draw off melting and condensing water and thus to secure a fairly dry atmosphere, the air circulating through the walls of the building.

Another completely new solution for using natural ice were the so-called swimmers, metal bodies being filled with ice and set to float at the surface of the fermenting wort. This method enabled reasonably exact temperature regulation, but only at the cost of much labor. The constant emptying and refilling of the swimmers were troublesome and involved the risk of unhealthy water or ice falling into the wort. Easier to handle were the above-mentioned attemperators through which the brewer now could pump ice-cold water instead of just well-water. If he already owned an attemperator this transition was simple. The same holds true for the counterflow and Baudelot coolers which now could be loaded with ice-water. A problem connected with the use of natural ice in these refrigerators was that the ice, coming from lakes and rivers, often contained foreign material which might clog the pipes (Tillmann 1972, p. 21).

Although few figures are available, it seems that ice demand increased constantly in the period 1840-1880, both in North America and in Europe. In Munich demand began to climb especially after 1858 (Sedlmayr 1951, p. 231). In 1846-1847 Spaten used 300 tons of ice, while selling 2.8 million liters (24,000 barrels) of beer, and in 1868-1869 the figures were 17,000 tons and 23 m.ls. (200,000 barrels), respectively.[4] In other words, between these years the firm's ice demand increased seven times faster than the amount of beer produced. F.J. Otto (1865, p. 171) concludes in a manual of chemical technology that "the best way of investing capital is to erect an ice-cellar and build up a large enough ice supply. Consequently, the use of ice ... expands more and more ..." The result was recurrent ice shortages which could only be overcome by purchasing expensive ice from far away.

---

4 These figures have been kindly supplied by Dr. Mikulas Teich.

After 1870, a brewery on the European Continent had a simple and fairly accurate rule-of-thumb concerning the need for ice: on average, the production of one pint of beer required one pint of ice (Fasbender 1881, pp. 443 f.; *Premier* ... 1908, Vol. 3, pp. 86 f.). In the early 1870s, Spaten needed roughly 25,000 tons of ice annually, whereas the smaller Philip Best brewery in the United States, where ice consumption was generally larger, used 60,000 tons of ice in 1880 alone (Baron 1962, p. 233 f.).

We learned in Chapter 8 that Munich natural ice prices averaged 1.5 guldens per ton during a normally cold year in the period surrounding 1870. Since one ton of beer represented an average retail price of 70 guldens, it follows that the expenses for cooling made up about 2% of the price in an ordinary year.[5] However, in the event of a mild winter ice costs could amount to as much as 10 guldens—that is, more than 10% of the beer retail price. Since beer prices had been regulated by the Bavarian authorities until 1868, the brewer had not been able to compensate himself after a mild winter by raising prices. This situation remained even after 1868—partly because of the public outrage that resulted when prices were raised; there were in the nineteenth century a number of "beer riots" in Bavaria.[6] Thus, it is not surprising that the brewer would want to control his outlays for refrigeration—especially since the price of barley and hops fluctuated almost as wildly as did natural ice (Jacobs and Richter 1935).

The Coming of Mechanical Refrigeration and Large-Scale Brewing

Natural ice was not only unreliable and expensive at times; it did moreover not allow beer to be produced economically year-round. Its use had made redundant the old Bavarian law forbidding brewing during the five summer months, but at most breweries production was still halted during a couple of months (Otto 1865, p. 172). Brewing during the hottest period only become conceivable after mechanical refrigeration had been adopted. How-

5 Struve (1893, pp. 100 f.); unfortunately, the wholesale price is not known.

6 Between 1872 and 1891 Munich summer beer prices fluctuated only between 0.24 and 0.28 marks/liter and winter prices between 0.20 and 0.24 (*Zeitschrift des koeniglich bayerischen statistischen Bureau* 1872, Vol. 4/1891, Vol. 23). For comparison: a worker at the Augsburg Machine Co. earned sixty-odd marks per month in the early 1870s (Kellenbenz 1981, p. 310).

ever, this does not mean that the purchase of an ice-machine immediately led to brewing year-round; in the case of Spaten this step was not taken until 1888 (Sedlmayr 1951, p. 131). In other words, it took eleven years for the firm to fully exploit the possibilities of the new technology. Furthermore, the acquisition of an ice-machine did not mean that the use of natural ice suddenly ceased; several firms were still using machines and natural ice alternatively in the early twentieth century (*Premier* ... 1908, Vol. 3, p. 83).

Small breweries continued to rely on natural ice well into the twentieth century, partly because ice-cellar design was improved in the face of competition from mechanical refrigeration (*Zeitschrift für Eis- und Kälte-Industrie* 1912-1913, Vol. 5, pp. 82 ff.). Most small firms continued to rely solely on natural ice well into the interwar period—small being defined as a brewery with a yearly production of less than 2 million liters (17,000 barrels) (Vetter 1921, p. 32). Rosenberg (1976, p. 203) has argued in connection with the struggle between sailing ships and steamers in the nineteenth century that we ought not view technical change as a one-way process: "That is, the 'old' technology continues to be improved after the introduction of the 'new,' thus postponing even further the time when the old technology is clearly outmoded." Similarly, Arne Kaijser (1986) has observed how the gas industry met the challenge from electricity around the turn of the century by supporting new innovations. Natural ice remained for many decades in the distribution chain and in small breweries, for example in railway cars and at retailers.

Initially, the structure and purpose of new technologies are often very similar to those of existing ones. The first automobiles looked like horse carriages without a horse. When Edison installed electricity in homes he consciously tried to bring its appearance close to that of the existing gas network. A similar conservatism prevailed when refrigeration was mechanized; the first machines were installed at breweries to produce ice, not immediately to cool the beer or air. A contemporary observer writes that:

> The first mode of applying artificial refrigeration to breweries which was most likely to suggest itself was to replace the natural product by one which could be manufactured as fast as required and when required, independently of climate or of season, and to furnish ice-cold water ... (Rossi 1894, Vol. 6, p. 168)

Natural ice was thus simply replaced by artificial ice, not by direct mechanical refrigeration. Since they had been more dependent on natural ice,

American brewers clung to ice-production longer than their European colleagues. On both continents several brewers began to sell ice along with beer as a way of keeping their ice-machines busy (Baron 1962, pp. 235 f.).

The wait-and-see attitude of most brewers was probably well justified. Workers were familiar with the handling of ice, whereas direct-acting refrigeration was a new and unfamiliar technology. An ice-machine failure would not bring immediate disaster, whereas the break-down of a directly-working refrigeration machine would. If a firm was foresighted enough to keep a fortnight's ice supply, then it stood a good chance of getting a defective machine started again before any beer was damaged. Nevertheless, the "fear that the equipment might fail" was wide-spread (Goosman 1925, Vol. 68, p. 478; cf. *Zeitschrift für die gesammte Kälte-Industrie* 1897, Vol. 4, p. 146). In many cases artificial ice did not even replace, rather only complemented natural ice. Several brewers who owned ice-machines felt that they could do well with natural ice in years with normal weather and use their machines only when the natural supply was insufficient or too expensive. Since the machines were costly to run, they were mainly seen as a kind of safety-net. Indeed a study from 1880 established that in the Vienna area there was enough natural ice in eight out of ten winters (in Fasbender 1881, pp. 446-53).

Artificial ice had several advantages compared to the natural product. It was more durable and easier to obtain in convenient sizes. Since it did not have to be stored for months before it was really needed, the brewer saved both ice and space. It was a general rule that he would use twice as much natural as artificial ice (Rossi 1894, Vol. 6, p. 168). If he distilled the water before turning it into ice, then the risk of infection was considerably lowered. However, ice (artificial as well as natural) had its drawbacks; it was bulky and wet; it could not afford exact temperature control; its moisture often caused mold when it was not combined with some kind of drying device. Moreover, as Linde pointed out in 1873 at the Brewers' Congress in Vienna, making ice in order to produce cold is quite an inefficient detour. The main alternatives were either to replace artificial ice with a circulating brine or to put the evaporator pipes directly in contact with the air or liquid to be cooled. There was also a hybrid system using both ice and brine, where the machine produced ice which in turn was used to cool down a circulating brine (Possanner 1894, p. 282). Brine and direct-evaporation could be applied anywhere within the brewery. In practice, the difference between them was minute, both applying a network of pipes, which, as in Figure 13.2, were usually installed close to the ceiling. Because moisture from the atmosphere condensed on the pipes, special drying apparatuses were not always required, but the ice had to be continuously removed by hand. The pipes could run through the whole building or be installed in separate rooms and combined with ventilators. Understandably enough, brewers were afraid that ammonia would escape and spoil their beer, and hence it took longer for the direct-evaporation system to take hold, and when it did catch on, it did so first in the United States (Rossi 1894, Vol. 7, pp. 15 f.; *Zeitschrift für die gesammte Kälte-Industrie* 1909, Vol. 16, p. 192).

Figure 13.2. Beer, ready for consumption, being poured into kegs at the *Löwenbrauerei* in Munich, ca 1890. Please note the refrigeration pipes in the ceiling; courtesy *Deutsches Museum*, Munich

Refrigeration was indispensable at three points of the brewing process: during wort cooling, fermentation, and storage. At each stage the late nineteenth-century brewer could choose to adopt one or more of the following principles: he could install a machine for brine or direct-expansion; he could use artificial or natural ice; he could pump cold well or stream water through his brewery; or he could rely solely on the elements. The passage from natural to artificial ice did not require substantial changes anywhere along the brewing process. The same holds true also for wort and fermentation cooling by means of water, ice, or machine. For instance, all three cooling principles could be used with the Baudelot contrivances and the attemperators. Thus, the step from one cooling source to another did not always imply a radical change for the brewer and his workers. Instead, there was often a high degree of continuity between the "old" and "new" technologies. This evolutionary character of refrigeration development was pronounced in all levels of the brewing process.

For reasons of convenience and economy, brewers usually wanted any novelty to be accommodated to existing structures where possible. This desire forced the manufacturers of refrigeration systems to be flexible. Although manufacturers were successful in closing and stabilizing the compressor design, other parts remained open—to a large extent as a result of consumer demand. The example of Linde is a case in point. The machine which the Dreher Co. bought in 1877 served the double purpose of cooling the air in the fermentation rooms and producing ice (Linde 1979, pp. 41 f.). Because of the limited space of its storage cellars, the *Dortmunder Actienbrauerei* in 1882 preferred a brine circulating system—the first system installed by the Linde Co. (pp. 55 f.). Like several subsequent breweries, the Dortmund brewery chose to combine the brine system with fresh water refrigeration and ice production. In this way it reached a higher degree of security and could take care of all three cooling steps. During the 1880s nearly half of the systems sold by the Linde Co. to breweries were designed to cool brine or fresh water. Roughly 30% were meant for ice production (LAG-W).

Various figures concerning the overall mechanization of brewing refrigeration in Germany, and German exports to the United States, show this process from a different perspective (*Wirtschaftliche* ... 1908). First of all, it must be repeated that in the second half of the nineteenth century the brewing industry was by far the largest purchaser of refrigeration equipment. The predominance of breweries was equally strong all over Europe and North America. Only toward the end of the century did the chemical industry in Germany and the meat packing and cold storage firms in the United States begin to make any significant inroads. The first period of upsurge—both concerning sales within Germany and transatlantic export—was 1883-1884. After that, figures decreased somewhat, but soon started to rise again. Domestic demand was particularly strong 1889-1890, when German machine firms installed roughly one hundred refrigeration machine systems at German breweries. Exports peaked in 1887, when about two dozen German machine systems were installed at American breweries. This situation differed substantially from that twenty years earlier, when one Hannover and one New York brewery had been first to purchase Carré machines (Baron 1962, p. 235; Hartl 1912, p. 61; cf. Braun 1983).

Behind these figures lay some peculiarities of the refrigeration business. We have seen that Gabriel Sedlmayr was shopping around for an ice-machine as early as in 1863, but that he abandoned the idea when the weather turned colder. This illustrates two important aspects of demand. First, the demand for refrigerating machines was very sporadic and haphazard, being directly connected with the weather situation. During the mild winters of 1862/63, 65/66, 69/70, and 72/73 the brewers repeatedly complained about the natural ice situation (*Bierbrauer* 1873, Vol. 4 (n.s.), pp. 46, 161; Fasbender 1881, pp. 447 ff.; Sedlmayr 1951, p. 146). Second, Sedlmayr's brewery was a large one, as were all the firms which initially invested in mechanical refrigeration. Similarly, a contemporary journal talks explicitly about "large" breweries as Carré's customers (*Bierbrauer* 1870, Vol. 1 (n.s.), pp. 30 f.).

During the 1880s the reliance of the refrigeration business on climate and the large breweries continued. The winter of 1883-1884 was disastrous (Linde 1979, p. 56). Typically, at least 20% of the breweries which ordered machines from the Linde Co. in the wake of this calamity were joint-stock companies.[7] Even though *Actienbrauereien* made up only 0.4% of all Bavarian breweries in 1884, they produced roughly 9% of all Bavarian beer (Feuchtmayr 1921-1922, Table IV). They were well equipped

7 I have arrived at this figure after checking the delivery lists of the Linde Co. in 1884 (LAG-W). The figure might be higher, since some firms might have chosen not to call themselves *Actienbrauereien*, even if they really were joint-stock companies.

with capital, and their number grew steadily. Franz Feuchtmayr (p. 27) argues that the concentration trend in the Bavarian brewing industry was heavily "promoted" (*fördert*) by the introduction of refrigerating machines, a conclusion similar to Robert Mansfeld's (1913, pp. 12, 50 f.). This statement is different from that of H.F. Tillmann (1972) which I critically quoted at the opening of this chapter. I suggest along with Feuchtmayr that the mechanization of brewery refrigeration was but one part of the trend toward factory brewing which had already started several decades earlier. Mechanical refrigeration fitted the large-scale, capital-intensive breweries quite well and enabled them to grow faster than their smaller competitors. Installing mechanical refrigeration was an extremely expensive affair, a point which may be illustrated by a Swedish case. When *Lyckholms Aktiebryggeri* bought a system in 1887, its value represented 1/5 of the total assets of the company and 1/2 of the value of one year's beer sales (Attman 1961, pp. 129, 207; *Lyckholms* ... 1933, p. 64). Furthermore, the purchase of a refrigeration machine system often involved the acquisition of one or two extra steam engines as well. The total energy consumption of a brewery typically doubled when refrigeration was mechanized (*Illustriertes* ... 1910). At Spaten three fourths of the steam engine power was used for refrigerating purposes in 1894.[8] Since most small brewers could not afford a steam engine, they could not consider buying an ice-machine until internal combustion engines became cheaper (*Zeitschrift für Eis- und Kälte-Industrie* 1913-1914, Vol. 6, p. 141). Since several middle-range breweries bought refrigeration systems although they could not really afford one, the result was serious economic trouble as the beer market receded.

In short, the coming of mechanical refrigeration did not cause "small-scale breweries [to] develop into large firms." Rather, it was facilitated by the already large brewing factories.

The Adoption of Machinery and the Capitalist Factory

It is beyond doubt that the large breweries were initially the social carriers of mechanical refrigeration on the customer side. However, there was a continuous debate during our period concerning just how large a firm

8 I owe this information to Dr. Miculas Teich.

should be in order to profit from an ice-machine. Gabriel Sedlmayr supported Linde's work at the same time as his former chief brewer Philipp Heiss (1975, pp. 225 f.) dismissed the value of mechanical refrigeration altogether in a textbook from the mid-1870s. In 1881 Franz Fasbender (1881, p. 453) recommended that "large" breweries purchase ice-machines, but on the same page quotes Theodor Langer's conclusion that such an investment would not be worthwhile for any brewer.

These contemporary disagreements over the value of mechanical refrigeration technology might have originated in an inherently faulty attempt at calculating what could not be quantified. In Chapter 10 I briefly showed the kind of data that were available to the potential customer. In brochures distributed by the machine companies, the brewer could find prices for various machine systems along with estimated running costs. These he could compare to the average natural ice prices, which he probably knew well. But how was he to judge the estimated running costs? A possible answer was to turn to companies which had already bought ice-machines. The problem, however, was that technology, environment, and staff differed between breweries. One brewer might already employ a fine technician, another one might have to hire new personnel. One brewery might be situated on the coast, another one in the mountains. Although these factors might have been quantifiable, at least in principle, others certainly were not. How could a brewer estimate the value of year-round production; the future natural ice and coal prices; the risk of workers striking against the new technology; the value of a dry and mold-free atmosphere; the value of a more even beer quality? The answer is: he could not, at least not with any large degree of exactness. And if he after all chose to invest in mechanical refrigeration, then he could not base his decision on a strict cost-benefit analysis. When ice-machines were still new devices, it was not possible to decide whether to invest in such a system only on the basis of economic calculations. Hence, it remains to explain why some brewers were more interested in investing in mechanical refrigeration than others.

It might be easier to address this problem, if we return once more to Weber's *General Economic History* and try to answer the question on a structural level. First, it could be suggested that the coming of mechanical refrigeration has to be seen as an integral part of the general mechanization process that capitalist industry has undergone since the eighteenth century.

Second, it may be implied that ice-machines were favored in that they enabled the brewer to better control and predict the brewing process.

We have seen that the social carriers of mechanical refrigeration were the large, factory-based breweries. In Weber's (1981, p. 169) ideal typical scheme of industry an extensive use of machines is seen as a significant characteristic of the capitalist factory:

> Where labor discipline within the shop is combined with technical specialization and co-ordination and the application of non-human sources of power, we are face to face with the modern factory.

A Weberian interpretation thus implies that ice-machines are by definition to be found in industries that work in a free market and whose production process is organized along the lines of the factory system. A capitalist factory is led by an entrepreneur who employs not only formally free labor but also apparatuses and machines—which in the nineteenth century were increasingly driven by steam engines. We saw in the beginning of this chapter that Weber made a direct connection between the specialization of work and the strivings toward labor-saving inventions. When work within the factory becomes more specialized, it also becomes easier to replace individual workers with machines:

> ... the mechanization of the production process through the steam engine liberated production from the organic limitations of human labor. Not altogether, it is true, for it goes without saying that labor was indispensable for the tending of machines. But the mechanizing process had always and everywhere been introduced to the definite end of releasing labor ... (Weber 1981, pp. 306 f.)

In this view, one driving force behind the introduction of mechanical refrigeration must have been the wish to reduce labor (cf. McGaw 1987 and Rosenberg 1976, Ch. 6). The handling of natural ice was a labor-intensive activity, thus indirectly fostering mechanization. Similarly, we have seen how this labor-saving tendency governed the work of machine firms, which made great efforts to design semi-automatic ice-machines, and breweries, which adopted devices like automatic alarm thermometers.

However, refrigeration machines may not only replace labor, it can also make the production process more reliable. The choice between natural ice and artificial refrigeration depended, for instance, on how highly the brewer valued the prospects of increasing the degree of control of the brewing process. Collins (1986, pp. 22 f.) discusses Weber's view of the modern, capitalist firm and writes that:

> What is distinctive about modern, large-scale, "rational" capitalism—in contrast to earlier, partial forms—is that it is methodical and predictable, reducing all areas of production and distribution as much as possible to a routine.

If we follow Weber's idea that increased control and prediction were central elements in the rationalization process (Beniger 1986, p. 15), then it may be suggested that mechanical refrigeration was preferred to natural ice because it enabled the brewer to better predict and control the brewing process, thus making it more reliable. Mechanical refrigeration was important not only in that it brought more exact temperature control, but maybe more so in that it made it possible to reduce the insecurity that plagued the use of natural ice. Even though coal prices fluctuated, natural ice prices were yet more unstable; even though workers were unreliable and might go on strike, the insecurity of the natural ice supply was still greater. For the factory brewer, the maximization of profits was certainly central, but so was the wish to be able to work in a predictable environment. We will see in the following chapter that such an environment included not only ice-machines and thermometers, but also science and personnel with an advanced education.

14. The Scientification of Brewing

From Brewhouse to School

Whereas the master brewer could control the brewing process on his own in the small craft brewery, several of his tasks had to be carried out by other persons and artifacts in the factory. Among these human and non-human *delegates* (Latour 1987a) were mechanics and ice-machines, helpers and thermometers, chemists and scientific devices, all of which should guarantee continual supervision. A commentator writes at the turn of the century that:

> The activity of the chemist promotes reliability in the production of beer... He relieves the master brewer from his controlling functions and thus makes it easier for him to produce durable beer. (in *Fest-Schrift* ... 1899, p. 22)

The chemist determined both the protein content of the barley and the amount of sulfuric acid in the hops, and supervised the fermentation process, making sure that pure yeast cultures were used. Chemical and biological analysis, like ice-machines, enabled breweries to control the various processes more efficiently.

Chemists were not the only scientifically educated people who found their way into the breweries. Brewery owners began increasingly to value college education highly, and during the nineteenth century a number of schools were founded to give a college-level education to aspiring brewers. Brewing training went from apprenticeship and internship in the brewery to formal education in schools—very much like mechanical engineering education went from the shop to school. An increasing emphasis on the chemical and biological principles of brewing came with this process of *academization*. This knowledge was transmitted in classrooms and laboratories with blackboards and instruments as central tools.

The forms of education and training cannot be separated from the nature of the production process. In order to appreciate fully the changes in brewing education, one must relate them both to developments of beer production and to scientific developments. The traditional way for a master to transmit knowledge to a new generation was to train apprentices. The guilds and civic authorities supervised this educational system by setting goals and arranging tests for journeyman and master. Official support for this traditional education was withdrawn in 1862 in Bavaria as a step toward liberalizing business practices. Rules had previously specified a two-year minimum before a brewer apprentice could become a journeyman and another five years to attain the status of master (Sedlmayr 1951, pp. 108 f.; Sedlmayr 1880, p. 17). Emphasis was on practical skills, and the teaching methods were verbal and personal.

Knowledge was acquired in this *professional culture* through personal experience and usually not transmitted by publicly available textbooks: "Until the 18th century, and even beyond, the skill of the master brewer was a well kept *secret*. Each brewer had his own particular methods to ensure success ..." (Wild, 1936, p. 9). There was little difference in principle between the training of brewers and of mechanics, for instance; both were geared toward the transmission of knowledge by experience and acquaintance (Göranzon 1983). We could speak of a *brewhouse* culture, somewhat analogous with Calvert's mechanical *shop* culture. In both cases, the opposite would be *school* culture.

The transition from the presuppositions, values, and routines of the brewhouse to those of the school was not always simultaneous with the coming of factory brewing. The academization of brewing education and the emergence of large-scale breweries in Germany were fairly close together in time, while in Britain they were separated by more than a century. Some London porter breweries had already reached a capital-intensive level of production in the eighteenth century without the founding of advanced schools. The relative insignificance of higher technical education in Britain, as opposed to Germany in particular, was a general phenomenon that was not limited to brewing or mechanical engineering. This "English disease" has been much discussed—often in a negative manner (Armytage 1976; Roderick and Stephens 1978). However, as the historian R.A. Buchanan (1982-1983) has stressed, British industry did well without advanced theoretical training. The British brewing industry is a case in point; it managed without school culture for more than a century. Hence, it cannot be maintained that academization was a prerequisite for the coming of factory brewing, but it is nevertheless safe to say that school culture simplified and speeded up the proliferation of industrial brewing in Germany and elsewhere (*Illustriertes* ... 1910, p. 100). Textbooks and well-organized courses were instrumental in the rapid dissemination of Bavarian brewing technology throughout Germany and in other countries like Denmark (*Zeitschrift für das gesamte Brauwesen* 1892, Vol. 15, p. 27).

The Academization of Brewing Training in Bavaria

The cradle of school culture brewing was in Bavaria, where it was generally connected with agricultural education (Struve 1893, 59 f., 102). The first German agricultural school, founded in 1804, included brewing classes. It was erected in Weihenstephan, a small town some ten miles north of Munich and to this day an agronomic center (Steuert 1905; *100 Jahre* ... 1965). Its first teacher, Max Schönleuter, arranged lectures on physical, chemical, and geological subjects in order to turn the practice of agriculture into a "comprehensive scientific system" (in Steuert 1905, p. 17). Despite this ambitious goal, brewing education in Weihenstephan appears to have been mainly practical, including on-site studies at the local brewery (Steuert 1905, pp. 187 ff.). Schönleuter's successor, Karl Wimmer, also tried to find a reasonable balance between the "auxiliary sciences" and practical training, but was forced to move the natural science classes to the Royal Academy of Science in Munich in the 1820s. Wimmer listed arithmetic, geometry, natural history, physics, mechanical engineering, chemistry, and physiology among these *Hilfswissenschaften* for agriculture. A proponent of school culture, he emphasized laboratory work and made sure the school bought a number of instruments, including hydrometers (saccharometers) and thermometers. The brewing laboratory included apparatus which enabled the students to experiment with various brewing processes on a small scale (p. 190).

The school was raised to the college (*Hochschule*) level after a thorough reorganization in 1852. A *Gymnasium* background, even including Latin, was now required. Although the majority of students had come from the homes of businessmen and teachers even before the reform, this measure effectively closed the school to several social groups—farmers, among them (Steuert 1905, pp. 73, 155, 165-169). The "cultivated bourgeoisie" (*Bildungsbürgertum*) came to dominate the college, at least numerically, just as it dominated several technical *Hochschulen*. Brewery owners from all over Germany sent their sons to Weihenstephan, where they attended professor Martin Knoblauch's lecture and laboratory classes and practiced at the "magnificent model brewery" nearby (p. 160). Success was short-lived, however (Raum 1965, pp. 18 f.). Cooperation problems between the brewery manager and the school board meant that brewing education at Weihenstephan was in trouble until 1865, when Karl Lintner, professor of chemistry and technology, arranged for a special brewing department to be founded. It soon gained wide acclaim: "Director Lintner and his invaluable colleague, Professor Dr. Holzner, brought the Weihenstephan brewing school to international fame within a decade ..." (Steuert 1905, p. 196). Lintner justly ascribed the success of the brewing college to its "absolutely scientific" (*vollkommen wissenschaftlich*) character and well-equipped establishments (*Bayerischer Bierbrauer* 1869, Vol. 4, pp. 126-129).

Figure 14.1 demonstrates that the broad curriculum ranged from mathematics and physics to brewing practice, with as much as one third of the time devoted to theoretical and experimental chemistry and to what we today would call biochemistry. Lintner's aim surely was to introduce such school culture ideals as theoretical and experimental classes into brewing education. This did not mean, however, that he failed to appreciate practical studies in an industrial setting. On the contrary, he emphasized the role of "practical experiments" (*praktische Übungen*) where the principles of the lecture hall and the laboratory could be applied on a large scale, but this in turn did not mean that he disliked vocational training. Lintner believed that "[p]ractical experiments should not replace vocational training ...," and wanted his students to have gone through two years of such *Praxis* in a real brewery before coming to Weihenstephan (in *Bayerischer Bierbrauer* 1877, Vol. 12, p. 95; cf. Lintner 1906, p. 238). If we paraphrased the sociologist Bruno Latour's (1984) study of Louis Pasteur (who, in Latour's interpretation, turned French society into a laboratory), then we could say that Lintner wanted to move the laboratory out of the school and turn the brewery into a laboratory.

Lintner's one-year brewing course at Weihenstephan attracted around thirty students per year, including a considerable number of foreigners. Every sixth pupil came from outside the German-speaking world during the period 1865-1879, whereas only 21% came from Bavaria and 63% from the rest of Germany or Austria-Hungary (Raum 1965, p. 25). The foreigners became very important transmitters of advanced brewing knowledge in general and of Bavarian brewing technology in particular. At a time when people with formal schooling were scarce, the Weihenstephan college served an obvious need, and it soon became a model institute for other schools (Holzner 1893, p. 4). Well over 80% of its students could find jobs in the brewing industry.[1] Its establishment of various laboratories and its emphasis on theoretical studies had not been totally accepted, however. For example, an official adviser to the Bavarian administration disliked the teachers' "incessant phrases about the advancement of science." He found the direction of the school overly ambitious and asserted that "at the end [of the course] all theoretical knowledge ... has declined to the level of simple statements that the students mechanically repeat by heart" (in Raum 1965, p. 23). Like Karl-Heinz Manegold (1970a) and Kees Gispen (1990) have observed for mechanical engineering education, not everyone embraced all the elements of brewing school culture.

Subject	%
Chemical laboratory work	19
Chemistry, incl. organic and fermentation chemistry	13
Mathematics	9
Engineering	9
Business administration	9
Cultivation of plants, incl. barley, wheat, and hops	6
Technical drawing	6
Physics, incl. statics, hydrodynamics, heat theory	5
Economics	5
Practical training in the brewery	5
Botany, incl. plant physiology, barely and yeast studies	5
Mechanics	3
Fermentation experimentation, incl. quantitative analysis	3
Microscopy	3
Total	100

In addition: review session, preceptorials, and study trips

Figure 14.1. The curriculum at the brewing department of the Agricultural Central School in Weihenstephan, outside Munich; compiled from *Bayerischer Bierbrauer* (1869, Vol. 4, 1877, Vol. 12) and Raum (1965)

1 *Bayerischer Bierbrauer* (1877, Vol. 12, pp. 92-96); the statistics showing the vocation of the students after their exams are ambiguous, since 19% come under the heading "Unknown;" but it seems safe to guess that around 90% of all graduates went to work in the brewing industry.

Weihenstephan was not the only place in Bavaria where brewers were educated. In the 1820s a certain professor Hermann gave the first lectures on brewing in Munich (Renatus 1982, p. 84; Struve 1893, p. 60). Linde's later supporter, Gabriel Sedlmayr (1880, p. 19) claimed that his own father had persuaded Hermann to begin these lectures. Whether this story is true or not, his mention of the role played by his father shows how highly Sedlmayr, Junior, valued "theoretical brewing lectures" (*ibid.*). His devotion to a well-balanced education was strong. The younger Sedlmayr later cooperated with the Munich Polytechnic as the owner of Spaten by letting a total of more than three hundred students undergo internships at his brewery (Lintner 1906, p. 235; Sedlmayr 1951, pp. 174 f.). He developed close ties with professor Georg Cajetan von Kaiser who lectured at the Polytechnic from the mid-1830s until his death in 1871 (Renatus 1982, pp. 85 f.).

Kaiser had come to Munich in 1834 and soon became a central figure among those individuals who were active in the industrialization of Bavarian production. He immediately took over the editorship of the "Bavarian Journal of Arts and Trade," the journal that Linde later edited; in 1837 Kaiser became Secretary of the Bavarian Polytechnic Society, which Linde later joined (Vogel 1872, p. 16). He retained both posts until 1868. Like his juniors, Sedlmayr and Linde, Kaiser had strong faith in the future of science in the productive realm. His biographer, August Vogel (1872, p. 18), writes that

> ... in his writings and lectures he managed to pave the way for a thoroughly scientific treatment [*durchaus wissenschaftliche Behandlung*] of the national Bavarian technology [of brewing], which had previously mainly been pursued empirically [*empirisch*].

Kaiser had an excellent position from which he could promote an academic and scientific approach to brewing, although this was not always an easy task. He often experienced hard opposition from what his biographer calls "practitioners" with "deep-rooted preconceptions" (*ibid.*), and responded by emphasizing that because his courses were given at a polytechnic, they aimed at the education of brewers—not of chemists (*ibid.*; Wild 1930, p. 12). He believed that an advanced scientific base could well be combined with technical and economic ability.

It is easy to analyze what the academization of brewing meant for Kaiser, because lecture notes made by one of his pupils in 1845 were published in 1930 (Wild 1930). This pupil was August Deiglmayr, the person who would later suggest that Linde develop his scientifically founded ice-machine! The editor of these lectures, Josef Wild, had found the notes among the papers of his father, who had once been Deiglmayr's classmate. It is clear from the notes that Kaiser did not want to burden his students with complicated formulae or highly abstract theories. Let us take his account of the alcoholic fermentation process as an example (in Wild 1930, pp. 85-93). Kaiser first explains what steps have to be taken in order that fermentation take its proper course. The temperature has to be controlled, and sugar and yeast have to be added to the wort. Kaiser describes by means of a table how the amount of yeast varies with the temperature. Knowledge is transmitted by rules which are easy to follow. He then goes on to give a quite superficial account of the nature of fermentation: under the liberation of heat, sugar is transformed into alcohol and carbonic acid as a result of the sugar combining with the oxygen of the yeast; the more sugar has been added, the quicker the fermentation takes place and the higher becomes the alcohol content; simultaneously, ether is somehow produced and the wort becomes blurred and agitated. Like the famous chemist Justus von Liebig, Kaiser believed that fermentation was a purely chemical process that did not involve living organisms.

Kaiser realized that his students were not future researchers. His lectures were grounded in the scientific knowledge of the time, but they were geared toward the everyday needs of a brewer. Not unlike Zeuner, Kaiser acted as a translator between science and technology. Deiglmayr's belief in the power of scientification presumably owed a lot to Kaiser's influence, just as Linde's method was heavily dependent on Zeuner's program.

Like Lintner, Kaiser attracted students from far away—13% came from outside Germany and Austria (Sedlmayr 1951, p. 174). There is in fact data concerning the education in Munich of one such student. A Swede, Alfred Sandwall (1935, pp. 307 ff.), spent parts of 1858-1859 in Munich, attending Kaiser's lectures at the Polytechnic and practicing at two breweries, one of them being Spaten. His studies ended with a formal examination in the town hall. Among the five examiners were, in addition to Kaiser, such prominent men as the brewery owner Josef Sedlmayr and, as chairman, a town councilor. Brewing was a serious and partly official concern in Munich.

A brewing school was set up in 1869 in another Bavarian town, Augsburg, in addition to the educational institutes in Weihenstephan and Munich (*Fest-Schrift* ... 1899). Its founder, Karl Michel, a former Weihenstephan student, wanted to give courses for both beginners and experienced brewers. In line with what above was called brewing school culture, Michel stressed experimentation. The laboratories of the brewing school were similar to those of any chemistry department (p. 16).

In the 1870s and 1880s brewing school culture also spread outside Bavaria. Max Delbrück founded an experimental and educational brewing institute in Berlin in 1883, and Americans established a "practical brewing school" in New York in 1876 followed in the next decade by three similar ones in the United States (Arnold and Penman 1933, p. 124; *Brauindustrie* ... 1932, p. 41). Toward the end of the nineteenth century the journeyman-master system had lost its importance for the large and medium-size breweries. Prospects were not good for young men who wanted only a practical education. Without a theoretical background he most likely would have ended up in a dead end. For the career-minded person of sufficient means, attending a brewing school had become a necessary step in acquiring professional status (Struve 1893, p. 267). At the turn of the century an observer commented that

> ... the present standpoint of the brewing industry is that it is very reluctant to give any advanced job to men who are only empirically educated [*empirisch gebildet*]. (*Fest-Schrift* ... 1899, p. 22)

By then, brewing education had begun to specialize.[2] There were courses for chief brewers, brewing technicians, and even brewing chemists in Germany (*ibid.*, pp. 21 f.; Struve 1893, p. 110).

The Coming of Chemistry and Biology

Science had found an undisputed position in a number of breweries by the end of the century. The process of the scientification of brewing had begun much earlier, however. In this section it will be shown how the sciences that we today call chemistry, biology, and biochemistry were continuously

2 For a discussion of the question of intellectual specialization in general and of specialization in the natural sciences in the nineteenth century in particular, see Liedman (1980, Ch. IV).

applied to brewing problems. Focus will be on theories and methods that were relevant to malting, alcohol fermentation, and analysis (Coleman 1971; *DHS* 1981; Partington 1964). We shall also see that scientification primarily concerned the large, industrially-organized breweries—in addition to state authorities.

In the eighteenth century Combrune and Richardson had already transplanted the thermometer and hydrometer from the scientific to the productive realm. Both men had regarded the introduction of these instruments as part of a more ambitious scientification program. Combrune (1758, p. xiii) had claimed that "... beer brewed upon clear and evident chemical principles, is neither naturally or accidentally subject to cloudiness, & c. nor to any disorder whatever." He believed that chemistry was the key to successful brewing, and showed a considerable familiarity with this science. Richardson had published a book in 1798 dealing not only with chemistry but also including sections on gravity, on the expansion and contraction of matter, and on evaporation. Richardson's (1798, p. 146) ambition had been to present "a new system ... supported by reason," even though he had known that it would give him "a host of enemies to encounter." These statements are important because they show, first, that a proponent of the scientification of brewing in the eighteenth century would invoke the power of reason and, second, that his project would not be readily accepted by everyone. Both men had been quite hard on those practically minded, "ignorant and illiterate" (Combrune 1758, p. xiv) brewers who were "strongly prejudiced against having recourse to books" (Richardson 1798, p. 146). It is difficult to judge just how widespread the effects of the scientification propaganda were in Britain. Before the mid-nineteenth century the contribution of science apparently was in analysis and control of existing practice and products rather than change and development (Mansfeld 1913, p. 8; Mathias 1959, p. 65). For instance, the thermometer and saccharometer were employed to analyze the various properties of a brew, not to suggest how they could be altered. While these scientific instruments only provided means to control the brewing products, a more elaborate kind of science was needed if the malting and brewing processes were to be thoroughly understood and modifications be recommended. The historian E.M. Sigsworth (1964-1965) has claimed that British practice was hardly affected at all by science before the turn of the twentieth century. His conclusion is reasonable when limited to the application of new theories, but it underestimates the role of chemical and other kinds of analysis which undoubtedly increased production reliability.

Around 1800 the focus moved across the Channel (Partington 1964, pp. 261 f., 307). The last Brit of significance in the following story was W. Irvine, who found in 1785 that some substance in the malt is active during the transformation of starch into sugar. Some twenty years later the Swiss pioneer of plant chemistry, Théodore de Saussure, suggested that this substance, which speeded up the malting process, was gluten—a protein in the grain. However, in 1833 his theory was attacked by two Frenchmen, J.F. Persoz and Anselme Payen, who isolated and named this substance "diastase." Today it belongs to what we call enzymes, the role of which is to activate the process of decomposing the starch. Persoz and Payen called diastase a "ferment," implying that its action was similar to that of yeast. They included malting under the very broad concept of fermentation, which at the time encompassed a large number of transformation processes, one of them being alcohol fermentation (*DHS* 1981, p. 148; Partington 1964, pp. 263, 301-309).

Brewers had known for a long time that the conversion of sugar into alcohol was speeded up in the presence of yeast. Toward the end of the eighteenth century, scientists began to debate about the nature of the process, whether it was purely chemical or involved the activity of living organisms. Most scientists around 1800 followed A.-L. Lavoisier and treated fermentation only in chemical terms. J.J. Berzelius introduced the term "catalytic force" in order to cover the activity of both yeast and diastase, and Justus von Liebig interpreted fermentation as a special case of oxidation, whereby oxygen moved from sugar to gluten. However, in the same decade a competing view was presented by microscopists who claimed that yeast was a living substance, a micro-organism. The problem developed into a famous conflict between Liebig and Louis Pasteur, the latter becoming the strongest advocate of the micro-organism theory. Pasteur's growing fame and experimental ability was largely responsible for temporarily closing the controversy in the 1870s (Latour 1984; cf. Engelhardt and Caplan 1987). It had become generally accepted by then that yeast consists of living cells, but shortly after the end of our period it was discovered that fermentation can take place without the presence of yeast cells. In 1897 E. Buchner managed to isolate the active ingredient from the yeast and support fermentation with only this enzyme present (*DHS* 1981, pp. 126 f.).

Several of these developments in the theory of malting and fermentation occurred in close contact with the productive sphere (Bernal 1965, p. 647). Payen had begun his career as director of a sugar factory, where he dealt with questions concerning the behavior of starch and sugars (Partington 1964, p. 429). Pasteur's interest in fermentation had been aroused as a young professor in Lille by problems in a local distillery, and he later wrote two books addressing the biochemical aspects of both wine and beer making (*ibid.*, pp. 749 f.; Pasteur 1876) Such connections between science and brewing are even easier to discern when it comes to chemical and biological analysis.

It is quite natural that a brewer carries out some kind of quality control at various points during the production process. In older times he or she relied mainly on the physical senses for checking the composition and temperature of wort and beer. This method was usually sufficient for a small-scale brewery, where the brewer and owner were the same person. The structural changes enforced by factory production created a need for quantitative and general methods, which could reduce the risk of making beer of uneven quality. There were also fiscal and political interests behind the development of better analytic techniques, in addition to such commercial needs. For tax reasons, governments often wanted to know how much raw materials each brewery used. In order to protect the public from foul products, they also wanted to check the actual contents of various beers (Michel 1907, Vol. 2, p. 191; Struve 1893, p. 47).

Late in the eighteenth century the most common variable to be analyzed —by means of an instrument called the beer balance (*Bierwaage*)—was the specific weight, or density, of wort and beer (Kaiser 1907; Lintner 1906; Michel 1906-1907; Planitz 1879; Struve 1893). Other things being equal, a lower density implies a larger alcohol content. Of course, this property interested the authorities, and when the Bavarian government found out that the beer balance was rather inaccurate, it commissioned the Munich Scientific Society to work out a more reliable method (Struve 1893, p. 48).

The more elaborate hallymetric beer test consequently appeared in the 1830s. It was designed by J.N. von Fuchs, a professor at the Munich Society, and was based on the solubility of salts in water; the hallymeter is a salt solution gauge. Fuchs introduced the hallymetric test in 1835, according to Heinrich Lüers (1951, pp. 7 f.) in direct response to the needs of the government. It enabled the analyst to determine the alcohol and carbon dioxide content of a beer and to decide how much malt and hops had been used when making it—important information for the taxation authorities (Michel 1906, Vol. 1, pp. 80-94). Fuchs's method caught on quite rapidly among government authorities and firms which could afford the expensive apparatus required (Michel 1906, Vol. 1, p. 92, 1907, Vol. 2, p. 16). Fuchs was in fact aware that scientification was an adventure primarily for the well-to-do, but he did not doubt that "science is the lodestar of practice [*Leitstern der Praktik*]" (in Michel 1907, Vol. 2, p. 5).

Several other methods of analysis were developed during the following decades. The most widely hailed were Steinheil's optic and Karl Balling's saccharometric tests. While the former was limited to the settling of the alcohol content, the latter could also be used for determining wort strength (Michel 1906, Vol. 1, p. 134, 1907, Vol. 2, p. 74; Balling 1843, 1855). Simultaneously, the number of German books and journals on the chemistry of brewing began to increase. These publications described methods of analyzing, for example, the composition of sugars, proteins, and ash, and they reproduced pictures helping to distinguish between various bacteria which are active during the fermentation process (Planitz 1879, p. 53; Lintner 1877). Laboratories were founded in the largest breweries, where analysis and other chemical investigations took place; compare Figure 14.2. After mid-century the so-called zymotechnician appeared, a scientist-engineer educated to analyze the behavior of enzymes. One of the Munich pioneers of this profession was Hans von der Planitz (Jörgensen 1909; Morgan 1980). In the 1870s he claimed that enzymology had left its purely empirical stage and reached the final "rational fusion of theory with practice" (Planitz 1879, p. 49).

The Institutionalization of Brewing Science

Planitz held a position at the Munich Scientific Brewing Station and was one of the central proponents of the scientification of brewing. This *Wissenschaftliche Station für Brauerei* was founded in 1876 on a proposal by Carl Lintner (Kieninger 1976; Lüers 1951). A decade after he had reorganized the brewing school at Weihenstephan and founded the journal "The

Figure 14.2. The "laboratory" at the *Löwenbrauerei* in Munich. Here, various kinds of chemical and biochemical analyses and other investigations were carried out under the direction of college-trained chemists and so-called zymotechnicians; courtesy *IHK-Wirtschaftsarchiv für München und Oberbayern*, Munich

Bavarian Beer-Brewer" (*Der Bayerische Bierbrauer*), Lintner thought it was also time to institutionalize brewing research. He raised the topic in a speech at the Third German Brewing Conference and quickly gained support from the leading brewers of the country. A couple of months later fifty-five of them met to constitute the station and to appoint a committee responsible for its erection. Two of the committee's seven members in fact belonged to the Sedlmayr family: Anton from the Spaten and Gabriel Junior from the *Franziskanerkeller* breweries (Lüers 1951, pp. 11 f.). Our old friend Gabriel, Linde's supporter, had been active in an earlier planning phase.

Work at the station was supposed to proceed along three lines. First, research would broaden "the scientific foundation [*wissenschaftliche Grundlagen*] of brewing" (Lintner 1906, p. 238 f.). Second, raw materials, instruments, and products would be examined and tested. Third, foul beer produced at any of the patron breweries would be analyzed. The guidelines thus contained a tension between general and particular interests (Lüers 1951, p. 45). Of course, each individual brewer wanted the station to address the practical problems concerning his brewery, but the station management was independent enough to publish results of common interest.

Even though Lintner remained a teacher at the Weihenstephan school, he allowed his journal to become the official organ of the station in 1878. It received a new name, "Journal for the Complete Brewing Trade" (*Zeitschrift für das gesamte Brauwesen*), and Louis Aubry, the director of the station, became co-editor. Each issue included a section with the latest news from the station; topics like the effect of the temperature on malting and lactic acid on mashing were addressed. The station quickly became popular, especially among the large and medium sized breweries who could afford to become members; the yearly fee was 100 marks per brewery, and each special test was extra. In the late 1880s more than two hundred firms helped to finance the station, and over one thousand assignments were carried out yearly (Lürs 1951, p. 22). At this time, a sister institute was born in Copenhagen: The Carlsberg Laboratory. Its aim was

> to test the doctrines already furnished by science and by continued studies to develop them into as fully [a] scientific basis as possible for the operations of malting, brewing and fermentation. (Holter and Möller 1976, p. 16)

Behind this formulation lay J.C. Jacobsen, the owner of the *Gamle Carlsberg* brewery and an old friend of both Gabriel Sedlmayr and Anton Dreher. Jacobsen introduced industrial and scientific brewing methods into Denmark, as his friends had done in Germany and Austria. They all belonged to the same pro-scientific school culture.

As a boy Jacobsen had attended lectures by the famous physicist, H.C. ˆÖrsted, and in the mid-1840s he had spent some time in Munich studying under Kaiser and learning the latest brewing techniques at Spaten. Interestingly enough, we know that Jacobsen heard Linde's Vienna speech of 1873 and was quite impressed. Convinced of the superiority of Linde's scientific approach, Jacobsen became one of the first brewers to order a refrigeration system from him five years later (Fraenkel 1897, pp. 273 ff.).

Published as *Meddeleiser fra Carlsberg Laboratoriet*, the early work of the Carlsberg Laboratory was particularly famous in the area of yeast cultivation (Olsen 1935, p. 186; Wettstein 1983). Under the direction of Emil Christian Hansen, and guided by Pasteur's theories the physiology department managed to isolate yeast cells of a certain kind and from them produce pure cultures. These cultures were practically applied in 1883, thus heralding for the industry a solution to one of its largest problems: bad yeast causing foul fermentation. The historians Arnold and Penman very aptly write that "Brewery fermentation was thereby reduced to an exact manipulation, subject to certain laws and controllable by the operative brewer." Just like thermometers and ice-machines, yeast cultivation enabled the brewery to predict the behavior of the brewing process. In the minds of these people, the *Leitbild* of "the predictable brewing process" developed.

The Munich and Copenhagen institutes were by no means the only ones founded in the second half of the nineteenth century, but they seem to have put more emphasis on research than most of the others, which were limited to analysis and testing. In the 1860s the first British analytic laboratories appeared in a few breweries in Burton-on-Trent (Sigsworth 1964-1965, pp. 537 ff.). German testing stations could be found, for instance, in Worms, Augsburg, Berlin, Memmingen (moved to Weihenstephan in 1892), and Nuremberg (*Illustriertes Brauer-Lexikon* 1910, p. 808; *Fest-Schrift* ... 1899; Schulze-Besse 1930, pp. 20 f.; Struve 1893, p. 222; *50 Jahre* ... 1937). Since it was felt that the more scientifically inclined Munich station primarily served the larger firms, the Memmingen and Nuremberg stations were founded by the Bavarian government with the explicit aim of supporting small breweries. The small breweries apparently regarded scientific research as a luxury they could not afford themselves.

In fact, not even the large breweries invested in their own research departments during the nineteenth century. Those firms that did employ scientifically-educated men assigned them tasks such as analysis, testing, and control rather than research duties. One of the first brewers to hire a chemist for such humble purposes was Dreher. Burdened with recurring quality problems, in 1852 he had asked his peer Sedlmayr whether he could recommend "an educated [*gebildeter*] brewer, who had studied chemistry as well" (in Sedlmayr 1951, p. 182). On Sedlmayr's suggestion, Dreher employed one of Kaiser's pupils: August Deiglmayr!

There were two reasons for devoting one part of this study to the brewing industry: breweries were the most important purchasers of refrigeration machinery; Linde's scientific approach was vigorously supported by some brewers, most notably Sedlmayr and Deiglmayr. It was no coincidence that these two men and their breweries have reappeared throughout this part. Spaten and Dreher were pioneering firms when it came to mechanizing production; they were among the first industrially organized breweries on the Continent; their directors valued college education and scientific methods highly. In short, their *organizational cultures* favored a scientific approach to technical problems. Sedlmayr and Deiglmayr acted in accordance with a long-standing tradition within their firms when sponsoring Linde. Of course, the Sedlmayr family and the Dreher Co. were not the only ones with a scientific approach to brewing, but they were certainly among its most active promoters. They chose to encourage Linde, instead of supporting an established machine firm, because they believed in the ability of science to solve technical problems. Linde's position as a member of the status group of college professors gave his allegedly scientific approach a flavor of seriousness and reliability.

This pro-scientific opinion might appear self-evident to the modern reader, but it was not so at the time. The majority of nineteenth-century brewers were still content with the methods of their parents and grandparents. For them, factory production based on scientific principles was not a serious alternative to their small-scale, empirical brewing techniques. While the typical craft brewer hailed historical continuity, the typical large-scale brewer supported any novelties that promised increased profits, rapid growth, and, last but not least, better means of control. In order to reach these goals the application of machinery and science had proved to be particularly efficacious. Hence, it is not unexpected to find that the mechanization and scientification of refrigeration technology were carried by the same industrial category: factory breweries operating on a large scale. Furthermore, it is not surprising that scientifically based methods of control were particularly pronounced in the German-speaking world, where the sensitive lager beer was produced, and where school culture was especially strong.

Linde's scientification project appeared at a time when the most influential brewers could appreciate it. Many brewers had successfully adopted chemical analysis and scientific instruments to control the brewing process and were now open to a scientific approach also in other areas. It is not difficult to find passages in the brewing literature from the early 1870s where science is praised. For instance, it is stated in the journal *Bierbrauer* (1874, Vol. 5 (n.s.), p. 21) that theoretical insights and scientific knowledge are necessary for "the brewer who strives for a higher degree of cultivation [*Bildung*]." The rational German brewer of that time obviously believed that *Bildung* was a prerequisite for achieving what today is sometimes called "excellence" in business. Science was not supported on purely fiscal grounds. The scientification (and mechanization) of refrigeration technology could not be defended by cost-benefit analyses alone; compare the discussion at the end of the previous chapter. Science (like machines) promised control and stability, and appeared to bring the firm closer to "the predictable brewing process."

In Weberian terms this means that the adoption of science to the production process is part of the development of practical rationality. When I discussed the unfolding of theoretical and formal rationality in Chapter 7, I focused on disenchantment and systematization, intellectual processes which aim at the creation of comprehensive *Weltbilder* that give the world meaning. I implied that these processes may also serve as a background for active participation in worldly events. Technical thermodynamics was an intellectually rational approach and tried to make its segment of the world understandable, but as soon as it was applied to solve concrete problems, it slid into the realm of practical rationality. The borderline between the intellectual and the practical was very fine for the scientist-engineer Linde; as an educator he focused on the former, as a practicing technician on the latter. This sociologically rooted difference in attitude has been described by Weber (1958e, p. 279):

> ... the intellectuals have always been the exponents of a rationalism which in their case has been relatively theoretical. The business classes (merchants and artisans) have been at least possible exponents of rationalism of a more practical sort.

Whereas the social locus of practical rationality is thus primarily to be found among businessmen and engineers, its historical locus lies in religions that combine a monotheistic belief in an almighty creator with an ethic of strict self-control. The Protestant notion of the "calling" (*Beruf*) illustrates this combination. Here, devout Christians follow the path which they believe that God has designed for them, regarding themselves as God's tools and priding themselves for taking part in a godly plan. The significant factor is that this plan forces them to act purposive-rationally in this world rather than to concentrate solely on otherworldly matters, even though they know that life in this world is nothing but a parenthesis on the road toward eternal life. This combination of "on the one hand, abnegation of the world, and on the other, mastery of the world," has been thoroughly analyzed by Weber (1958c, p. 327) in his article "Religious Rejections of the World and Their Directions."[3] There, as elsewhere, Weber (p. 325) puts the Protestant's combination of rejection of and ascetic activity in this world in opposition to the mystic's passive, contemplative rejection of the world:

> Active asceticism operates within the world; rationally active asceticism, in mastering the world, seeks to tame what is creatural and wicked through work in a worldly 'vocation' [Beruf] (inner-worldly asceticism). Such asceticism contrasts radically with mysticism, if the latter draws the full conclusion of fleeing from the world (contemplative flight from the world).

Here is the ideological roots of capitalism. The Protestant in general, and the Calvinist in particular, is an ascetic, while he or she labors unselfishly in his or her calling. A prerequisite for his or her mastering the world is that he or she masters his or her own character and actions; that is, the coming of practical rationality in this world goes hand in hand with the increasing control of personal conduct (Abramowski 1961, pp. 20-39; Schluchter 1979, pp. 35 f.). Instead of maximizing profits for his or her own short-term well-being, the Protestant in a self-sacrificing way seeks to glorify God by reinvesting profits, thus starting the process of accumulation of capital which is characteristic of all truly capitalist endeavors (Weber 1930).

This famous capitalist thesis of Weber's is not the central concern for the present analysis. More important is the connection between inner-worldly, active asceticism and mastery of the world, which has been discussed, among others, by Wolfgang Schluchter (1980) in his book "The Rationality of Ruling the World." The central thesis of Schluchter's book is that the Weberian approach leads to the following conclusion:

---

3 Orig: "Zwischenbetrachtung: Theorie der Stufen und Richtungen religiöser Weltablehnung" (Weber 1920, Vol. I, pp. 536-573).

> The religious ethic and rational metaphysics of the Occident are directed toward a rationality of cultivating and working the world [*Weltbearbeitung*]—yes, even toward ruling the world [*Weltbeherrschung*]. (p. 22)

This tendency toward ruling the world is interpreted by Schluchter (p. 21) as an outcome of "practical rationality." Weberian practical rationality thus combines, on the one hand, a "pragmatic and this-worldly predisposition" (Kalberg 1980, p. 1152) with a purposive-rational approach to problem-solving and, on the other hand, abnegation of the world with ruling it.

This line of thought has been extensively elaborated upon by philosophers connected to the Frankfurt School of Critical Theory (cf. Held 1980; Jay 1973; Kellner 1984). Max Horkheimer and Theodor Adorno (1969) have shown how the abnegation of the world can be found in the scientific attitude of turning the world into an object, and how purposive rationality —or subjective or instrumental rationality, as they usually say—has created a technocratic society, based on minute control (cf. Horkheimer 1941, 1985). Herbert Marcuse (1968, p. 207) has emphasized in his paper "Industrialization and Capitalism in the Work of Max Weber" that what he calls technical rationality is really "irrational." Technical rationality with its focus on industrialization and "conquest of nature," has "become destructive." This criticism of purposive-rational action later returned with Georg Henrik von Wright's (1987) plea for a value-rational attitude aiming at what is good for mankind and the world.

Weber himself never went so far in his critique, but he did tie the active asceticism of Protestantism to a scientific attitude toward practical problems:

> Scientific progress and Protestantism must not at all be unquestioningly identified. The Catholic church has indeed occasionally obstructed scientific progress; but the ascetic sects of Protestantism have also been disposed to have nothing to do with [pure] science, except in a situation where material requirements of everyday life were involved. On the other hand it is its specific contribution to have placed science in the service of technology and economics. (Weber 1981, p. 368)

A Weberian interpretation of the events described in this chapter would hence imply that the increasing use of scientific instruments and methods by the brewing industry was an outcome of the unfolding of practical rationality. Whereas the small-scale craft brewer relied on traditional methods with which he was personally acquainted, the large-scale factory brewer turned, in a rational manner, to science for help:

> Finally, through the union with science, the production of goods was emancipated from all the bonds of inherited tradition, and came under the dominance of the freely roving intelligence. (Weber 1981, p. 306)

While the employment of chemists and zymotechnicians might not have enabled the brewery director literally to rule the world, it did make it possible for him to control the organic and inorganic components of the brewing process better. Just like ice-machines made the process more predictable, pure yeast cultures made fermentation more reliable. Both machinery and science were means to reach one of his goals: a drinkable and durable product that could find ever expanding markets.

Conclusion

Rationality: The Common Denominator of Science, Technology, and Business

The original question of this study was why science, technology, and business have become so closely united in our society that they often appear as a "seamless web." Advanced technology and science belong, almost by definition, to modern industry; advanced industrial products are prerequisites for modern research. Not only "Big Science" projects are dependent on industrial techniques, virtually every single scientist and engineer is as well. Not only large, multi-national companies utilize cutting-edge research results, many small, knowledge-intensive firms also do. In order to address the topic a historical case was chosen: the scientification of refrigeration technology and the growing use of science and machinery by the brewing industry in the nineteenth century. There were at least three reasons for this choice. First, both mechanical refrigeration and science were carried by the largest brewing companies in the world. Second, although the social and intellectual roots of the seamless web date back to the Renaissance and the Reformation, the last century is commonly considered conclusive for the institutionalization of the ties between science, technology, and business. Third, surprisingly little historical work has been done in the area of early, pre-domestic refrigeration.

Max Weber's theory of the rationalization of the Occident proved to be particularly helpful for interpreting the scientification process. Rationalization processes can be found in many cultures, but only in the West has such an array of factors converged: the removal of magic powers from the world; the systematization of thought and conduct; the wish to rule and manipulate the world; the accumulation and long-term investment of capital. Some of these factors may be found elsewhere, but only in the culture of the Occident have they come together and begun to reinforce each other. The Western rationalization process can be said to consist of three analytic elements: the unfolding of theoretical, formal, and practical rationality. While the first two concepts capture the attempts of religious leaders and intellectuals to make life intelligible by presenting an abstract and comprehensive world-view, the last one describes how a self-sacrificing attitude to this world has enabled the Catholic monk and the Calvinist bourgeois to control not only his or her own life, but also his or her surroundings.

When the Weberian approach is described in this way, it may seem far too abstract and of little assistance. Its usefulness can better be proven by applying it directly to the empirical case of the present study, thus allowing it to draw together factors and events that otherwise might have been treated in isolation.

The core event of this study was the early attempt of the scientist-engineer Carl Linde to translate certain concepts, results, methods, and ontological positions from the science of thermodynamics into the technology of mechanical refrigeration. Linde addressed in a theoretically rational way what was originally a very concrete problem—how to construct a workable ice-machine. He first stipulated that the most efficient refrigeration process ought to be identical with the reverse Carnot cycle and then determined what refrigerant it ought to apply. He deduced what an optimal ice-machine should look like and what degree of efficiency would be its possible maximum. The outcome of this exercise was the "disenchantment" not only of nature, but also of mechanical refrigeration *per se*. By treating heat, temperature, and work as strictly defined concepts and applying the unforgiving laws of "the mechanical theory of heat" in a rigorous manner, Linde allowed no mystic forces to enter the world of refrigeration. By criticizing the ruling standard and prevalent trajectories of contemporary ice-machine design on principal grounds, he attempted to remove old spells from the area of mechanical refrigeration.

Linde's educational background and teaching activity concerned "technical thermodynamics" and "school culture." By playing down the role of manual training, school culture proponents like Reuleaux and Zeuner—who were also Linde's teachers—brought the methods of mechanical engineering closer to those of science. When Linde opened a laboratory of theoretical mechanical engineering in 1875, this was a conscious act to foster a professional culture based on scientific ideals. The student should carry out experiments, and sometimes even research, in the laboratory—a site which complemented the lecture hall. Linde's work was an integral part of technical thermodynamics, a technological research and development program founded by Zeuner. It is obvious from the exemplar of this program, the "Fundamentals," that Zeuner regarded scientific results and methods to be of paramount importance to technology. Just like Linde would later do, Zeuner saw it as his task to act as a translator between the spheres of science and technology.

The emergence of school culture and technical thermodynamics come under the headings of rationalization of thoughts and institutions. Kerstin Lindskoug (1979) suggests in a book on Weber's social theory that these two processes, together with "victory of reason," are typical to the passage from traditional to modern society. While the rationalization of thoughts covers the "growth of knowledge and the development of science" (p. 9), the rationalization of institutions includes the construction of bureaucratic, predictable bodies. The proponents of school culture—in mechanical engineering, as well as in brewing—considered both components crucial. On the one hand, the scientification of technology, the systematization of teaching routines, and the introduction of what Weber called "the rational experiment" represent the process of intellectualization. On the other hand, the replacement of on-the-job training by "regular curricula and special examinations" (Weber 1958a, p. 241) is concurrent, in two ways, with the development of modern bureaucracy. The technical and agricultural colleges were, in themselves, bureaucratic institutes, but they also supplied industry with rationally-behaving "bureaucrats." When machine firms and breweries grew, their organizations becoming less personal and more formalized and they needed personnel with clearly defined skills and knowledge—mechanical engineers and chemists, for instance.

After the brewing industry had enrolled him to build a real ice-machine, Linde slowly moved away from academe. But even as an inventor-entrepreneur, he continued to receive direct support from school culture. His firm, *Gesellschaft für Linde's Eismaschinen*, was a knowledge-intensive company that depended heavily on a continuous supply of college-educated engineers. Together with financiers from the machine industry, purchasers from the brewing industry, manufacturers from Augsburg and other towns, these engineers made up an agency network that supported the Linde project from the mid-1870s onward. After its foundation in 1879, the Linde

Co. became the primary social carrier of the Linde refrigeration machine system, thus fulfilling a number of functions: motivation and organization; legal and economic power; information about scientific, technological, and economic factors; resources for diffusion, marketing, research, development, and design; skills to operate and maintain its machine systems.

Much of the Linde Co.'s research, development, and design work was close to technical thermodynamics in both form and content. Thus it is not surprising to find Linde interested in transferring its scientific ideals of intersubjectivity and formally rational rules from technology to the marketplace. The early history of the Munich Refrigeration Testing Station incorporated all aspects of rationality. Linde's primary reason for founding this institute was to establish his own design as the ruling standard of mechanical refrigeration. But, in addition to this practically economic reason, there was also a theoretical one. His adversary, Pictet, had claimed to employ a method whereby the entropy law was invalidated. To Linde such a claim meant that magic powers had returned to refrigeration technology. Linde had introduced the laws of thermodynamics in his endeavor to create clarity in this realm of technology. If Pictet-Grübs had beaten the Linde Co., theoretical rationality would also have lost. The interesting thing, however, is that Linde could only win if practically rational methods were applied; theoretical arguments would not have sufficed. Instead, it was paramount that intersubjectively clear, formalized testing procedures were agreed upon, before the test series could begin. Just like the formalization of the legal system is meant to bring order into the dealings between citizens, the creation of uniform tests means that the rules of the game are made clear to everyone.

What were the effects of the scientification of refrigeration technology? The most important impact was a shift of focus from absorption to vapor compression. This shift was initiated when Linde established that the behavior of absorption machines was a presumptive anomaly in the field of mechanical engineering, and it can be regarded as the formulation of a new "path-selective" *Leitbild* for this field (Marz and Dierkes 1992, p. 9). From Linde's time onward vapor compression has generally been regarded as the superior ideal type. Neither absorption nor air expansion have disappeared, but their areas of application have become more limited. There are at least four reasons why vapor compression overtook the other classificatory ideal types.

First and foremost is the success of the Linde Co. vapor compression system. Due to their scientific reputation, high design quality, and fuel-efficient performance, the Linde machines sold extremely well in the 1880s. Paradoxically, however, it appears that the technical carefulness of the Linde design and the meticulous manufacturing skills of the Augsburg Machine Co. were more important than its scientific basis! Linde had originally pleaded for a thermodynamically more efficient refrigerant, but the final outcome of his development work was the application of ammonia, a working fluid that had already been used by the leading absorption manufacturers for more than a decade. He had also called for a machine that followed the theoretically perfect Carnot cycle, but compared with earlier systems, his own design does not appear to have come much closer to this ideal. Nevertheless, there are indications that Linde's machines produced in the early 1880s almost 75% more ice per energy unit than some German absorption systems and, a decade later, over 20% more than his closest vapor compression competitors managed to do.

The Introduction quoted the economic historian, Nathan Rosenberg, as he asked to what extent science influenced the technologies that emerged during the Second Industrial Revolution. An important conclusion drawn from the present study is that the impact of thermodynamics was a recognizable but not a decisive factor in the development of mechanical refrigeration before 1890. During our period of study the first scientific seeds were sown, but it was not until later that a full harvest could be reaped. In other words, this case study does not falsify M.C. Duffy's statement discussed in Chapter 7, that the science of heat did not begin to exercise a substantial impact before the 1890s.

A further reason for the victory of vapor compression is that Linde gave his classificatory ideal type an enormous backing by positing the reverse Carnot cycle as a *Leitbild*, and by claiming that vapor compression had the largest practical potential to reach this optimum. He picked a standard for the theoretically most efficient process from the science of thermodynamics and compared it with existing machines. Linde showed through a theoretical and practical analysis that vapor compression had the brightest future. The analysis appeared impressive and unassailable to many of his colleagues.

Third, the ensuing interest in vapor compression can in part be explained by its similarity to the steam engine cycle. The Carnot *Leitbild* was based on studies of the steam engine, a prime mover central to mechanical engineering. It was comparatively easy for people in the technical thermodynamics school to transform diagrams and formulae from the steam engine to the vapor compression area. They often denounced absorption off-hand, because this ideal type was *a priori* regarded as too complicated to analyze. Scientification had its limits.

Fourth, the rational attitude of scientification meant that factors like calculation and quantification were emphasized to the neglect of so-called softer ones. For instance, fuel economy became more important than safety. Linde himself acknowledged that an air expansion machine was less dangerous to use, but he valued the lower coal consumption of a vapor compression system more.

These four reasons indicate that Ruth Schwartz Cowan's study of American domestic refrigeration, included in her book *More Work for Mother* (1983), needs to be complemented. Cowan attributes the victory of vapor compression around 1910 primarily to the collective efforts of General Electric and the largest electric utilities to convince customers to choose compressor refrigerators (which ran on electricity) instead of absorption ones (which were fueled by gas). In her interpretation, vapor compression won out because of vested economic interests. I agree basically, although I believe that Cowan has undervalued the strength of engineering tradition. Even if it had not been unanimously accepted as the ruling standard of mechanical refrigeration, vapor compression had already established itself as the most promising ideal type before the turn of the century. Absorption had always remained stronger in the United States than in Europe, but vapor compression gained ground as the scientific approach to problems of refrigeration technology grew. Economic interests and corporative strength were not the only driving forces; engineering attitudes presumably also played an important role.

Scientification had further effects. The emphasis on practically rational factors like degree of efficiency meant that poisonous ammonia outpaced the less efficient but fairly harmless carbon dioxide as a refrigerant in vapor compression machinery. This is the same ideal that would later contribute to the extensive use of freons (fluorocarbons - CFC). The attempts to compare various machines led to the establishment of standard testing procedures at the turn of the century. Linde and others began to teach refrigeration engineering courses, and this field slowly emerged as a sub-discipline of mechanical engineering. However, this part of the academization process lies beyond the scope of this study. It suffices to say that Linde's work continued to influence refrigeration technology well into the twentieth century. It did so socially through a technological school, cognitively through a research and development program, and technically through the establishment of an archetype. Indirectly, it has contributed to the emission of gases that now threaten the ozone layer around the earth.

On the consumer side, the most influential social carrier of mechanical refrigeration was the brewing industry; the carriers of a scientific approach —both to brewing and ice-machine design—were the very largest breweries. It is thus not surprising that Linde was initially enrolled by representatives of the largest breweries on the European Continent. Linde's membership in the Weberian status group of college professors was decisive for August Deiglmayr of Dreher and Gabriel Sedlmayr of Spaten, for it gave his allegedly scientific approach to mechanical refrigeration a touch of seriousness and reliability. Sedlmayr had close contacts with the brewing colleges of Bavaria and appreciated higher technical education; himself a chemist, Deiglmayr appreciated the theoretically, formally, and practically rational attitude of science. Chemistry and what nowadays is labeled biochemistry had enabled these breweries to make the brewing process intelligible, controllable, and predictable. In the second half of the 1800s fermentation was no longer a mystic process, chemical analysis had been adopted at various points of the brewing process, and yeast cultivation had reduced the risk of "foul beer" being produced.

Their interest in Linde's work could also be explained by reference to a common ideology of scientification, ideology here meaning a set of assumptions, values, and imperatives (Liedman 1984). We have met many agents whose statements, beliefs, and acts constituted this ideology. Among them were not only Linde, Zeuner, and Sedlmayr, but also technical college reformers like Bauernfeind, politicians such as Escher, and brewing educators like Kaiser and Lintner. All of them shared a conviction that technology would benefit from closer contacts with science. The central imperative of the scientification ideology was: translate the results, concepts, and methods of science in such a manner that they can be made to bear on technological problems! It was a call for an increase in the information flow from science to technology. We have seen how Linde echoed this imperative in the editor's introduction to the "Bavarian Journal of Industry and Trade," how Zeuner did the same in the "Fundamentals," how Jacobsen did so when describing the goals of the Carlsberg Laboratory, and how Bauernfeind did so at the opening of the Munich Polytechnic. Parallel to the basic imperative was a number of values and assumptions concerning technological knowledge. The ideology praised the quantification and systematization of data, along with a reductive method of analysis and a deductive mode of presentation, where calculation was an important step. It held that each technological problem had an optimal solution. If a problem was very complex, it should be cut into a number of smaller problems, each of which might have an ideal solution. However, the ideal could never be reached in practice, so that sensible approximations were hence needed in the actual design process. We have seen how Linde established the Carnot cycle as the optimum for all ice-machines and deduced technological rules from general principles; how Zeuner developed approximations in order to make scientific results useful to the everyday engineer; and how Reuleaux used systematization as the first step on the road toward scientification. We encountered Combrune who supported the quantification of temperature measurements by making propaganda for the use of thermometers, and zymotechnicians who introduced a reductive enzyme analysis into the brewery.

If their belief in the power of science and rationality might explain why Sedlmayr and Deiglmayr supported Linde's work, it does not by itself explain why they and other brewers wanted to substitute mechanical for non-mechanical refrigeration. Many brewers wanted to reduce their reliance on natural ice, because this product was bulky and cumbersome to handle; it was often accused of being unwholesome, and its supply was often insecure. However, the interest in mechanical refrigeration cannot be explained merely by reference to the disadvantages of natural ice.

The organizational cultures of Spaten and Dreher are essential on the agency level; these breweries had a long-standing tradition of staying at the cutting edge of technology and scientific instrumentation. In the 1810s Sedlmayr Senior had already pioneered by introducing a new malt drying method and the first brewery steam engine into Bavaria. Two decades later the young Sedlmayr and his friend Dreher toured Great Britain, paying close attention to all brewing devices—instruments like thermometers and saccharometers, among them. Their goal was to adopt British technology, the most modern at the time. Mechanization became a routine path for these firms, and when a promising ice-machine appeared it was natural for their firms to welcome it.

On the structural level, this emphasis on machinery and various implements was typical for a capital-intensive brewing company. It is not surprising from a Weberian perspective to find that the social carriers of brewing mechanization in general and of mechanical refrigeration in particular were the large-scale, factory breweries oriented toward an anonymous market. Collins (1986, p. 25) has pointed out that Weber emphasized that the emergence of a mass market and of large companies serving such a market were prerequisites for mechanization. In accordance with Weber's (1981, p. 276 f.) description of the capitalist firm, such companies were run by an entrepreneur applying "rational capital accounting" which needs technologies whose performance can be easily quantified and calculated; they sold their product on a free market and hired workers on a free labor market; they acted in a society with a predictable legal and administrative system. While small-scale, craft brewers hardly showed any interest in ice-machines, capitalist factory establishments like Spaten and Dreher were more likely to invest in such machinery. Only the largest breweries had the potential to afford it; with their industrial structure, they were already familiar with various apparatus; they often already employed mechanics and steam engines. Hence, when mechanical refrigeration made its breakthrough in the 1880s, it did so in factory brewing. Contrary to what H.F. Tillmann (1972) has claimed, this technology did not allow small firms to grow during our period. Rather, it enabled the very largest firms to become even bigger, thus contributing to a concentration of the trade.

Unlike the small, locally-oriented brewery, the large factory counterpart relied on a wide and impersonal market and needed to produce a durable beer with an even quality—preferably year-round. These demands required minute control of processes and products. A crucial factor was temperature control, where mechanical refrigeration in combination with thermometry appeared very promising. The thermometer provided intersubjective information and was especially suitable for the large brewery where staff turnover could be substantial. Like the saccharometer, it had clear ties with the sphere of science. Like the ice-machine, the thermometer was connected to all the following brewing processes: increased predictability and calculability, as well as mechanization and scientification. Like science, mechanical refrigeration and thermometry were adopted because they contributed to the rationalization of brewing, theoretically by substituting degrees for demons, formally by replacing personal skills with intersubjective knowledge, and practically by allowing for better control.

The main thesis of the present study is that the scientification, intellectualization, and systematization of technology, as well as the increasing degree of quantification and calculability of engineering in order to make production more predictable and easy to control, are all parts of the overall rationalization of the Occident, as Weber understood it.

Toward a Weberian History and Sociology of Technology

This case study has not only attempted to interpret the scientification of refrigeration and brewing technology in Weberian terms; it has also tried to apply, more generally, a Weberian approach to the study of history and sociology of technology. Rather than having contributed to the development of Weberian sociology proper, it has suggested what consequences a Weberian methodology could have for our views and treatments of problems in the area of science, technology, and society. In this regard it has partly followed Randall Collins' *Weberian Sociological Theory* (1986).

Perhaps most significant in this connection is the unequivocal denunciation of any kind of determinism—technological, social, or economic alike. Weber's view of society and history was always multidimensional (Abramowski 1966). Although the title of the present study, as well as a common reading of Weber's *Protestant Ethic*, may indicate that Weber was an idealist, such a conclusion would be premature. He paid great attention to the impact of ideas on the path of history, but he never lost sight of economic and other material factors. It is perfectly legitimate for the historian to focus on ideologic elements, if he or she is driven in that direction because of interest or the research questions chosen (Holton and Turner 1989). However, problems emerge when the historian believes that all events may be explained by reference to ideas only.

Thus a Weberian approach implies non-reductionism—except on one score. Weber was a methodological individualist and maintained that societies and groups never act on their own, only their individual members do (Cohen 1981). Social scientists may rightly discuss structural phenomena, but they are not allowed to regard them as real entities. A nominalist, Weber regarded structures as analytical tools without ontological existence (Kocka 1986a).

Similarly, all classificatory and analytic concepts exist only in the mind of the scholar, "ideal type" being a case in point. The ideal typical capitalist, whose deliberations are always based on strict calculation, may be impossible to find in practice, but his or her fictitious existence may still be of great help to the economist or the economic historian (Giddens 1971). In the same vein, classificatory ideal types may be of great importance to the historian of technology. By dividing artifacts into groups and attributing certain characteristics to them, the historian simplifies both analysis and presentation. For example, although by definition a tricycle is no bicycle, it makes perfect sense to include it in a history of the bicycle.

Although Weber is famous for his grand historical schemes, they never preclude an agency perspective. His methodological individualism includes a focus on persons acting meaningfully and with certain motives and interests. Weber (1958e, p. 280) writes in a much debated passage that interests "*directly* govern men's conduct" (my emph.). However, he goes immediately on to say that

> very frequently the "world images" that have been created by "ideas" have, like switchmen, determined the tracks along which action has been pushed by the dynamic of interests.

In line with the analysis of the ideology of scientification given above, we could thus say that a Weberian approach requires us to discuss what *Weltbilder* and values determine human acts. Various visions or *Leitbilder*, as well as influential archetypes or *Vorbilder* must be paradigmatic in technology studies.

The agency perspective furthermore implies that structural change is never an autonomous process. Collins (1986) has pointed out that it is always driven by certain groups in society—often in opposition to other groups. A Weberian view thus highlights the importance of social conflict to technological change (Hård 1993). In our story scientification was primarily fostered by certain engineering professors, politicians, and factory brewers; their opponents were concerned parties with other educational ideals, as well as craft brewers and laborers. It was no automatic process. It is important to stress, like Wolfgang Schluchter (1979) and Wolfgang Mommsen (1987) do, that a Weberian approach does not imply a unilinear, evolutionary view of history. Artur Bogner (1989) thus seems to be on the wrong track when he claims that Weberian history is irreversible. Weber's almost dialectic discussion of the interplay between charismatic and bureaucratic political leadership reveals that history may well go back and forth (Beetham 1985). For instance, toward the end of the nineteenth century, the influence of the opponents of school culture and excessive scientification grew and the pendulum swung back (Manegold 1970a).

Another aspect of Weber's anti-evolutionism is found in his history of industrial organization, where he forcefully argues that factory production did not grow out of craft work, but represented a developmental line of its own. Transferred to the history of artifacts, this position—which is a necessary consequence of Weber's methodology of types—means that the shift from one classificatory ideal type to another represents a radical change, whereas a modification of the *Stand der Technik* within one ideal typical group is a gradual passage.

In short, a Weberian approach to the history and sociology of technology would be anti-evolutionary and anti-determinist; it would allow for the influence of ideologies, but it would not exclude economic and material factors; it would combine an agency perspective with structural discussions; it would assume that social phenomena—including technology—are constituted through a process of conflict.

References

Abbreviations

ABPTV	Archiv des Bayerischen Polytechnischen Vereins, in DM-S
ADB	Allgemeine Deutsche Biographie
BIGB	Bayerisches Industrie- und Gewerbe-Blatt
DHI	Dictionary of the History of Ideas
DHS	Dictionary of the History of Science
DM-S	Deutsches Museum, Munich, Sondersammlung
DPJ	Dingler's polytechnisches Journal
DS	Dictionary of Science
EPSZ	Eidgenössische Polytechnische Schule, Zurich
ETH	Eidgenössische Technische Hochschule, Zurich
FDMT	Fontana Dictionary of Modern Thought
LAG-H	Archive of the Linde AG, Höllriegelskreuth
LAG-W	Archive of the Linde AG, Wiesbaden
MA	Maschinenfabrik Augsburg
MAN-HA	Historisches Archiv, MAN AG, Augsburg
MPICE	Minutes of Proceeding of the Institution of Civil Engineers
NBG	Nouvelle Biographie Générale
PSK	Polytechnische Schule/Technische Hochschule, Karlsruhe
SBED	Scribner-Bantam English Dictionary
SM-NS	Stadtarchiv, Munich, Nachlass von Herrn Kommerzienrat Fritz Sedlmayr
THM	Polytechnische Schule/Technische Hochschule, Munich
VDI	Verein deutscher Ingenieure
ZVDI	Zeitschrift des Vereins deutscher Ingenieure

Archives

Bayerischer Polytechnischer Verein, in DM-S
Deutsches Museum, Munich, Sondersammlung
ETH-Bibliothek, Zurich
Lehrstuhl A für Thermodynamik, Technische Universität, Munich
Linde AG, Höllriegelskreuth
Linde AG, Wiesbaden
MAN AG, Augsburg, Historisches Archiv
Patent- och registreringsverket, Stockholm
Stadtarchiv, Munich
Svenska bryggareföreningens arkiv, in Uppsala universitetsbibliotek

Periodicals

Allgemeine Zeitschrift für Bierbrauerei und Malzfabrikation. 1878-1879, Vols. 6-7.

American Society of Mechanical Engineers, Transactions of the. 1892-1893, Vols. 13-14.

Der Bayerische Bierbrauer. 1866-1877, Vols. 1-12.

Bayerisches Industrie- und Gewerbe-Blatt (previously *Bayerisches Kunst- und Gewerbe-Blatt*). 1869-1895, Vols. 1-27.

Bericht über die Königl. Polytechnische Schule zu München für das Studienjahr ... 1868-1877. Munich.

Bericht über die Königl. Technische Hochschule zu München für das Studienjahr ... 1877-1879, 1908-1909. Munich.

Der Bierbrauer. Monatsberichte über die Fortschritte des gesamten Brauwesens. 1870-1879, Vols. 1-10 (new series).

Carlsberg Laboratoriet, Meddelelser fra. 1877.

Der Civilingenieur. Zeitschrift für das Ingenieurwesen. 1854, Vol. 1 (new series).

Deutsche Brauindustrie. 1888-1890, Vols. 13-15.

Dingler's polytechnisches Journal. 1850, Vol. 115; 1860-1863, Vols. 158-170.

Engineering. 1868.

Gesellschaft für Geschichte und Bibliographie des Brauwesens, Jahrbuch der. 1928-1941.

Ice and Refrigeration (later: *Industrial Refrigeration*). 1891-1902, Vols. 1-22.

Institution of Civil Engineers, Minutes of Proceedings of the. 1882, Vol. 68.

Mechanics' Magazine. 1851, 1869.

Polytechnisches Centralblatt. 1857, 1860, 1863.

The Practical Mechanic's Journal. 1862/63-1863/64, Vols. 8-9.

Programm der Eidgen. Polytechnischen Schule für das Schuljahr ... 1855/56-1864. Zurich.

Programm der Königl. Bayerischen Technischen Hochschule zu München für das Jahr ... 1877/78-1902/03. Munich.
Programm der Polytechnischen Schule zu München für das Jahr ... 1868/69-1876/77. Munich.
Scientific American. 1861, Vol. 5; 1868-1883, Vols. 19-48.
Society of Arts, Journal of the. 1854, Vol. 2.
Teknisk tidskrift. 1874, Vol. 4.
Zeitschrift des königlich bayerischen statistischen Bureau. 1869-1891, Vols. 1-23.
Zeitschrift des Vereins deutscher Ingenieure. 1868-1870, Vols. 12-14.
Zeitschrift für das gesamte Brauwesen. Organ der wissenschaftlichen Station für Brauerei in München. 1880, Vol. 3; 1887-1889, Vols. 10-12; 1892, Vol. 15.
Zeitschrift für die gesammte Kälte-Industrie. 1894-1909, Vols. 1-16.
Zeitschrift für Eis- und Kälte-Industrie. 1910/11-1913/14, Vols. 3-6; 1922, Vol. 22.

Bibliography

ABRAMOWSKI, Günter. 1966. *Das Geschichtsbild Max Webers. Universalgeschichte am Leitfaden des okzidentalen Rationalisierungsprozesses.* Stuttgart: Klett.
Abridgements of Specifications Relating to Ice-Making Machines, Ice Safes, and Ice Houses, A.D. 1819-1866. 1877. London.
ACHAM, Karl. 1984. "Über einige Rationalitätskonzeptionen in den Sozialwissenschaften," in Schnädelbach, pp. 32-69.
AGASSI, Joseph. 1966. "The Confusion Between Science and Technology in the Standard Philosophies of Science," *Technology and Culture*, Vol. 7, pp. 348-366.
AHLSTRÖM, Göran. 1982. *Engineers and Industrial Growth: Higher Technical Education and the Engineering Profession During the 19th and Early 20th Centuries: France, Germany, Sweden and England.* London and Canberra: Croom Helm.
AITKEN, Hugh G.J. 1976. *Syntony and Spark. The Origins of Radio.* Princeton, NJ: Princeton University Press.
AITKEN, Hugh G.J. 1978. "Science, Technology, and Economics: The Invention of Radio as a Case Study," in Krohn *et al.*, pp. 89-111.
ALBRECHT, Helmut. 1987. *Technische Bildung zwischen Wissenschaft und Praxis. Die Technische Hochschule Braunschweig 1862-1914.* Hildesheim: Georg Olm.
Allgemeine Deutsche Biographie. 1967-1971/1875-1912. Berlin: Duncker & Humblot.
ANDERSON, Oscar E., Jr. 1953. *Refrigeration in America: A History of a New Technology and Its Impact.* Princeton, NJ: Princeton University Press.
ANDORFER, Ludwig. 1929. *Die Rationalisierung in der Brauindustrie unter Berücksichtigung ihrer Einwirkung auf die Arbeiterschaft.* Nuremberg: F. Carl.
ARMYTAGE, W.H.G. 1976. *A Social History of Engineering.* Whitstable, Kent: Faber and Faber.
ARNOLD, John P., and PENMAN, Frank. 1933. *History of the Brewing Industry and Brewing Science in America.* Chicago: Inset.

ATTMAN, Artur. 1961. *Bryggerinäringen i Göteborg, II, 1810-1961*. Gothenburg: AB Pripp och Lyckholm.

BALLING, Karl J.N. 1843. *Die sacharometrische Bierprobe*. Prague: Borrosch & André.

BALLING, Karl J.N. 1855. *Anleitung zur Vornahme der sacharometrischen Bierprobe*. Prague: Calve.

BALLING, Karl J.N. 1865/1845. *Die Bierbrauerei, wissenschaftlich begründet und praktisch dargestellt*, Vol. 2, 3rd ed. Prague: Calve.

BARON, Stanley. 1962. *Brewed in America: A History of Beer and Ale in the United States*. Boston and Toronto: Little Brown.

BARTH, Ernst. 1973. *Entwicklungslinien der deutschen Maschinenbauindustrie von 1870 bis 1914*. Berlin: Akademie-Verlag.

BAUERNFEIND, Carl Max, ed. 1869. *Reden und Vorträge zur Einweihungsfeier der neuen Technischen Hochschule in München*. Munich.

BECKER, Raymond B. 1972. *John Gorrie, M.D., Father of Air Conditioning and Mechanical Refrigeration*. New York: Carlton.

BECKER, Walter. 1962. "Die Entwicklung der deutschen Maschinenbauindustrie von 1850 bis 1870," in Schröter, Alfred, and Becker, Walter, *Die deutsche Maschinenbauindustrie in der industriellen Revolution*. Berlin: Akademie-Verlag, pp. 135-285.

BECKMAN, Olof. 1976. *Värmelära*. Stockholm: AWE/Geber.

BECKMAN, Svante. 1990. *Utvecklingens hjältar. Om den innovativa individen i samhällstänkandet*. Stockholm: Carlssons.

BEER, John J. 1981/1959. *The Emergence of the German Dye Industry*. New York: Arno Press.

BEETHAM, David. 1985. *Max Weber and the Theory of Modern Politics*. Cambridge: Polity.

BEHREND, Gottlieb. 1883, 1900. *Eis- und Kälteerzeugungs-Maschinen nebst einer Anzahl ausgeführter Anlagen zur Erzeugung von Eis, Abkühlung von Flüssigkeiten und Räumen*, 1st and 4th eds. Halle a.S: Knapp.

BEHREND, Gottlieb. 1898. "Ueber künstliche Kälteerzeugung und Kälteindustrie," *Sammlung gemeinverständlicher Vorträge*, (new series) Row XIII, Vol. 297. Hamburg: Verlags-Anstalt.

BELOFSKY, Harold. 1991. "Engineering Drawing—A Universal Language in Two Dialects," *Technology and Culture*, Vol. 32, pp. 23-46.

BENIGER, James R. 1986. *The Control Revolution: Technological and Economic Origins of the Information Society*. Cambridge, MA: Harvard University Press.

BERG, Maxine. 1980. *The Machinery Question and the Making of Political Economy 1815-1848*. Cambridge: Cambridge University Press.

BERGGREN, Christian. 1990. *Det nya bilarbetet. Konkurrensen mellan olika produktionskoncept i svensk bilindustri*. Lund: Arkiv.

BERNER, Boel. 1990. "Kunskap för förändring - om dynamik och tröghet i sociotekniska system," in *Energin, makten och framtiden. Samhällsvetenskapliga perspektiv på teknisk förändring*. Stockholm: Allmänna förlaget, pp. 52-73.

BERGSTRÖM, Lennart. 1985. "Teorier om den tekniska kunskapens natur. En teknikfilosofisk litteraturöversikt med fallstudie," *TRITA-HOT*, No. 1004. Stockholm: Royal Institute of Technology.

BERNAL, J.D. 1965/1954. *Science in History*, 4 vols., 3rd ed. London: Pelican.

BERTHOIN ANTAL, Ariane. 1992. *Corporate Social Performance: Rediscovering Actors in their Organizational Contexts*. Frankfurt a.M. and Boulder, Col.: Campus and Westview.

BERTILSSON, Margareta. 1985. "Om rätt och moral; synpunkter på Max Webers rättslära," *Statsvetenskaplig tidskrift*, No. 1, pp. 25-38.

Die Bierfrage in Bayern im Jahre 1861. 1861. Munich: Lindauer.

BIJKER, Wiebe E. 1987. "The Social Construction of Bakelite: Toward a Theory of Invention," in Bijker *et al.*, pp. 159-187.

BIJKER, Wiebe E., HUGHES, Thomas P., and PINCH, Trevor J., eds. 1987. *The Social Construction of Technological Systems: New Directions in the Sociology and History of Technology*. Cambridge, MA: MIT Press.

BIJKER, Wiebe E., and LAW, John, eds. 1992. *Shaping Technology—Building Societies: Studies in Sociotechnical Change*. Cambridge, MA: MIT Press.

BIRR, Kendall A. 1966. "Science in American Industry," in Van Tassel, David, and Hall, Michael, eds., *Science and Society in the United States*. Homewood, Ill.: Dorsey, pp. 35-80.

BIUCCHI, B.M. 1973. "The Industrial Revolution in Switzerland," in Cipolla, Ch. 10.

BJÖRCK, Henrik. 1986. "'På de tillfälliga uppfinningarnas oroliga haf': Tekniska tidskrifter i Sverige 1800-1870," *Polhem*, Vol. 4, pp. 57-126.

BJÖRCK, Henrik. 1987. "Bilder av maskiner och ingenjörskårens bildande," *Polhem*, Vol. 5, pp. 267-310.

BJÖRKMAN, Torsten, and LUNDQVIST, Karin. 1981. *Från MAX till PIA. Reformstrategier inom arbetsmiljöområdet*. Lund: Arkiv.

BOEHM, Laetitia, and SCHÖNBECK, Charlotte, eds. 1989. *Technik und Bildung*. Dusseldorf: VDI-Verlag.

BOGNER, Artur. 1989. *Zivilisation und Rationalisierung. Die Zivilisationstheorien Max Webers, Norbert Elias' und der Frankfurter Schule im Vergleich*. Opladen: Westdeutscher Verlag.

BOLIN-HORT, Per. 1990. *Work, Family and the State: Child Labour and the Organization of Production in the British Cotton Industry, 1780-1920*. Lund: Lund University Press.

A. Borsig, Berlin 1837-1902. Festschrift zur Production der 5000. Lokomotive. 1902. Berlin.

BOURDIEU, Pierre. 1984/1979. *Distinction: A Social Critique of the Judgement of Taste*. London: Routledge & Kegan Paul.

BOURDIEU, Pierre. 1988/1984. *Homo Academicus*. Cambridge: Polity.

BOURNE, John. 1873-1874. "Contribution to the Bibliography of Mechanical Refigeration," *MPICE*, Vol. 37, pp. 271-282.

Die Brauindustrie in den Vereinigten Staaten in ihrer technischen und wirtschaftlichen Entwicklung. 1932. Berlin: Gesellschaft für die Geschichte und Bibliographie des Brauwesens.

BRAUN, Hans-Joachim. 1977. "Methodenprobleme der Ingenieurwissenschaft, 1850 bis 1900," *Technikgeschichte*, Vol. 44, pp. 1-18.

BRAUN, Hans-Joachim. 1981. "Franz Reuleaux und der Technologietransfer zwischen Deutschland und Nordamerika am Ausgang des 19. Jahrhunderts," *Technikgeschichte*, Vol. 48, pp. 112-130.

BRAUN, Hans-Joachim. 1983. "Technologietransfer im Maschinenbau von Deutschland in die USA 1870 bis 1939," *Technikgeschichte*, Vol. 50, pp. 238-252.
BRAUN, Hans-Joachim. 1992. "Introduction," *Social Studies of Science*, Vol. 22, pp. 213-230.
BRAVERMAN, Harry. 1974. *Labor and Monopoly Capital: The Degradation of Work in the Twentieth Century*. New York and London: Monthly Review Press.
BRING, Samuel E., ed. 1935. *Svenska bryggareföreningen 1885-1935*. Stockholm: Almqvist & Wiksell.
BRUNNER, Otto, CONZE, Werner, and KOSELLECK, Reinhart, eds. 1972-1984. *Geschichtliche Grundbegriffe: Historisches Lexikon zur politisch-sozialen Sprache in Deutschland*, Vols. 1-5. Stuttgart: Klett-Cotta.
BRUSH, Stephen G. 1976. *The Kind of Motion We Call Heat: A History of the Kinetic Theory of Gases in the 19th Century*, Vol. 1. Amsterdam and New York: North-Holland.
BRYANT, Lynwood. 1966. "The Silent Otto," *Technology and Culture*, Vol. 7, pp. 184-200.
BRYANT, Lynwood. 1973. "The Role of Thermodynamics in The Evolution of Heat Engines," *Technology and Culture*, Vol. 14, pp. 152-165.
BRYANT, Lynwood. 1976. "The Development of the Diesel Engine," *Technology and Culture*, Vol. 17, pp. 432-446.
BUCHANAN, R.A. 1983. "Gentlemen Engineers: The Making of a Profession" *Victorian Studies*, Vol. 26, pp. 407-429.
BUCHANAN, R.A. 1985. "The Rise of Scientific Engineering in Britain," *British Journal for the History of Science*, Vol. 18, pp. 218-233.
BÜCHNER, Fritz. 1940. *Hundert Jahre Geschichte der Maschinenfabrik Augsburg-Nürnberg*. Nuremberg: M.A.N.-AG.
BUCHNER, Otto. 1864. *Die Mineralöle, insbesondere Photogen, Solaröl und Petroleum*. Weimar: Bernhard Friedrich Voigt.
BULLOCKS, Alan, and STALLYBRASS, Oliver, eds. 1977. *The Fontana Dictionary of Modern Thought*. London: Fontana.
BUNGE, Mario. 1979. "Philosophical Inputs and Outputs of Technology," in Bugliarello, George, and Doner, Dean B., eds., *The History and Philosophy of Technology*. Urbana, Ill.: University of Illinois Press, pp. 262-281.
BURGER, Thomas. 1976. *Max Weber's Theory of Concept Formation: History, Laws, and Ideal Types*. Durham, NC: Duke University Press.
BURSTALL, Aubrey F. 1963. *A History of Mechanical Engineering*. London: Faber and Faber.
BÜSCHER, Gustav. 1942. *Festes Wasser, flüssige Luft. Carl von Lindes Kampf um Kältegrade*. Berlin: Wilhelm Limpert.
BYNUM, W.F., BROWNE, E.J., and PORTER, Roy, eds. 1981. *Dictionary of the History of Science*. Princeton, NJ: Princeton University Press.
CALLON, Michel. 1987. "Society in the Making: The Study of Technology as a Tool for Sociological Analysis," in Bijker *et al.*, pp. 83-103.
CALVERT, Monte A. 1967. *The Mechanical Engineer in America, 1830-1910: Professional Cultures in Conflict*. Baltimore, MD: John Hopkins Press.

CARDWELL, Donald S.L. 1971. *From Watt to Clausius: The Rise of Thermodynamics in the Early Industrial Age*. Ithaca, NY: Heinemann.

CARDWELL, Donald S.L., and HILLS, Richard L. 1976. "Thermodynamics and Practical Engineering in the Nineteenth Century," *History of Technology*, Vol. 1, pp. 1-20.

Carl von Lindes Kältemaschine und ihre Bedeutung für die Entwicklung der modernen Lagerbierbrauerei. 1929. Berlin.

CARNOT, Sadi. 1978/1824. *Réflexions sur la puissance motrice du feu*. Paris: J. Vrin.

CARRÉ. 1860. "Note sur un appareil propre à produire du froid," *Comptes rendus hebdomadaires des séances de l'Académie des sciences*, Vol. 51, pp. 1023-1027.

CHANDLER, Alfred D., Jr. 1977. *The Visible Hand: The Managerial Revolution in American Business*. Cambridge, MA: Belknap.

CHECKLAND, P.B. 1981. *Systems Thinking, Systems Practice*. Chichester: Wiley.

CIPOLLA, Carlo M., ed. 1973. *The Fontana Economic History of Europe: The Emergence of Industrial Societies*, 2 vols. London: Collins and Fontana.

CLAUSIUS, Rudolf. 1863. "Technische Physik," vorgetragen von Prof. Clausius im Schuljahre 1862/63 am Eidgenössischen Polytechnikum in Zürich, bearbeitet von Heinrich Berchtold, Zürich in August 1863, at ETH-Bibliothek, Zurich, Hs. 797: 1, *mimeograph*. Zurich.

CLAUSIUS, Rudolf. 1864. *Abhandlungen über die mechanische Wärmetheorie. Erste Abtheilung*. Braunschweig: Friedrich Vieweg & Sohn.

CLAUSIUS, Rudolf. 1867. *Abhandlungen über die mechanische Wärmetheorie. Zweite Abtheilung*. Braunschweig: Friedrich Vieweg & Sohn.

CLEMEN, Rudolf A. 1923. *The American Livestock and Meat Industry*. New York: Ronald Press.

CLEMEN, Rudolf A. 1946. *Georg H. Hammond (1838-1886): Pioneer in Refrigerator Transportation*. New York: Newcomen Society.

COCHRAN, Thomas C. 1981. *Frontiers of Change: Early Industrialism in America*. New York: Oxford University Press.

COHEN, Ira J. 1981. "Introduction to the Transaction Edition: Max Weber on Modern Western Capitalism," in Weber, pp. XV-LXXXIII.

COLEMAN, Joseph James. 1882. "Air Refrigerating Machinery and its Applications," *MPICE*, Vol. 68, pp. 146-169.

COLEMAN, William. 1971. *Biology in the Nineteenth Century: Problems of Form, Function, and Transformation*. New York: Wiley.

COLLINS, Randall. 1981. "On the Micro-foundations of Macro-sociology," *American Journal of Sociology*, Vol. 86, pp. 984-1014.

COLLINS, Randall. 1986. *Weberian Sociological Theory*. Cambridge: Cambridge University Press.

COLLINS, Randall. 1990. "Ethical Controversies of Science and Society: A Relation Between Two Spheres of Social Conflict," *manuscript*. Riverside, CA: University of California.

COLLINS, Randall. 1990a. "Market Closure and the Conflict Theory of the Professions," in Burrage, Michael, and Torstendahl, Rolf, eds., *Professions in Theory and History: Rethinking the Study of the Professions*. London: Sage, pp. 24-43.

COMBRUNE, M. 1758. *An Essay of Brewing: With a View of Establishing the Principles of the Art*. London: Dodsley.

CONSTANT, E.W., II. 1980. *The Origins of the Turbojet Revolution*. Baltimore: John Hopkins University Press.

CONSTANT, E.W., II. 1987. "The Social Locus of Technological Practice: Community, System, or Organization," in Bijker *et al.*, pp. 223-242.

COWAN, Ruth Schwartz. 1983. *More Work for Mother: The Ironies of Household Technology from the Open Hearth to the Microwave*. New York: Basic.

CUMMINGS, Richard O. 1949. *The American Ice Harvests: A Historical Study in Technology, 1800-1918*. Berkeley and Los Angeles: University of California Press.

DAHLANDER, G.R. 1866. *Om den tekniska undervisningen i några af Europas Länder*. Gothenburg: D.F. Bonnier.

DAHLBECK, S.P. 1866. *Det Tekniska Undervisningsväsendet uti Tyskland, Schweitz och Sverige. Iakttagelser under en vetenskaplig resa, sommaren år 1864*. Helsinki: privately published.

DANIELS, George H. 1970. "The Big Questions in the History of American Technology," *Technology and Culture*, Vol. 11, pp. 1-21.

DAVID, Paul. 1975. *Technical Choice, Innovation and Economic Growth: Essays on British and American Experience in the Nineteenth Century*. Cambridge: Cambridge University Press.

DEANE, Phyllis. 1965. *The First Industrial Revolution*. Cambridge: Cambridge University Press.

DE GEER, Hans. 1978. *Rationaliseringsrörelsen i Sverige. Effektivitetsidéer och socialt ansvar under mellankrigstiden*. Stockholm: Studieförbundet näringsliv och samhälle.

DELBRÜCK, Max, ed. 1910. *Illustriertes Brauerei-Lexikon*. Berlin: Parey.

DELBRÜCK, Max, and STRUVE, Emil. 1903. *Beiträge zur Geschichte des Bieres und der Brauerei*. Berlin: Parey.

DENNIS, Norman, HENRIQUES, Fernando, and SLAUGHTER, Clifford. 1969/1956. *Coal is Our Life: Analyses of a Yorkshire Mining Community*. London: Tavistock.

DESAI, Ashok V. 1968. *Real Wages in Germany, 1871-1913*. Oxford: Clarendon.

DESSAUER, Friedrich. 1958. *Streit um die Technik*. Frankfurt a.M. and Memmingen: Knecht.

Die Deutsche Brauindustrie der Gegenwart. 1930. Mannheim: J. Bensheimer.

DICKSON, David. 1974. *Alternative Technology and the Politics of Technical Change*. London: Fontana.

DIECKMANN, Johann. 1961. *Max Webers Begriff des "modernen okzidentalen Rationalismus."* Cologne: University of Cologne.

DIENEL, Hans-Liudger. 1991. "Eis mit Stil. Die Eigenarten deutscher und amerikanischer Kältetechnik," in Täubrich and Tschoeke, pp. 100-111.

DIERKES, Meinolf. 1988. "Organisationskultur und Leitbilder als Einflußfaktoren der Technikgenese - Thesen zur Strukturierung eines Forschungsfeldes," in Hoffmann, Ute, ed., *Ansätze sozialwissenschaftlicher Analyse von Technikgenese*, Verbund sozialwissenschaftliche Technikforschung, Mitteilungen, Vol. 3. Munich: Institut für Sozialwissenschaftliche Forschung, pp. 49-62.

DIERKES, Meinolf. 1989. *Technikgenese in organisatorischen Kontexten. Neue Entwicklungslinien sozialwissenschaftlicher Technikforschung*. FS II 89-104. Berlin: Wissenschaftszentrum Berlin für Sozialforschung.

DIERKES, Meinolf, and HOFFMANN, Ute, eds. 1992. *New Technology at the Outset: Social Forces in the Shaping of Technological Innovations*. Frankfurt a.M. and New York: Campus and Westview.

DIERKES, Meinolf, HOFFMANN, Ute, and MARZ, Lutz. 1992. *Leitbild und Technik. Zur Entstehung und Steuerung technischer Innovationen*. Berlin: edition sigma.

DIERKES, Meinolf, and KNIE, Andreas. 1989. "Technikgenese. Zur Bedeutung von Organisationskulturen und Konstruktionstraditionen in der Entwicklung des "Motorenbaus und der mechanischen Schreibmaschine," in Lutz, Burkart, ed., *Technik in Alltag und Arbeit*, Verbund sozialwissenschaftliche Technikforschung, Mitteilungen, Vol. 6. Berlin: edition sigma.

DIERKES, Meinolf, and MARZ, Lutz. 1991. "Technikakzeptanz, Technikfolgen und Technikgenese. Zur Weiterentwicklung konzeptioneller Grundlagen der sozialwissenschaftlichen Technikforschung," in Jaufmann, Dieter and Kissler, Ernst eds., *Einstellung zum technischen Fortschritt. Technikakzeptanz im nationalen und internationalen Vergleich*. Frankfurt a.M. and New York: Campus.

DIESEL, Eugen. 1983. *Diesel. Der Mensch, das Werk, das Schicksal*. Munich: Heyne.

DIESEL, Rudolf. 1893. *Theorie und Konstruktion eines rationellen Wärmemotors zum Ersatz der Dampfmaschine und der heute bekannten Verbrennungsmotoren*. Berlin: Springer.

DILLARD, Dudley. 1986/1967. *Västeuropas och Förenta staternas ekonomiska historia*. Lund: Gleerup.

DÖDERLEIN, Gustav. 1903. *Prüfung und Berechnung ausgeführter Ammoniak-Kompressions-Kältemaschinen an Hand des Indikator-Diagramms*. Munich: Oldenbourg.

DOSI, Giovanni. 1982. "Technological Paradigms and Technological Trajectories: A Suggested Interpretation of the Determinants and Directions of Technical Change," *Research Policy*, Vol. 11, pp. 147-162.

DOSI, Giovanni, *et al.* eds. 1988. *Technical Change and Economic Theory*. London and New York: Pinter.

DUFFY, M.C. 1983. "Mechanics, Thermodynamics and Locomotive Design: The Machine-ensemble and the Development of Industrial Thermodynamics," *History and Technology*, Vol. 1, pp. 45-78.

EDLUND, Claes, HERMÉREN, Göran, and NILSTUN, Tore. 1986. *Tvärskap. Samarbete och kunskapsutbyte över ämnesgränser*. Lund: Studentlitteratur.

EDQUIST, Charles. 1977. *Teknik, samhälle och energi*. Malmö: Zenit & Bo Cavefors.

EDQUIST, Charles, and EDQVIST, Olle. 1978. *Social Carriers of Technology for Development*. Report No. 123. Lund: Research Policy Institute.

EDQUIST, Charles, and EDQVIST, Olle. 1979. *Social Carriers of Techniques for Development*. Report No. R3. Stockholm: SAREC.

ELLUL, Jacques. 1964/1954. *The Technological Society*. New York: Vintage.

ELSTER, Jon. 1983. *Explaining Technical Change: A Case Study in the Philosophy of Science*. Cambridge and Oslo: Cambridge University Press and Universitetsforlaget.

EMERY, F.E., and TRIST, E.L. 1960. "Socio-technical Systems," in Churchman, C.W., and Verhulst, M., eds., *Management Science, Models and Techniques*, Vol. 2. Oxford: Pergamon, pp. 83-97.

Encyclopædia Britannica. 1969. 24 vols. Chicago: William Benton.

The Encyclopedia Americana. 1945. 30 vols. New York and Chicago.

ENGELHARDT, H. Tristam, Jr., and CAPLAN, Arthur L., eds. 1987. *Scientific Controversies: Case Studies in the Resolution and Closure of Disputes in Science and Technology*. Cambridge: Cambridge University Press.

ERIKSSON, Bengt Erik. 1987. "Historisk sociologi som löfte," *Sociologisk forskning*, Vol. 24, pp. 3-11.

EWING, J.A. 1923/1908. *The Mechanical Production of Cold*. Cambridge: Cambridge University Press.

FABER, Karl-Georg. 1982/1971. *Theorie der Geschichtswissenschaft*. Munich: C.H. Beck.

FASBENDER, Franz. 1881-1885. *Die mechanische Technologie der Bierbrauerei und Malzfabrikation unter Mitwirkung erfahrener Fachleute und tüchtiger Ingenieure bearbeitet*, 3 vols. Vienna and Leipzig: Gebhardt.

FERGUSON, E. 1979. "The American-ness of American Technology," *Technology and Culture*, Vol. 20, pp. 3-24.

Fest-Schrift herausgegeben zur Erinnerung an die 30jährige Lehrtätigkeit im Braufache des Herrn Karl Michel. 1899. Munich.

Festschrift zur Feier des 25jährigen Bestehens der Gesellschaft ehemaliger Studierender der Eidgenössischen polytechnischen Schule in Zürich. 1894. Zurich: Jegher.

FEUCHTMAYR, Franz. 1921-1922. "Die Konzentration im Braunbierbraugewerbe des rechtsrheinischen Bayerns von den 70er Jahren bis 1921," Dissertation, *manuscript*. Munich: Ludwig-Maximilians-Universität.

FOX, Robert. 1971. *The Caloric Theory of Gases from Lavoisier to Regnault*. Oxford: Clarendon.

FRAENKEL, A. 1897. *Gamle Carlsberg. Et Bidrag til dansk Industri Historie og industriel Udviklingshistorie*. Copenhagen: H. Hagerups Boghandel.

FRÄNGSMYR, Tore, HEILBRON, J.L., and RIDER, Robin E. eds., 1990. *The Quantifying Spirit in the 18th Century*. Berkeley, CA: University of California Press.

Gabriel Sedlmayr Brauerei zum Spaten München. ca. 1911. Brochure at DM-S. Munich.

GEISER, Karl. 1890. *Die Bestrebung zur Gründung einer eidgenössischen Hochschule*. Berne: Wyss.

GERTH, H.H., and MILLS, C. Wright, eds. 1958. *From Max Weber: Essays in Sociology*. New York: Oxford University Press.

GIDDENS, Anthony. 1972. *Politics and Sociology in the Thought of Max Weber*. London: MacMillan.

GISPEN, Cornelis W.R. 1985/1981. "Technical Education and Social Status: The Emergence of the Mechanical Engineering Occupation in Germany: 1820-1890," Dissertation, *mimeograph*. Berkeley, CA: University of California.

GISPEN, Kees. 1990. *New Profession, Old Order: Engineers and German Society, 1815-1914*. Cambridge: Cambridge University Press.

GLETE, Jan. 1987. *Ägande och industriell omvandling. Ägargupper, skogsindustri, verkstadsindustri 1850-1950*. Stockholm: Studieförbundet näringsliv och samhälle.

GODELIER, Maurice. 1972/1966. *Rationality and Irrationality in Economics*. New York: Monthly Review Press.

GOOD, David F. 1984. *The Economic Rise of the Habsburg Empire, 1750-1914*. Berkeley, CA: University of California Press.

GOOSMAN, J.C. 1924-1926. "History of Refrigeration," *Ice and Refrigeration*, Vol. 66-71, passim.

GÖRANZON, Bo, ed. 1983. *Datautvecklingens filosofi. Tyst kunskap och ny teknik.* Stockholm: Carlsson & Jönsson.

GRABOW, Gerd. 1984. "Das Werken und Wirken von Gustav Anton Zeuner (1828 bis 1907)," *Freiberger Forschungshefte*, Vol. D160. Leipzig.

GRASHOF, Franz. 1864. "Über die der Organisation von polytechnischen Schulen zu Grunde zu legenden Principien," *ZVDI*, Vol. 8, pp. 592-618.

GROSS, N.T. 1973. "The Industrial Revolution in the Habsburg Monarchy, 1750-1914," in Cipolla, Ch. 4.

GRÜNER, Gustav. 1967. *Die Entwicklung der höheren technischen Fachschulen im deutschen Sprachgebiet*. Braunschweig: Westermann.

GYR, Peter. 1981. "Joseph Wolfgang von Deschwanden (1819-1866), Erster Direktor des Eidgenössischen Polytechnikums in Zürich," Dissertation, *mimeograph*. Zurich: Universität Freiburg.

HABAKKUK, H.J. 1967/1962. *American and British Technology in the Nineteenth Century: The Search for Labour-Saving Inventions*. Cambridge: Cambridge University Press.

HABER, Samuel. 1964. *Efficiency and Uplift: Scientific Management in the Progressive Era, 1890-1920.* Chicago and London: University of Chicago Press.

HABERMAS, Jürgen. 1968. *Technik und Wissenschaft als "Ideologie."* Frankfurt a.M.: Suhrkamp.

HABERMAS, Jürgen. 1981. *Theorie des kommunikativen Handelns*, 2 vols. Frankfurt a.M.: Suhrkamp.

HABERMAS, Jürgen. 1984. *Vorstudien und Ergänzungen zur Theorie des kommunikativen Handelns*. Frankfurt a.M.: Suhrkamp.

HABICH, G.E. 1869/1862. *Die Schule der Bierbrauerei*, 2nd ed. Leipzig: Spamer.

HABICH, G.E. 1883/1866. *Die Praxis der Bierbraukunde*, 4th ed. Halle a.S.: Knapp.

HALL, Henry. 1888. "The Ice Industry of the United States," in *United States Department of the Interior, Census Office: Report on Power and Machinery Employed in Manufactures*. Tenth Census. Washington, D.C.

HALLENDORFF, C.J. Herman. 1967. *Slagsten och automat.* Stockholm: Seelig.

HÅRD, Mikael. 1979. "Vetenskapsakademierna. En komparativ och kvantitativ studie med tonvikten lagd på akademierna i Berlin och Stockholm vid mitten av 1700-talet," *manuscript*. Gothenburg: Gothenburg University, Dept. of History of Science and Ideas.

HÅRD, Mikael. 1981. *Ingenjören i slutet av 1800-talet*, Report 69, Ser. 2. Gothenburg: Gothenburg University, Dept. of Theory of Science.

HÅRD, Mikael. 1982. "Agricultural Chemistry and Plant Nutrition Theory in France, 1790-1830," *manuscript*. Princeton, NJ: Princeton University, Dept. of History.

HÅRD, Mikael. 1986. "Forskning, skolning, bildning. Carl Linde som teknikens institutionsbyggare, 1875-1906," *Dædalus, Sveriges Tekniska Museums Årsbok*, Vol. 55, pp. 60-69.

HÅRD, Mikael. 1992. *Technology in Flux. Local Practices and Global Patterns in the Development of the Diesel Engine*. FS II 92-103. Berlin: Wissenschaftszentrum Berlin für Sozialforschung.

HÅRD, Mikael. 1993. "Beyond Harmony and Consensus: A Social Conflict Approach to Technology," *Science, Technology, & Human Values*, Vol. 18 (forthcoming).

HÅRD, Mikael. 1993a. "Technological Drift in Science: The Making of Radio Astronomy in Sweden, 1942-1976," in Lindqvist, Svante, ed., *Science on the Periphery: Swedish Physics in the 20th Century*. Canton, MA: Science History Publications (forthcoming).

HARTL, C. 1912. "Die wirtschaftliche Organisation des deutschen Braugewerbes in Vergangenheit und Gegenwart," *Veröffentlichungen der Wirtschaftlichen Abteilung des Vereins 'Versuchs- und Lehranstalt für Brauerei in Berlin,'* Vol. 6. Berlin: Parey.

HAUSER, Albert. 1961. *Schweizerische Wirtschafts- und Sozialgeschichte*. Erlenbach-Zurich and Stuttgart: Rentsch.

HEIMPEL, Karl. 1894. "Über Kühlmaschinen," *Die Technischen Blätter, Vierteljahresschrift des Deutschen Polytechnischen Vereines in Böhmen*, Vol. 25, Nos. 3 & 4, reprint.

HEISS, Philipp. 1875/1853. *Die Bierbrauerei mit besonderer Berücksichtigung der Dickmaischbrauerei*, 6th ed. Augsburg: Lampert.

HEKMAN, Susan J. 1983. *Weber, the Ideal Type, and Contemporary Social Theory*. Notre Dame, IN: University of Notre Dame Press.

HELD, David. 1980. *Introduction to Critical Theory: Horkheimer to Habermas*. Berkeley, CA and London: Hutchinson.

HELMERS, Sabine. 1990. *Theoretische und methodologische Beiträge der Ethnologie zur Unternehmenskulturforschung*. FS II 90-106. Berlin: Wissenschaftszentrum Berlin für Sozialforschung.

HELMERS, Sabine. 1991. *Perspectives on Links Between Professional Culture and Technology Development: Evidence from a Case Study in the Field of Medical Technology*. FS II 91-107. Berlin: Wissenschaftszentrum Berlin für Sozialforschung.

HENDERSON, W.O. 1975. *The Rise of German Industrial Power 1834-1914*. Berkeley and Los Angeles, CA: University of California Press.

HENRIQUES, Pontus. 1917-1927. *Skildringar ur Kungl. tekniska högskolans historia*, 2 vols. Stockholm: Norstedt.

HERMBSTÄDT, Sigismund. 1826/1813. *Chemische Grundsätze der Kunst, Bier zu brauen*, 3rd ed. Berlin.

HESSELMAN, Jonas. 1948. *Teknik och Tanke. Hur en motor kommer till*. Stockholm: Sohlmans.

HIEBERT, Erwin N. 1962. *Historical Roots of the Principle of the Conservation of Energy*. Madison, WI: State Historical Society of Wisconsin.

HIRN, G.-A. 1865. *Théorie méchanique de la chaleur, première partie. Exposition analytique et expérimentale*. Paris: Gauthier-Villars.

HOBSBAWM, E.J. 1968. *Industry and Empire: From 1750 to the Present Day*. Harmondsworth, Middles.: Penguin.

HOBSBAWM, E.J. 1981/1975. *Kapitalets tidsålder*. Stockholm: Tiden.

HOFFMANN, Walther G. 1965. *Das Wachstum der deutschen Wirtschaft seit der Mitte des 19. Jahrhunderts*. Berlin: Springer.

HOFMANN, Hannes. 1962. *Die Anfänge der Maschinenindustrie in der deutschen Schweiz 1800-1875*. Zurich: Fretz & Wasmuth.

HOLMER, Jan. 1988. "Dekvalificering, polarisering, eller rekvalificering?" *manuscript*. Gothenburg: Gothenburg University.

HÖLSCHER, L. 1982. "Industrie, Gewerbe," in Brunner *et al.* 1972-1984, Vol. 3, pp. 237-304.

HOLTER, Heinz, and MØLLER, K. Max, eds. 1976. *The Carlsberg Laboratory 1876/1976*. Copenhagen: Rhodes.

HOLTON, Robert J., and TURNER, Bryan S. 1989. *Max Weber on Economy and Society*. London and New York: Routledge & Kegan Paul.

HOLZNER, Georg. 1893. "Dr. Emil Struve über die Entwicklung des Bayerischen Braugewerbes im neunzehnten Jahrhundert," *Zeitschrift für das gesammte Brauwesen*, Vol. 16, reprint.

HORKHEIMER, Max. 1941. "The End of Reason," *Studies in Philosophy and Social Science*, Vol. 9, pp. 366-388.

HORKHEIMER, Max. 1985/1947. *Zur Kritik der instrumentellen Vernunft*. Frankfurt a.M.: Fischer.

HORKHEIMER, Max, and ADORNO, Theodor W. 1969/1944. *Dialektik der Aufklärung: Philosophische Fragmente*. Frankfurt a.M.: Fischer.

HOUNSHELL, David A. 1984. *From the American System to Mass Production: The Development of Manufacturing Technology in the United States*. Baltimore, MD: John Hopkins University Press.

HUGHES, Thomas P. 1971. *Elmer Sperry: Inventor and Engineer*. Baltimore, MD and London: John Hopkins Press.

HUGHES, Thomas P. 1983. *Networks of Power: Electrification in Western Society, 1880-1930*. Baltimore, MD, and London: John Hopkins University Press.

HUGHES, Thomas P. 1987. "The Evolution of Large Technological Systems," in Bijker *et al.*, pp. 51-82.

Des Ingenieurs Taschenbuch. 1870, 1887. 8th ed., 13th ed. Berlin: Verein "Hütte."

JACOB, Max. 1917. "C. Lindes Lebenswerk," *Die Naturwissenschaften*, Vol. 5, pp. 417-423.

JACOBS, Alfred, and RICHTER, Hans. 1935. "Die Grosshandelspreise in Deutschland von 1792 bis 1934," *Sonderhefte des Instituts für Konjunkturforschung*, Vol. 37.

JANOSKA-BENDL, Judith. 1965. *Methodologische Aspekte des Idealtypus. Max Weber und die Soziologie der Geschichte*. Berlin: Duncker & Humblot.

JAY, Martin. 1973. *The Dialectical Imagination: A History of the Frankfurt School and the Institute of Social Research, 1923-1950*. London: Heinemann.

JOERGES, Bernward. 1988. "Large Technical Systems: Concepts and Issues," in Mayntz and Hughes, pp. 9-36.

JOHANSSON, H. 1983. "Arctic," *Motalabygd*.

JOKISCH, Rodrigo, ed. 1982. *Techniksoziologie*. Frankfurt a.M.: Suhrkamp.

JÖRGENSEN, Alfred. 1909/1886. *Die Mikroorganismen der Gärungsindustrie*, 5th ed. Berlin: Parey.

KAIJSER, Arne. 1986. *Stadens ljus. Etableringen av de första svenska gasverken*. Stockholm: Liber.

KAISER, G.C. von. 1907/1835. "Zur Geschichte der Bierproben," in Michel 1906-1907, Vol. 2, pp. 9-16.

KAIZL, Josef. 1879. "Der Kampf um Gewerbereform und Gewerbefreiheit in Bayern von 1799-1868," in Schmoller, G., ed., *Staats- und sozialwissenschaftliche Forschungen*, Vol. 2, No. 1. Leipzig.

KALBERG, Stephen. 1980. "Max Weber's Types of Rationality: Cornerstones for the Analysis of Rationalization Processes in History," *American Journal of Sociology*, Vol. 85, pp. 1145-1179.

KALIDE, Wolfgang. 1976. *Thermodynamik der Kühl- und Kälteanlagen*. Munich and Vienna: Hanser.

KARLQVIST, Anders. 1983. *Teknik och samhälle. En systemanalytisk introduktion*. Tema T Report No. RB-83-4. Linköping: University of Linköping.

KASPEROWSKI, Adam. 1834. *Die Dampfbierbräuerey*. Leipzig: Hermann und Langbein.

KASSON, John F. 1976. *Civilizing the Machine: Technology and Republican Values in America, 1776-1900*. Harmondsworth, Middles.: Penguin.

KELLENBENZ, Hermann. 1981. *Deutsche Wirtschaftsgeschichte: II. Vom Ausgang des 18. Jahrhunderts bis zum Ende des Zweiten Weltkriegs*. Munich: C.H. Beck.

KELLNER, Douglas. 1984. *Herbert Marcuse and the Crisis of Marxism*. London: MacMillan.

KELLY, Patrick, and KRANZBERG, Melvin, eds. 1978. *Technological Innovation: A Critical Review of Current Knowledge*. San Francisco: San Francisco Press.

KENNGOTT, Eva-Maria. 1990. *Der Organisationskulturansatz. Ein mögliches Programm zur Konzeption von Entscheidungsverhalten in Organisationen*. FS II 90-103. Berlin: Wissenschaftszentrum Berlin für Sozialforschung.

KENWOOD, A.G., and LOUGHEED, A.L. 1983. *The Growth of the International Economy 1820-1980: An Introductory Text*. London: Allen & Unwin.

KERN, Horst, and SCHUMANN, Michael. 1984. *Das Ende der Arbeitsteilung? Rationalisierung in der industriellen Produktion: Bestandsaufnahme, Trendbestimmung*. Munich: C.H. Beck.

KIENINGER, Helmut. 1976. *Hundert Jahre Wissenschaftliche Station für Brauerei in München e.V., 1876-1976*. Nuremberg.

KIRK, Alexander C. 1873-1874. "On the Mechanical Production of Cold," *MPICE*, Vol. 37, pp. 244-270.

KLEIN, R. 1888. *Aus dem industriellen Leben*. Berlin: A. Braun.

KLUCKHOHN, August. 1878-1879. "Ueber die Gründung und bisherige Entwicklung der k. technischen Hochschule zu München," in *Bericht* ..., pp. 45-62.

KNIE, Andreas. 1989. *Das Konservative des technischen Fortschritts. Zur Bedeutung von Konstruktionstraditionen, Forschungs- und Konstruktionsstilen in der Technikgenese*. FS II 89-101. Berlin: Wissenschaftszentrum Berlin für Sozialforschung.

KNIE, Andreas. 1991. *Diesel - Karriere einer Technik. Genese und Formierungsprozesse im Motorenbau*. Berlin: edition sigma.

KNIE, Andreas. 1991a. "'Generierung' und 'Härtung' technischen Wissens: Die Entstehung der mechanischen Schreibmaschine." *Technikgeschichte*, Vol. 58, pp. 101-26.

KNIE, Andreas. 1992. *Gemachte Technik. Zur Bedeutung von 'Fahnenträgern,' 'Promotoren' und 'Definitionsmacht' in der Technikgenese*. FS II 92-104. Berlin: Wissenschaftszentrum Berlin für Sozialforschung.

KNIE, Andreas. 1992a. "The Vain Search for Alternatives: Closure Processes in Internal-Combustion Engine Design, 1960-1990," *paper* presented at the Annual Meeting of the Society for the History of Technology, Uppsala, August 16-20.

KNIE, Andreas, BUHR, Regina, and HASS, Marion. 1992. *Auf der Suche nach den strategischen Orten der Technikgestaltung. Die Schreibmaschinen-Entwicklung der Mercedes-Büromaschinen-Werke zwischen den Jahren 1907 und 1940.* FS II 92-101. Berlin: Wissenschaftszentrum Berlin für Sozialforschung.

KNIGHT, Edward H. 1876. *Knight's American Mechanical Dictionary*. New York: Hurd & Houghton.

KOCKA, Jürgen. 1969. *Unternehmensverwaltung und Angestelltenschaft am Beispiel Siemens 1847-1914. Zum Verhältnis von Kapitalismus und Bürokratie in der deutschen Industrialisierung*. Stuttgart: Klett.

KOCKA, Jürgen. 1975. *Unternehmer in der deutschen Industrialisierung*. Göttingen: Vandenhoeck & Ruprecht.

KOCKA, Jürgen, ed. 1986. *Max Weber, der Historiker*. Göttingen: Vandenhoeck & Ruprecht.

KOCKA, Jürgen. 1986a. "Max Webers Bedeutung für die Geschichtswissenschaft" in Kocka 1986, pp. 13-27.

KÖNIG, Wolfgang. 1989. "Technische Vereine als Bildungseinrichtungen," in Boehm and Schönbeck, pp. 260-277.

KÖNIG, Wolfgang, and WEBER, Wolfhard. 1990. *Netzwerke, Stahl und Strom, 1840 bis 1914*. Berlin: Propyläen.

KORISTKA, Carl. 1863. *Der höhere polytechnische Unterricht in Deutschland, in der Schweiz, in Frankreich, Belgien und England*. Gotha: Besser.

KRANZBERG, Melvin. 1967. "The Unity of Science-Technology," *American Scientist*, Vol. 55, pp. 48-66.

KRANZBERG, Melvin. 1968. "The Disunity of Science-Technology," *American Scientist*, Vol. 56, pp. 21-34.

KROHN, Wolfgang, LAYTON, Jr., Edwin T., and WEINGART, Peter. 1978. *The Dynamics of Science and Technology: Social Values, Technical Norms and Scientific Criteria in the Development of Knowledge*. Dordrecht and Boston: Reidel.

KRUG, K. 1981. "Zur Herausbildung der Technischen Thermodynamik am Beispiel der wissenschaftlichen Schule von G.A. Zeuner," *NTM-Schriftenreihe für Geschichte der Naturwissenschaften, Technik und Medizin*, Vol. 18, pp. 79-97.

KRUMPER, Josef. 1916. "Einige Lebens-Erinnerungen ... mit Bezug auf die 'Maschinenfabrik Augsburg' in Augsburg und 'Werk Augsburg' der Maschinenfabrik Augsburg-Nürnberg A.G.," *manuscript*, at MAN-W.

KUCZYNSKI, Jürgen. 1947. *Die Bewegung der deutschen Wirtschaft von 1800 bis 1946, 16 Vorlesungen*. Berlin and Leipzig: Volk und Wissen.

KUHN, Thomas S. 1955. "Carnot's Version of 'Carnot's Cycle,'" *American Journal of Physics*, Vol. 23, pp. 91-95.

KUHN, Thomas S. 1959. "Energy Conservation as an Example of Simultaneous Discovery," in Clagett, Marshall, ed. *Critical Problems in the History of Science*. Madison, WI: University of Wisconsin Press, pp. 321-356.

KUHN, Thomas S. 1970/1962. *The Structure of Scientific Revolutions*, 2nd ed. Chicago and London: University of Chicago Press.

KÜPPERS, Günther. 1978. "On the Relation Between Technology and Science: Goals of Knowledge and Dynamics of Theories. The Example of Combustion Technology, Thermodynamics and Fluid Mechanics," in Krohn *et al.*, pp. 113-133.

KÜTTLER, Wolfgang, and LOZEK, Gerhard. 1986. "Der Klassenbegriff im Marxismus und in der idealtypischen Methode Max Webers," in Kocka, pp. 173-192.

KUZNETS, Simon. 1978. "Technological Innovations and Economic Growth," in Kelly and Kranzberg, pp. 335-356.

LACEY, A.R. 1976. *A Dictionary of Philosophy*. London: Routledge & Kegan Paul.

LANDES, David S. 1969. *The Unbound Prometheus: Technological Change and Industrial Development in Western Europe from 1750 to the Present*. Cambridge: Cambridge University Press.

LANG, Alexander. 1905. "Franz Reuleaux und die Maschinenwissenschaft," *Zeitschrift für Sozialwissenschaft*, Vol. 8, pp. 804-809.

LARRAIN, Jorge. 1979. *The Concept of Ideology*. London: Hutchinson.

LASH, Schott, and WHIMSTER, Sam, eds. 1987. *Max Weber, Rationality and Modernity*. London: Allen & Unwin.

LATOUR, Bruno. 1984. *Les microbes. Guerre et paix suivi de irréductions*. Paris: A.M. Metaile.

LATOUR, Bruno. 1987. *Science in Action: How to Follow Scientists and Engineers Through Society*. Cambridge, MA: Harvard University Press.

LATOUR, Bruno. 1987a. "Sociology of a Door," *manuscript*. Paris: École Nationale Supérieure des Mines.

LAW, John. 1987. "Technology and Heterogeneous Engineering: The Case of Portuguese Expansion," in Bijker *et al.*, pp. 111-134.

LAZONICK, William. 1985. "The Self-Acting Mule and Social Relations in the Workplace," in MacKenzie and Wajcman, pp. 93-108.

LAUDAN, Rachel. 1982. "Conference Report: Models of Scientific and Technological Change: Center for Philosophy of Science, University of Pittsburgh, April 9-12, 1981," *Technology and Culture*, Vol. 23, pp. 78-80.

LAUDAN, Rachel, ed. 1984. *The Nature of Technological Knowledge: Are Models of Scientific Change Relevant?* Dordrecht: Reidel.

LAYTON, Edwin T., Jr. 1971. "Mirror-Image Twins: The Communities of Science and Technology in 19th-Century America," *Technology and Culture*, Vol. 12, pp. 562-580.

LAYTON, Edwin T., Jr. 1971a. *The Revolt of the Engineers: Social Responsibility and the American Engineering Profession*. Cleveland: Press of Case Western Reserve University.

LAYTON, Edwin T., Jr. 1974. "Technology as Knowledge," *Technology and Culture*, Vol. 15, pp. 31-41.

LAYTON, Edwin T., Jr. 1979. "Scientific Technology, 1845-1900: The Hydraulic Turbine and the Origins of American Industrial Research," *Technology and Culture*, Vol. 20, pp. 64-89.

LEDOUX. 1878. Théorie des machines à froid, *Annales des mines*, 7th Ser., Vol. 14, pp. 121-208.

LEECH, Harper, and CARROLL, John C. 1938. *Armour and His Times*. New York and London: D. Appleton-Century.

LEIJON, Svante, *et al.* 1988. *Den nya tekniken - förändring eller anpassning*. Gothenburg: BAS.

LIEDMAN, Sven-Eric. 1980. *Surdeg. En personlig bok om idéer och ideologier*. Stockholm: Författarförlaget.

LIEDMAN, Sven-Eric. 1983/1977. *Motsatsernas spel. Friedrich Engels och 1800-talets vetenskap*. Malmö: Arkiv.

LIEDMAN, Sven-Eric. 1984. "Om ideologier," in *Om ideologier och ideologianalys*. Gothenburg: Gothenburg University, Dept. of History of Science and Ideas, pp. 1-51.

LIEDMAN, Sven-Eric. 1986. "Institutions and Ideas: Mandarins and Non-Mandarins in the German Academic Intelligentsia," *Comparative Studies in Society & History*, Vol. 28, pp. 119-144.

LINDBERG, Bo, and NILSSON, Ingemar. 1978. "Sunt förnuft och historisk inlevelse. Den nordströmska traditionen," in Forser, Tomas, ed., *Humaniora på undantag? Humanistiska forskningstraditioner i Sverige*. Stockholm: PAN/Norstedts, pp. 79-107.

LINDE, Carl. 1868. *Ueber einige Methoden zum Bremsen der Lokomotiven und Eisenbahnzüge*. Munich.

LINDE, Carl. 1869. "Ueber die Verwertung der Wärme zu mechanischer Arbeit," *BIGB*, Vol. 1, pp. 328-331, 363-366.

LINDE, Carl. 1870. "Ueber die Wärmeentziehung bei niedrigen Temperaturen durch mechanische Mittel," *BIGB*, Vol. 2, pp. 205-210, 321-326, 363-367.

LINDE, Carl. 1870a. "Ueber Luftdampfmaschinen," *BIGB*, Vol. 2, pp. 22-25, 92-95.

LINDE, Carl. 1871. "Verbesserte Eis- und Kühlmaschine," *BIGB*, Vol. 3, pp. 264-272.

LINDE, Carl. 1874. "Ueber Kälte-Erzeugungs-Maschinen," *BIGB*, Vol. 6, pp. 65-71.

LINDE, Carl. 1875-1876. "Theorie der Kälteerzeugungsmaschinen," *Verhandlungen d. Vereins z. Beförd. d. Gewerbefleisses*, Vol. 54, pp. 357-367, Vol. 55, pp. 185-196.

LINDE, Carl. 1893. "The Refrigerating Machine of To-Day," *Trans. Am. Soc. Mech. Engineers*, Vol. 14, pp. 1414-1434.

LINDE, Carl. 1894. "Zur Theorie der Kohlensäure-(Kaltdampf-)maschinen," *ZVDI*, Vol. 38, pp. 161-165.

LINDE, Carl. 1895. "Zur Theorie der Kohlensäure-(Kaltdampf-)maschine. (Ein experimenteller Beitrag)," *ZVDI*, Vol. 39, pp. 124-127.

LINDE, Carl. 1902. "Ungleichwertigkeit von Ammoniak, Kohlensäure und schwefliger Säure in Kompressions-Kaltdampfmaschinen," *Zeitschrift f. d. gesammte Kälte-Industrie*, Vol. 9, pp. 101-106.

LINDE, Carl. 1979/1916. *Aus meinem Leben und von meiner Arbeit*. Munich: Oldenbourg.

LINDEMANN, Fritz O.A. 1971. "Rationalisierung," in *Management-Enzyklopädie*, Vol. 5. Munich: Verlag Moderne Industrie, pp. 44-52.

LINDNER, Helmut. 1982. "Technische Entwicklung und das Problem der Mehrfacherfindung," in Jokisch, pp. 394-408.

LINDQVIST, Svante. 1984. *Technology on Trial: The Introduction of Steam Power Technology into Sweden, 1715-1736*. Stockholm: Almqvist & Wiksell International.

LINDQVIST, Svante. 1988. "Disseminering av vetenskap i institutionella strukturer. En aspekt på kunskapens relativisering," *TRITA-HOT*. No. 7002, Stockholm: Royal Institute of Technology.

LINDSKOUG, Kerstin. 1979. *Hänförelse och förnuft. Om karisma och rationalitet i Max Webers sociologi*. Lund: Dialog.

LINTNER, Carl. 1877. *Lehrbuch der Bierbrauerei: Nach dem heutigen Standpunkte der Theorie und Praxis*. Braunschweig.

LINTNER, Carl. 1906. "Das Brauwesen," in *Darstellungen aus der Geschichte der Technik der Industrie und Landwirtschaft in Bayern*. Munich: Oldenbourg, pp. 234-246.

LOHMANN, Hans-Dieter. 1972. "Über das historische Wechselverhältnis zwischen Produktion und kältephysikalischer Forschung (Ein Beitrag zur Geschichte der Entwicklung der Wissenschaft zur Produktivkraft)," *NTM-Schriftenreihe f. Gesch. d. Naturw. Technik u. Med.*, Vol. 9, pp. 1-22.

LOHMANN, Hans-Dieter. 1980. "Die Herausbildung der technischen Thermodynamik im 19. Jahrhundert in Deutschland," *Dresdener Beiträge z. Geschichte d. Technikwissenschaften*, Vol. 2, pp. 68-85.

LOHMANN, Hans-Dieter. 1981. "Die Rolle Gustav Anton Zeuners (1828-1907) bei der Herausbildung der Technischen Thermodynamik," *Rostocker Wissenschaftshist. Manuskr.*, No. 7, pp. 63-68.

LORENZ, H. 1899. "Die Wirkungsweise und Berechnung der Ammoniak-Absorptions-Maschinen," *Zeitschrift f. d. gesammte Kälte-Industrie*, Vol. 6, No. II, reprint.

LOVERDO, J. de. 1903. *Le Froid Artificiel et ses Applications Industrielles, Commerciales et Agricoles*. Paris: C.H. Dunod.

LÜERS, Heinrich. 1951. *Fünfundsiebzig Jahre Wissenschaftliche Station für Brauerei in München 1876-1951*. Nuremberg.

LUKACS, Georg. 1968/1923. "Geschichte und Klassenbewusstsein," *Georg Lukács Werke, Frühschriften*, Vol. 2. Neuwied and Berlin: Luchterhand.

LUNDQUIST, Agne. 1983. "Max Weber. Förord," in Weber, Max, *Ekonomi och samhälle. Förståendesociologins grunder*, Vol. 1. Lund: Argos, pp. IX-XXXIX.

Lyckholms bryggeri 1881-1931. 1933. Gothenburg: Aktiebolaget Pripps & Lyckholm.

MCCARTY, Harry C. 1902. "Slaughtering and Meat Packing," *United States Census Office: Census Reports, Vol. IX, Twelfth Census of the United States, Taken in the Year 1900, Manufactures, Part III*. Washington, D.C.

MCGAW, Judith. 1987. *Most Wonderful Machine: Mechanization and Social Change in Berkshire Paper Making, 1801-1885*. Princeton: Princeton University Press.

MACKENZIE, Donald, and WAJCMAN, Judy, eds. 1985. *The Social Shaping of Technology: How the Refrigerator Got Its Hum*, Milton, Keynes: Open University Press.

MACKENZIE, Donald, and WAJCMAN, Judy. 1985a. "Introductory Essay: The Social Shaping of Technology," in idem. 1985, pp. 2-25.

MCKINNEY, John C. 1970. "Sociological Theory and the Process of Typification," in McKinney and Tiryakin, pp. 235-270.

MCKINNEY, John C., and TIRYAKIN, Edward A., eds. 1970. *Theoretical Sociology: Perspectives and Developments*. New York: Appleton-Century-Crofts.

MACMANUS, R.D. 1925. *The Nation's Meat*. New York: Industries Publishing Co.

MACH, Ernst. 1883. *Die Mechanik in ihrer Entwicklung historisch-kritisch dargestellt*. Leipzig: Brockhaus.

MACK, Pamela E. 1990. *Viewing the Earth: The Social Construction of the Landsat Satellite System*. Cambridge, MA: MIT Press.

MANEGOLD, Karl-Heinz. 1969. "Das Verhältnis von Naturwissenschaft und Technik im 19. Jahrhundert im Spiegel der Wissenschaftsorganisation," *Technikgeschichte in Einzeldarstellungen*, Vol. 11, pp. 141-187.

MANEGOLD, Karl-Heinz. 1970. "Die Entwicklung der Technischen Hochschule Hannover zur wissenschaftlichen Hochschule. Ein Beitrag zum Thema 'Verwissenschaftlichung der Technik im 19. Jahrhundert,'" *Technikgeschichte in Einzeldarstellungen*, Vol. 16, pp. 13-46.

MANEGOLD, Karl-Heinz. 1970a. *Universität, Technische Hochschule und Industrie: Ein Beitrag zur Emanzipation der Technik im 19. Jahrhundert unter besonderer Berücksichtigung der Bestrebungen Felix Kleins*. Berlin: Duncker & Humblot.

MANEGOLD, Karl-Heinz. 1978. "Technology Academised: Education and Training of the Engineer in the 19th Century," in Krohn *et al.*, pp. 137-158.

MANSFELD, Robert. 1913. "Kapitalkonzentration im Brauereigewerbe," *Veröffentlichungen der Wirtschaftlichen Abteilung des Vereins 'Versuchs- und Lehranstalt für Brauerei in Berlin,'* Vol. 8. Berlin.

MARCUSE, Herbert. 1964. *One-Dimensional Man: Studies in the Ideology of Advanced Industrial Society*. London: Routledge & Kegan Paul.

MARCUSE, Herbert. 1968/1965. "Industrialization and Capitalism in the Work of Max Weber," in idem., *Negations: Essays in Critical Theory*. London: Allen Lane.

MARUO, Kanehira. 1992. "The Three-Way 'Catalysis:' A History of a Rhethorical Closure Around Automobile Emission Control Technology," *paper* presented at the Annual Meeting of the Society for the History of Technology, Uppsala, August 16-20.

MARX, Karl. 1982/1867. *Das Kapital. Kritik der politischen Ökonomie*, Vol. 1, 4th ed. Berlin: Dietz.

MARX, Leo. 1964. *The Machine in the Garden: Technology and the Pastoral Ideal in America*. New York: Oxford University Press.

MARZ, Lutz, and DIERKES, Meinolf. 1992. *Leitbildprägung und Leitbildgestaltung. Zum Beitrag der Technikgenese-Forschung für eine prospektive Technikfolgen-Regulierung*. FS II 92-105. Berlin: Wissenschaftszentrum Berlin für Sozialforschung.

MATHES, Heinz Dieter. 1981. "Rationalisierung," in *Handwörterbuch der Wirtschaftswissenschaft*, Vol. 6. Stuttgart and New York: Gustav Fischer, pp. 399-406.

MATHIAS, Peter. 1959. *The Brewing Industry in England 1700-1830*. Cambridge: Cambridge University Press.

MAUEL, Kurt. 1969. "Die Aufnahme naturwissenschaftlicher Erkenntnisse und Methoden durch die Ingenieure im 19. Jahrhundert," *Technikgeschichte in Einzeldarstellungen*, Vol. 11, pp. 189-219.

MAUERSBERGER, Klaus. 1980. "Die Herausbildung der technischen Mechanik und ihr Anteil bei der Verwissenschaftlichung des Maschinenwesens," *Dresdener Beiträge zur Geschichte der Technikwissenschaften*, Vol. 2, pp. 1-52.

MAUERSBERGER, Klaus. 1984. "Quellen und Herausbildung technikwissenschaftlicher Methoden in Mechanik und Maschinenbau," *Dresdener Beiträge zur Geschichte der Technikwissenschaften*, Vol. 8, pp. 17-23.

MAYNTZ, Renate, and HUGHES, Thomas P., eds. 1988. *The Development of Large Technological Systems*, Frankfurt a.M.: Campus.

MAYR, Otto, and POST, Robert C., eds. 1981. *Yankee Enterprise: The Rise of the American System of Manufactures*. Washington, D.C.: Smithsonian Institution Press.

MENDELSSOHN, K. 1977/1966. *The Quest for Absolute Zero: The Meaning of Low Temperature Physics*. London: Weidenfeld & Nicolson.

MENDOZA, E. 1961. "A Sketch for a History of Early Thermodynamics," *Physics Today*, Vol. 14, No. 2, pp. 32-42.

MENSCH, Gerhard. 1979/1975. *Stalement in Technology: Innovations Overcome the Depression*. Cambridge, MA: Ballinger.

MEYER, Kirstine. 1913. *Die Entwicklung des Temperaturbegriffs im Laufe der Zeiten*. Braunschweig: Friedrich Vieweg & Sohn.

MICHEL, Carl. 1880. *Lehrbuch der Bierbrauerei nach dem neuesten Standpunkte der Wissenschaft und Praxis*, 3 vols. Augsburg: Schlosser'sche Buchhandlung.

MICHEL, Carl. 1906-1907. *Beiträge zur Entwicklungsgeschichte der Bierbrauerei*, 3 vols. Munich.

MICHELSON, J. 1907. "Die bayerische Grossindustrie und ihre Entwicklung seit dem Eintritt Bayerns in das Deutsche Reich," Dissertation, *mimeograph*. Erlangen: Friedrich-Alexander-Universität.

MILWARD, Alan S., and SAUL, S.B. 1977. *The Development of the Economies of Continental Europe 1850-1914*. London: Allen & Unwin.

MITCHEL, G. Duncan, ed. 1979. *A New Dictionary of Sociology*. London: Routledge & Kegan Paul.

MITZMAN, Arthur. 1971. *The Iron Cage: An Historical Interpretation of Max Weber*. New York: Knopf.

MOMMSEN, Wolfgang. 1974. *The Age of Bureaucracy: Perspectives on the Political Sociology of Max Weber*. Oxford.

MOMMSEN, Wolfgang. 1987. "Personal Conduct and Societal Change," in Lash and Whimster, pp. 35-51.

MONCKTON, H.A. 1966. *A History of English Ale and Beer*. London: Bodley Head.

MORGAN, Neil. 1980. "The Development of Biochemistry in England Through Botany and the Brewing Industry (1870-1890)," *History & Philosophy of the Life Sciences*, Vol. 2, pp. 141-166.

MÜLLER, August Ernst. 1845. *Lehrbuch der Ober- und Untergährung des Bieres*. Braunschweig: Friedrich Vieweg & Sohn.

MÜLLER, Jens, REMMEN, Arne, and CHRISTENSEN, Per. 1984. *Samfundets teknologi, teknologiens samfund*. Herning, DK: Systime.

MÜNCH, Richard. 1981. "Über Parsons zu Weber: Von der Theorie der Rationalisierung zur Theorie der Interpretation," in Sprondel and Seyfarth, pp. 108-156.

MURRAY, Patrick. 1982. "The Frankfurt School Critique of Technology," in Durbin, Paul, ed., *Research in Philosophy and Technology*, Vol. 5. Greeenwich, CT: JAI Press, pp. 223-248.

NELSON, Daniel. 1975. *Managers and Workers: Origins of the New Factory System in the United States, 1880-1920*. Madison, WI: University of Wisconsin Press.

NORDIN, Ingemar. 1988. *Teknologins rationalitet. En teori om teknikens struktur och dynamik*. Stockholm: Timbro.

Nouvelle Biographie Générale (Universelle). 1852-1866. 46 vols. Paris.

OECHSLI, Wilhelm. 1905. "Geschichte der Gründung des Eidgenössischen Polytechnikums mit einer Übersicht seiner Entwicklung 1855-1905," *Festschrift zur Feier des fünfzigjährigen Bestehens des Eidg. Polytechnikums*, Vol. 1. Frauenfeld.

OGBURN, William F. 1923. *Social Change with Respect to Culture and Original Nature*. London: Allen & Unwin.

OLDHAM, Bernard C. 1946-1947. "Evolution of Machine and Plant Design," *mimeograph*. London: The Institute of Refrigeration.

OLSON, Erik. 1935. "Bryggeriindustrien i teknikens tidevarv," in Bring, pp. 175-206.

Om fabrikation af artificiel is och frusna karaffer med användande af Raoul Pictets system för ismaskiner. 1881. Stockholm: A.L. Norman.

Om framställandet af artificiel köld i bryggerier genom apparater efter Raoul Pictets system. 1881. Stockholm: A.L. Norman.

OTTO, Fr. Jul. 1865. "Die Bierbrauerei, die Branntweinbrennerei und die Liqueurfabrikation," in Bolley, P., ed., *Handbuch der chemischen Technologie*, Vol. 4, Gr. l. Braunschweig: Friedrich Vieweg & Sohn.

PARKIN, Frank. 1982. *Max Weber*. Chichester and London: Ellis Horwood and Tavistock.

PARSONS, Talcott. 1970. "Some Problems of General Theory in Sociology," in McKinney and Tiryakin, pp. 27-68.

PARTINGTON, J.R. 1964. *A History of Chemistry*, Vol. 4. London: MacMillan.

PASSER, Harold C. 1953. *The Electrical Manufacturers, 1875-1900: A Study in Competition, Entrepreneurship, Technical Change, and Economic Growth*. Cambridge, MA: Harvard University Press.

PASTEUR, L. 1876. *Études sur la bière*. Paris: Gauthier-Villars.

PAUPIE, Franz Andreas. 1794. *Die Kunst des Bierbrauens, physisch, chemisch und ökonomisch beschrieben*. Prague: Widtmann.

PAWLOWITSCH, A. 1978. "Zum wissenschaftlichen Schaffen Gustav Zeuners aus heutiger Sicht," *Maschinenbautechnik*, Vol. 27, pp. 484-487.

PERREN, Richard. 1978. *The Meat Trade in Britain 1840-1914*. London: Routledge & Kegan Paul.

PFETSCH, Frank R. 1978. "Innovationsforschung in historischer Perspektive. Ein Überblick," *Technikgeschichte*, Vol. 45, pp. 118-133.

"The Pictet Artificial Ice Company (Limited)." 1878. *Pamphlet*, at Yale University Library. New York.

PIERCE, Bessie L. 1937-1957. *A History of Chicago*. 3 vols. New York and London: Knopf.

PINCH, Trevor J., and BIJKER, Wiebe E. 1987. "The Social Construction of Facts and Artifacts: Or How the Sociology of Science and the Sociology of Technology Might Benefit Each Other," in Bijker *et al.*, pp. 17-50.

PLANITZ, Hans von der. 1879. *Das Bier und seine Bereitung einst und jetzt*. Munich: Oldenbourg.

POSSANNER, Benno Freiherr von. 1894. *Technologie der Landwirtschaftlichen Gewerbe, I. Band: Das Wasser und die Wärme. Die Stärkefabrication. Die Bierbrauerei*. Vienna: Hof- und Staatsdruckerei.

PRECHTL, Joh. Jos. 1833. *Handbok för bryggning och maltberedning*. Stockholm: Georg Scheutz.

Premier Congrès International du Froid, Paris 5 au 12 octobre 1908. 1908. 3 vols. Paris: Secrétariat général de l'Association International du Froid.

PRICE, Derek J. de Solla. 1965. "Is Technology Historically Independent of Science? A Study in Statistical Historiography," *Technology and Culture*, Vol. 6, pp. 553-568.

PRICE, Derek J. de Solla. 1982. "The Parallel Structures of Science and Technology," in Barnes, Barry, and Edge, David, eds. *Science in Context: Readings in the Sociology of Science*. Milton, Keynes, pp. 164-176.

PRICE, Derek J. de Solla. 1986. *Little Science, Big Science ... and Beyond*. New York: Columbia University Press.

PRICE, Roger. 1981. *An Economic History of Modern France, 1730-1914*. London: MacMillan.

PSYCHOPEDIS, Kosmas. 1984. *Geschichte und Methode. Begründungstypen und Interpretationskriterien der Gesellschaftstheorie: Kant, Hegel, Marx und Weber*. Frankfurt a.M. and New York: Campus.

RADKAU, Joachim. 1989. *Technik in Deutschland. Vom 18. Jahrhundert bis zur Gegenwart*. Frankfurt a.M.: Suhrkamp.

RAMMERT, Werner. 1992. "Research on the Generation and Development of Technology: The State of the Art in Germany," in Dierkes and Hoffmann, pp. 62-89.

RANKINE, William John Macquorn. 1859. *A Manual of the Steam Engine and Other Prime Movers*. London and Glasgow: R. Griffin.

RAUM, H. 1965. "Die Brauerschule in Weihenstephan von 1865 bis 1895," in *100 Jahre Fakultät ...*, pp. 17-33.

RENATUS, Elisabeth. 1982. "Ueber Bier-Untersuchungen und Fehler, welche dabei gemacht werden können: Beiträge des Polytechnischen Vereins in Bayern zur Entwicklung der Brauwissenschaft im 19. Jahrhundert," Dissertation, Technische Universität Mannheim, *mimeograph*. Munich.

"Report of the Commissioner of Corporations of the Beef Industry, March 3, 1905." 1905, in *United States 58th Congress, 3rd Session,* House of Representatives, Doc. No. 382. Washington, D.C.

REULEAUX, Franz. 1861. *Der Constructeur. Ein Handbuch zum Gebrauch beim Maschinen-Entwerfen*. Braunschweig: Friedrich Vieweg und Sohn.

REULEAUX, Franz. 1865. "Maschinenbaukunde." Vorträge von Herrn F. Reuleaux, Professor am Königl. Gewerbe-Institut in Berlin etc. etc., gehalten am Eidgenöss. Polytechnikum zu Zürich im Schuljahr 1863/64, at ETH-Bibliothek, Zurich, *manuscript*. Karlsruhe.

REULEAUX, Franz. 1875. *Theoretische Kinematik: Grundzüge einer Theorie des Maschinenwesens*. Berlin.

RICHARDSON, John. 1784. *Statistical Estimates of the Materials of Brewing: or, a Treatise on the Application and Use of the Saccharometer*. London: privately published.

RICHARDSON, John. 1798. *The Philosophical Principles of the Science of Brewing*. York: G. Peacock.

RICHMOND, Georg. 1893. "Notes on the Refrigeration Process and Its Proper Place in Thermodynamics," *Transactions of the American Society of Mechanical Engineers*, Vol. 14, pp. 183-250.

RIEDNER, Wilhelm. 1941. "Technische Hochschule München," in *Die deutschen technischen Hochschulen. Ihre Gründung und geschichtliche Entwicklung*. Munich: Verlag der deutschen Technik, pp. 223-242.

RINGER, Fritz. 1969. *The Decline of the German Mandarins: The German Academic Community, 1890-1933*. Cambridge, MA: Harvard University Press.

RIP, Arie, and BELT, Henk van der. 1988. "Constructive Technology Assessment: Toward a Theory," *manuscript*. Enschede: University of Twente.

RODERICK, Gordon W., and STEPHENS, Michael D. 1973. "Science and Technology at English Universities and Colleges, and the Economic Development During the 19th Century," *Technikgeschichte*, Vol. 40, pp. 226-250.

RODERICK, Gordon W., and STEPHENS, Michael D. 1978. *Education and Industry in the 19th Century: The English Disease?* London: Longman.

ROGERS, Kenneth C. 1979. *Fundamentals First: The Story of Stevens Institute of Technology*. New York: Newcomen Society in North America.

ROLT, L.T.C. 1986/1965. *Tools for the Job: A History of Machine Tools to 1950*. London: B.T. Batsford.

RONGE, Grete. 1955. "Die Züricher Jahre des Physikers Rudolf Clausius," *Gesnerus*, Vol. 12, pp. 73-108.

ROSENBERG, Nathan. 1976. *Perspectives on Technology*. Cambridge: Cambridge University Press.

ROSENBERG, Nathan. 1982. *Inside the Black Box: Technology and Economics*. Cambridge: Cambridge University Press.

ROSENBERG, Nathan. 1982a. "The Growing Role of Science in the Innovation Process," in Bernard, Carl Gustaf, Crawford, Elisabeth, and Sörbom, Per, eds., *Science Technology and Society in the Time of Alfred Nobel*. Oxford: Pergamon, pp. 231-246.

ROSENBERG, Nathan. 1990. "Why do Firms do Basic Research (With Their Own Money)?," *Research Policy*, Vol. 19, pp. 165-174.

ROSENFELD, L. 1941. "La genèse des principes de la thermodynamique," *Bulletin de la Société royale des sciences de Liège*, Vol. 10, pp. 199-212.

ROSSI, Auguste J. 1893-1894. "Artificial Refrigeration in Breweries," *Ice and Refrigeration*, Vols. 5-7, passim.

ROSSI, Pietro. 1986. "Max Weber und die Methodologie der Geschichts- und Sozialwissenschaften," in Kocka, pp. 28-50.

ROTH, Guenther. 1987. "Rationalization in Max Weber's Developmental History," in Lash and Whimster, pp. 75-91.

ROTH, Guenther, and SCHLUCHTER, Wolfgang. 1979. *Max Weber's Vision of History: Ethics and Methods*. Berkeley, CA: University of California Press.

RUNCIMAN, W.G., ed. 1978. *Max Weber: Selections in Translation*. Cambridge: Cambridge University Press.

RUSSELL, Stewart. 1986. "The Social Construction of Artefacts: A Response to Pinch and Bijker," *Social Studies of Science*, Vol. 16, pp. 331-346.

RYDBERG, Sven. 1983. *Möte med Munters*. Stockholm: Gullers.

SACHS, Wolfgang. 1984. *Die Liebe zum Automobil. Ein Rückblick in die Geschichte unserer Wünsche*. Reinbek: Rowohlt.

SANDWALL, Sven. 1935. "Svenska bryggareföreningen 1885-1935," in Bring, pp. 207-339.

SARTORIUS VON WALTERSHAUSEN, A. 1920. *Deutsche Wirtschaftsgeschichte, 1815-1914*. Jena: Fischer.

SAVAGE, Stephen P. 1981. *The Theories of Talcott Parsons: The Social Relations of Action*. London: MacMillan.

SCHARL, Benno. 1814. *Beschreibung der Braunbier-Brauerey im Königreiche Baiern*. Munich: Lindauer.

SCHLUCHTER, Wolfgang. 1979. *Die Entwicklung des okzidentalen Rationalismus: Eine Analyse von Max Webers Gesellschaftsgeschichte*. Tübingen: Mohr.

SCHLUCHTER, Wolfgang. 1980. *Rationalismus der Weltbeherrschung. Studien zu Max Weber*. Frankfurt a.M.: Suhrkamp.

SCHLUCHTER, Wolfgang. 1989. *Rationalism, Religion, and Domination: A Weberian Perspective*. Berkeley, CA: University of California Press.

SCHMIDT, Gert. 1981. "Technik und kapitalistischer Betrieb. Max Webers Konzept der industriellen Entwicklung und das Rationalisierungsproblem in der neueren Industriesoziologie," in Sprondel and Seyfarth, pp. 168-188.

SCHMOOKLER, Jacob. 1966. *Invention and Economic Growth*. Cambridge, MA: Harvard University Press.

SCHNABEL, Franz. 1925. "Die Anfänge des technischen Hochschulwesens," in *Festschrift anläßlich des 100jährigen Bestehens der Technischen Hochschule Fridericiana zu Karlsruhe*. Karlsruhe: Müller.

SCHNÄDELBACH, Herbert, ed. 1984. *Rationalität: Philosophische Beiträge*. Frankfurt a.M.: Suhrkamp.

SCHOLL, Lars U. 1981. "Der Ingenieur in Ausbildung, Beruf und Gesellschaft 1856 bis 1881," in Ludwig, Karl-Heinz, ed., *Technik, Ingenieure und Gesellschaft. Geschichte des Vereins Deutscher Ingenieure 1856-1981*. Dusseldorf: VDI-Verlag, pp. 1-66.

SCHRÖTER, M. 1887. *Untersuchungen an Kältemaschinen verschiedener Systeme. Erster Bericht an den Ausschuss des Polytechnischen Vereins zu München*. Munich: Oldenbourg.

SCHRÖTER, M. 1890. *Untersuchungen an Kältemaschinen verschiedener Systeme. Zweiter Bericht an den Ausschuss des Polytechnischen Vereins zu München*. Munich: Oldenbourg.

SCHRÖTER, Moritz. 1908-1909. "Naturwissenschaft und Technik. Festrede gehalten bei der Akademischen Feier der k. Technischen Hochschule zu München am 7. Dezember 1908," in *Bericht ...*, appendix.

SCHRYOCK, Richard. 1962/1948. "American Indifference to Basic Science," in Barber, Bernard, and Hirsch, Walter, eds., *The Sociology of Science*. New York, pp. 98-110.

SCHULZE-BESSE, H. 1930. "Die wissenschaftlichen Institute und Organe der deutschen Brauindustrie," in *Deutsche Brauindustrie ...*, pp. 17-23.

SCHUMACHER, E.F. 1973. *Small Is Beautiful: Economics as if People Mattered*. London and New York: Harper & Row.

SCHUMPETER, Joseph A. 1935. "The Analysis of Economic Change," *Review of Economic Statistics*, Vol. 17, pp. 2-10.

SCHUMPETER, Joseph A. 1978/1942. *Can Capitalism Survive?* New York: Harper & Row.

SCHWARZ, Alois. 1888. *Die Eis- und Kühlmaschinen und deren Anwendung in der Industrie*. Munich: Oldenbourg.

SEDLMAYR, Fritz. 1937, 1951. *Geschichte der Spatenbrauerei unter Gabriel Sedlmayr dem Älteren und dem Jüngeren 1807-1874, sowie Beiträge zur bayerischen Brauereigeschichte dieser Zeit*, 2 vols. Nuremberg: Hans Carl.

SEDLMAYR, Gabriel. 1880. "Entwicklung und gegenwärtiger Stand der Bierbrauerei in der Stadt München," *Festschrift für die Theilnehmer an dem IV. Deutschen Brauertag in München, Juli 1880*. Munich: Lokal-Comite f. d. Brauertag, pp. 3-30.

SHINN, Terry. 1980. *L'école polytechnique, 1794-1914*. Paris: Presses de la fondation nat. d. sci. pol.

SIGSWORTH, E.M. 1964-1965. "Science and the Brewing Industry, 1850-1900," *Economic History Review*, Vol. 17, pp. 536-550.

SITTE, Camillo. 1888. "Die Grundformen im Möbelbaue und deren Entwicklung," *Wochenschrift des Niederösterreichischen Gewerbe-Vereins*, Vol. 49, reprint.

SMITH, Edgar C. 1942-1943. "Some Pioneers of Refrigeration," *Transactions of the Newcomen Society*, Vol. 13, pp. 99-107.

SPECK, Joseph, ed. 1980. *Handbuch wissenschaftstheoretischer Begriffe*. Göttingen: Vandenhoeck und Ruprecht.

SPRONDEL, Walter M., and SEYFARTH, Constans, eds. 1981. *Max Weber und die Rationalisierung sozialen Handelns*. Stuttgart: Enke.

STAUDENMAIER, John M. 1985. *Technology's Storytellers: Reweaving the Human Fabric*. Cambridge, MA: MIT Press.

STETEFELD, Richard. 1911. "Lage und Bau der Keller. Natureiskühlung und künstliche Kühlung in Bierbrauereien," in Leyser, E., *Die Malz- und Bierbereitung. Ein Lehr- und Nachschlagebuch*, Vol. 2, Part 2. Stuttgart: M. Waag.

STEUERT, Ludwig. 1905. *Die Kgl. Bayerische Akademie Weihenstephan und ihre Vorgeschichte. Festschrift zur Jahrhundertfeier 2. bis 4. Juni 1905*. Berlin: Parey.

STRANDH, Sigvard. 1979. *Maskinen genom tiderna*. Stockholm: Generalstabens litografiska anstalt.

STRASSMANN, Wolfgang Paul. 1959. *Risk and Technological Innovation: American Manufacturing Methods During the Nineteenth Century*. Ithaca, NY: Cornell University Press.

STRÖKER, Elisabeth. 1983. "Philosophy of Technology: Problems of a Philosophical Discipline," in Durbin, Paul T., and Rapp, Friedrich, eds., *Philosophy and Technology*. Dordrecht: Reidel, pp. 323-336.

STRUVE, Emil. 1893. "Die Entwicklung des bayerischen Braugewerbes im 19. Jahrhundert. Ein Beitrag zur deutschen Gewerbegeschichte der Neuzeit," *Staats- und Socialwissenschaftliche Forschungen*, Vol. XII, No. I. Leipzig.

SWOBODA, Karl. 1868. *Die Eisapparate der Neuzeit. Erläuterung und Beschreibung der in dem letzten Decennium in Anwendung gekommenen Eismaschinen*. Weimar: Bernhard Friedrich Voigt.

TÄUBRICH, Hans-Christian. 1991. "Eisbericht. Vom Handel mit dem natürlichen Eis," in Täubrich and Tschoeke, pp. 50-67.

TÄUBRICH, Hans-Christian, and TSCHOEKE, Jutta, eds. 1991. *Unter Null. Kunsteis, Kälte und Kultur*. Munich: C.H. Beck.

TAYLOR, Frederick W. 1967/1911. *The Principles of Scientific Management*. New York and London: W.W. Norton & Co.

Technische Hochschule München, 1868-1968. 1968. Munich.

TELLIER, Ch. 1910. *Histoire d'une invention moderne: le Frigorifique*. Paris: C. Delagrave.

THAUSING, Julius E. 1882, 1893/1877. *Die Theorie und Praxis der Malzbereitung und Bierfabrikation*, 2nd and 4th ed. Leipzig: J.M. Gebhardt.

THÉVENOT, Roger. 1978. *Essai pour une histoire du froid artificiel dans le monde*. Paris: Inst. Internat. d. Froid.

THOMPSON, John B. 1984. *Studies in the Theory of Ideology*. Cambridge: Polity Press.

THOMSON, William. 1852. "Additional Note on the Preceding Paper," *Philosophical Transactions of the Royal Society of London*, pp. 78-82.

TILLMANN, Hans Friedrich. 1972. "Der Einfluß der Kältetechnik auf die Entwicklung des Braugewerbes," Thesis, *mimeograph*. Bochum: Ruhr-Universität.

TROTT, A.R. 1981. *Refrigeration and Air-Conditioning*. Maidenhead, Berks.: McGraw-Hill.

TRUESDELL, C. 1980. *The Tragicomical History of Thermodynamics, 1822-1854*. New York: Springer.

TUCHEL, Klaus. 1964. *Die Philosophie der Technik bei Friedrich Dessauer, ihre Entwicklung, Motive und Grenzen*. Frankfurt a.M.: Knecht.

TWINING, Alexander C. 1857. *The Manufacture of Ice on a Commercial Scale and with Commercial Economy by Steam or Water Power*. New Haven, CT: Thomas J. Stafford.

ULRICH, H. 1970. *Die Unternehmung als produktives soziales System*. Berne and Stuttgart: Haupt.

UNFER, Louis. 1951. "Swift and Company: The Development of the Packing Industry, 1875 to 1912," Thesis, *mimeograph*. Urbana, Ill.: University of Illinois.

Uppfinningarnas bok. 1925. Vol. 2. Stockholm: P.A. Norstedt & Söner.

USHER, Abbot P. 1954. *A History of Mechanical Inventions*. Cambridge, MA: Harvard University Press.

UVAROV, E.B., CHAPMAN, D.R., and ISAACS, Alan, eds. 1971. *A Dictionary of Science*. Harmondsworth, Middles.: Penguin.

VAN WYLEN, Gordon J., and SONNTAG, Richard E. 1985. *Fundamentals of Classical Thermodynamics*. New York: Wiley.

VETTER, Theodor. 1921. "Die Konzentration in der bayerischen Brauindustrie bis zum Eintritt Bayerns in die Reichsbiersteuergemeinschaft," Dissertation, *mimeograph*. Heidelberg: Ruprecht-Carl-Universität.

VINCENTI, W.G. 1979. "The Air Propeller Tests of W.F. Durand and E.P. Lesley: A Case Study in Technological Methodology," *Technology and Culture*, Vol. 20, pp. 712-751.

VINCENTI, W.G. 1982. "Control-Volume Analysis: A Difference in Thinking between Engineering and Physics," *Technology and Culture*, Vol. 23, pp. 145-174.

VINCENTI, W.G. 1984. "Technological Knowledge without Science: The Innovation of Flush Riveting in American Airplanes," *Technology and Culture*, Vol. 25, pp. 540-576.

VOGEL, August. 1872. *Zur Erinnerung an Dr. Cajetan von Kaiser*. Munich: Manz.

WAGNER, Ladislaus von. 1870. *Die Bierbrauerei nach dem gegenwärtigen Standpunkte der Theorie und Praxis des Gewerbes*. Weimar: Bernhard Friedrich Voigt.

WEBER, Max. 1920. *Gesammelte Aufsätze zur Religionssoziologie, I-III*. Tübingen: Mohr.

WEBER, Max. 1922. *Gesammelte Aufsätze zur Wissenschaftslehre*. Tübingen: Mohr.

WEBER, Max. 1922a. *Grundriss der Sozialökonomik, III. Abteilung: Wirtschaft und Gesellschaft*. Tübingen: Mohr.

WEBER, Max. 1923. *Wirtschaftsgeschichte. Abriss der universalen Sozial- und Wirtschafts-Geschichte*. Munich and Leipzig: Duncker & Humblot.

WEBER, Max. 1924. *Gesammelte Aufsätze zur Soziologie und Sozialpolitik*. Tübingen: Mohr.

WEBER, Max. 1930/1904-1905. *The Protestant Ethic and the Spirit of Capitalism*. London: Allen & Unwin.

WEBER, Max. 1949. *The Methodology of the Social Sciences*. Glencoe, Ill.: Free Press.

WEBER, Max. 1949a/1904. "'Objectivity' in Social Science and Social Policy," in Weber 1949, pp. 49-112.

WEBER, Max. 1958/1918. "Parlament und Regierung im neugeordneten Deutschland," in idem., *Gesammelte politische Schriften*. Tübingen: Mohr (Paul Siebeck), pp. 294-431.

WEBER, Max. 1958a/1922. "Bureaucracy," in Gerth and Mills, pp. 196-244.

WEBER, Max. 1958b/1922. "Class, Status, Party," in Gerth and Mills, pp. 180-195.

WEBER, Max. 1958c/1915. "Religious Rejections of the World and Their Directions," in Gerth and Mills, pp. 323-359.

WEBER, Max. 1958d/1919. "Science as a Vocation," in Gerth and Mills, pp. 129-156.

WEBER, Max. 1958e/1922-1923. "The Social Psychology of the World Religions," in Gerth and Mills, pp. 267-301.

WEBER, Max. 1964/1922. *The Theory of Social and Economic Organization*. New York: Free Press.

WEBER, Max. 1965/1922. *The Sociology of Religion*. London: Methuen & Co.

WEBER, Max. 1981/1923. *General Economic History*. New Brunswick and London: Transaction Books.

WEINGART, Peter. 1982. "Strukturen technologischen Wandels. Zu einer soziologischen Analyse der Technik," in Jokisch, pp. 112-141.

WEISS, John Hubbel. 1982. *The Making of Technological Man: The Social Origins of French Engineering Education*. Cambridge, MA: MIT Press.

WETTSTEIN, D. von. 1983. "Carlsberg Laboratorium - Den Fysiologiske Afdelning," *Carlsbergfondet, Frederiksbergmuseet, Ny Carlsbergfondet, Årsskrift 1983*. Copenhagen.

WHIMSTER, Sam, and LASH, Scott. 1987. "Introduction," in Lash and Whimster, pp. 1-31.

WHITESIDE, George H. 1897. "Dr. John Gorrie," *Ice and Refrigeration*, Vol. 12, pp. 351-357.

WIENER, Philip P., ed. 1968-1974. *Dictionary of the History of Ideas: Studies of Selected Pivotal Ideas*, 5 vols. New York: Scribners.

WILD, Josef, ed. 1930. *Brauwissenschaft vor 85 Jahren. Vorlesungen über Brauerei von Professor G.C. von Kaiser München*. Berlin: Gesellschaft für die Geschichte und Bibliographie des Brauwesens.

WILD, Josef. 1936. "Der Braumeister in der Entwicklungsgeschichte des Brauwesens," in *Gesellschaft ...*

WILLIAMS, Edwin B., ed. 1979/1977. *The Scribner-Bantam English Dictionary*. New York: Bantam.

WINNER, Langdon. 1977. *Autonomous Technology: Technics-out-of-Control as a Theme in Political Thought*. Cambridge, MA: MIT Press.

Die Wirtschaftliche Bedeutung der deutschen Kälte-Industrie im Jahre 1908. 1908. Munich: Oldenbourg.

WISE, George. 1985. "Science and Technology," *Osiris*, 2nd Ser., Vol. 1, pp. 229-246.

WISLICKI, Alfred. 1985. "Transformability of Basic Models of Machines," *History and Technology*, Vol. 2, pp. 235-244.

WOLF Co., The Fred W. 1900. "Nineth Catalog," *pamphlet*, at New York Public Library. Chicago.

WOLF, Rudolf. 1880. *Das Schweizerische Polytechnikum. Historische Skizze zur Feier des 25jährigen Jubiläums im Juli 1880*. Zurich: Höhr.

WOOLRICH, W.R. 1947. "Mechanical Refrigeration - Its American Birthright," *Refrigerating Engineering*, Vol. 53, pp. 196-199, 246-250, 305-308, 346.

WOOLRICH, W.R. 1967. *The Men Who Created Cold: A History of Refrigeration*. New York: Exposition Press.

WRIGHT, Georg Henrik von. 1987. *Vetenskapen och förnuftet. Ett försök till orientering*. Stockholm: Bonniers.

YAGI, Eri. 1981. "Analytical Approach to Clausius' First Memoir on Mechanical Theory of Heat (1850)," *Historia Scientiarum*, Vol. 20, pp. 77-94.

YEAGER, Mary. 1981. *Competition and Regulation: The Development of Oligopoly in the Meat Packing Industry*. Greenwich, CT: JAI Press.

ZEUNER, Gustav A. 1862. "Theoretische Mechanik," vorgetragen von Prof. Dr. Zeuner im 2ten Semester des Schuljahres 1861/62 am Eidgenössischen Polytechnikum in Zürich, I. Theil. Bearbeitet von Heinrich Berchtold, Zürich im September 1862, at ETH-Bibliothek, Zurich, *mimeograph*. Zurich.

ZEUNER, Gustav A. 1865. "Theoretische Maschinenlehre." Vorträge des Herrn Dr. Gustav Zeuner, Professor der Mechanik und theoret. Maschinenlehre am Eidgenössischen Polytechnikum in Zürich, at ETH-Bibliothek, Zurich, *mimeograph*. Berlin.

ZEUNER, Gustav A. 1866/1859. *Grundzüge der mechanischen Wärmetheorie mit Anwendungen auf die der Wärmelehre angehörigen Theile der Maschinenlehre*, 2nd ed. Leipzig: Felix.

ZEUNER, Gustav A. 1869-1870. "Mechan. Wärmetheorie, Dampfmaschinenlehre," lecture notes by M. Kussevich, at ETH-Bibliothek, Zurich, *manuscript*. Zurich.

ZEUNER, Gustav. 1881. "Zur Theorie der Kalt-Dampfmaschinen. Mit einem Anhange: Ueber das Verhalten der Ammoniakdämpfe," *Der Civilingenieur*, Vol. 27 (n.s.), pp. 449-494.

ZILSEL, Edgar. 1941-1942. "The Sociological Roots of Science," *American Journal of Sociology*, Vol. 47, pp. 544-562.

ZIMMERMANN, A.F. 1842. *Der Bier-Brauer als Meister in seinem Fache*. Berlin: Schroeder.

ZORN, Wolfgang. 1962. "Kleine Wirtschafts- und Sozialgeschichte Bayerns 1816-1933," *Bayerische Heimatforschung*, No. 14. Munich-Pasing.

ZORN, Wolfgang. 1975. "Bayerns Gewerbe, Handel und Verkehr (1806-1970)," in Spindler, Max, ed., *Handbuch der bayerischen Geschichte, Vierter Band, Das Neue Bayern, 1870-1970*. Munich: C.H. Beck, pp. 781-845.

ZWECKBRONNER, Gerhard. 1991. "Was wollen die Technikwissenschaften?," in Hermann, Armin, and Schönbeck, Charlotte, eds., *Technik und Wissenschaft*. Dusseldorf: VDI-Verlag, pp. 377-380.

50 Jahre Kältetechnik 1879-1929 Geschichte der Gesellschaft für Linde's Eismaschinen A.-G. Wiesbaden. 1929. Berlin: VDI-Verlag.

50 Jahre Versuchsanstalt für Bierbrauerei der Bayerischen Landesgewerbeanstalt Nürnberg 1887-1937. 1937. Landshut.

75 Jahre Linde, 21 Juni 1954. Als Jubiläumsgabe unseren Angehörigen und Freunden gewidmet. 1954. Wiesbaden: Linde Co.

"100 Jahre Eidgenössische Technische Hochschule. Le centenaire de l'École Polytechnique Fédérale," 1955. *Schweizerische Hochschulzeitung*, Sonderheft, Vol. 28.

100 Jahre Fakultät für Brauwesen Weihenstephan 1865-1965. 1965. Munich: Technical University of Munich.

1815-1915. Hundert Jahre technische Erfindungen und Schöpfungen in Bayern. 1922. Jahrhundertschrift des polytechnischen Vereins in Bayern. Munich and Berlin.

Index